Carolyn Eberhard
CORNELL UNIVERSITY

GENERAL BIOLOGY
LABORATORY MANUAL

to Accompany

Biology

Claude A. Villee   Eldra Pearl Solomon   P. William Davis

and

World of Biology
THIRD EDITION

P. William Davis   Eldra Pearl Solomon

Illustrated by

Monica Howland and Fine Line Illustrations, Inc.

SAUNDERS COLLEGE PUBLISHING

Philadelphia   New York   Chicago
San Francisco   Montreal   Toronto
London   Sydney   Tokyo   Mexico City
Rio de Janeiro   Madrid

Address orders to:
383 Madison Avenue
New York, NY 10017

Address editorial correspondence to:
West Washington Square
Philadelphia, PA 19105

Text Typeface: 9/10 Souvenir Light
Compositor: The Kingswood Group, Inc.
Acquisitions Editor: Edward Murphy
Project Editor/Copy Editor: Robin C. Bonner
Art Director: Carol R. Bleistine
Text Design: Phoenix Studio, Inc.
Cover Design: Larry Didona
Text Artwork: Monica Howland and Fine Line Illustrations, Inc.
Production Manager: Tim Frelick
Assistant Production Manager: JoAnn Melody

Cover credit: The brooding anemone, *Epiactis prolifera*, from Washington State, © Charles
Seaborn; Animals Animals, © 1986, Richard Kolar, subject—Nautilus Interior, Nautilus
Pompilius.

GENERAL BIOLOGY LABORATORY   ISBN 0-03-063174-2

56   066   987654321

CBS COLLEGE PUBLISHING
Saunders College Publishing
Holt, Rinehart and Winston
The Dryden Press

PREFACE

This manual is designed to be used in the laboratory section accompanying a general biology course. The order of topics is similar to that in the accompanying textbooks *Biology* and *World of Biology*. However, the descriptive material in this laboratory manual is sufficiently comprehensive and detailed that it can be used with other texts. Page and figure references cited in this manual are to *Biology* by Villee et al. A correlation chart of topics for *World of Biology* by Davis and Solomon can be found on pages 367 and 368; the separate *Instructor's Manual* provides a further correlation.

The content and form of most of these exercises have successfully met the needs of many instructors. In keeping with the emphasis of the Villee, Solomon, and Davis text, topics on animal and plant tissue structure and DNA have been introduced. There are many new or redrawn figures, and a special insert of color plates illustrates some material that is especially hard to present as line drawings. A description of the metric system is given in an appendix. A short reference list for students appears at the end of each topic in the laboratory manual, and references are included in the instructor's manual. Finally, there are three open-ended projects at the end of the manual for courses in which students are asked to independently carry out work that is less structured. Directions for writing a laboratory report and for statistical analysis to complement the projects are given in appendices.

To accommodate the varying requirements of instructors teaching biology laboratory, 32 topics have been included—more than would ordinarily be covered in a two-semester course. Among these topics is introductory material important to both majors and nonmajors taking laboratory: seven topics on the diversity of living organisms, six topics emphasizing vertebrate anatomy, and two topics discussing the angiosperms. Other topics in this manual, such as those on genetics, muscle physiology, and animal behavior, help students learn how to gather and analyze data and to design experiments. We believe it is necessary that a general biology course provide a thorough introduction to the basic biology of plants and animals because many students, including biology majors, do not pursue studies in these areas. Moreover, those who do take more advanced courses often find that the instructor assumes they are familiar with material that in fact was not emphasized or was eliminated altogether from their introductory biology courses.

Each topic begins with formal objectives that describe what knowledge or skills the student should be able to demonstrate after completing the exercise. Key topics then state the subjects and concepts relevant to each exercise. The exercises contain questions concerning information recall, concepts, and analysis of laboratory material to stimulate student discussion during the laboratory period. Worksheets are provided at the end of many topics for students to use to record data and observations for particular experiments. These sheets can then be collected for grading at the end of the laboratory period. An index is provided for the convenience of both student and instructor in using the manual.

The exercises present techniques such as pipeting, chromatography, and the use of the spectrophotometer and kymograph. We have tried to minimize the use of complicated procedures and elaborate equipment wherever possible so that each experiment is feasible in some form at most colleges and universities. The major recurrent budget items for these exercises are preserved fetal pigs and live material. Although we encourage the use of live material, we have often provided for the use of preserved material as well in the event that live material is unavailable or too expensive.

Three projects for independent study are given at the end of the manual in which groups of students are asked to design or conduct, and analyze experiments with plant hormones, plant nutrition, and pond microecosystems. The projects emphasize input from the students rather than the use of elaborate equipment, and they have been used successfully with students who had varying levels of preparation.

The separate *Instructor's Manual* for this laboratory manual, which may be obtained from the publisher free of charge, suggests how many topics may be combined, shortened, or expanded. It also provides lists of material and equipment needed for these exercises, sources for specific supplies, directions for preparing solutions and handling live material, and an estimate of the cost of each exercise. A list of reference books, films, and film loops is also included. Requests for the *Instructor's Manual* should be addressed to: Customer Service, CBS College Publishing, 383 Madison Avenue, New York, NY 10017.

The foundation for these laboratory exercises is based upon a long association with colleagues in Introductory Biology at Cornell University: Antonie W. Blackler, the late William T. Keeton, Melvin Kreithen, Carol Hardy McFadden, Neil Campbell, William McFarland, P. Richard Ecklund, and Robert Turgeon. We are indebted to all of our colleagues at Cornell and Ithaca College for their support, suggestions, and contributions large and small: Renee Alexander, Robert Anderson, Jeanne Appling, Alan Bennett, Everette Busbee, Judith Byrnes, Donna Hill Canney, Nancy Clum, Gary Creason, Lin Davidson, Jan Factor, Gail Ferstandig, Sue Giffen, Jon Glase, Larry Greenberg, Monica Howland, Barry Ingber, Leanne Ketcham, Debra Kirchhof-Glazier, Marie Knowlton, Joshua Korman, Martha Lackey, Carolyn Louie, Martha Lyon, Carol Mapes, Michael Meredith, Elizabeth Mort, Sharman O'Neill, Donald Rhodes, Helen Roland, William Schrader, Buffy Silverman, Paul Sisco, Ann Snook, Daniel Solomon, Adrian Srb, George Swenson, Craig Tendler, Eileen Whalen, Richard Wodzinski, Nancy Wolf, and Hal Yingling.

We are extremely grateful to Monica Howland for researching and preparing many new and revised figures at short notice and under somewhat arduous conditions, as well as critiquing many of the exercises.

We also wish to acknowledge the following individuals who offered instructive comments on the manual manuscript at some point: Betty D. Allamong, Ball State University; Robert Amy, Southwestern at Memphis; Paul Davidson, Rollins College; John Erickson, Western Washington University; Cesar Fermin, Florida Institute of Technology; Eileen Gregory, Rollins College; Terry William Hill, Southwestern at Memphis; Russell C. Hollingsworth, Tarrant County Junior College, Northeast; Pius Horner, San Bernadino Valley College; Virginia Keville, Salem State College; Stephen Klein, Schenendehowa Central High School; William Leonard, University of Nebraska; Karen Loftin, University of Houston; Carmita Love, Community College of Philadelphia; W. Wallace Martin, Randolph Macon College; Roger Sawyer, University of South Carolina; Allen Schroeder, Gettysburg College; Robert Smith, San Bernadino Valley College; Gail Stetten, Johns Hopkins Hospital; and Joseph Wood, University of Missouri.

We are grateful to Sara Jane Hymes for typing the instructor's manual manuscript, and to the Saunders editorial staff: Michael Brown, Edward Murphy, their assistants, and Robin Bonner for bringing the manual to fruition against all odds.

Finally we wish to express our gratitude to the literary executor of the late Sir Ronald Fisher, F. R. S., Dr. Frank Yates, F. R. S., and Longman Group, Ltd. in London for permission to reprint material from their book, *Statistical Tables for Biological, Agricultural, and Medical Research* (6th edition, 1974).

Ithaca, New York
April 1985   C. E.

CONTENTS

TO THE STUDENT

OBJECTIVES

At the beginning of each topic in this manual is a list of specific Objectives describing the subject areas and skills that you should master upon completion of the topic. In addition, there are other, broader objectives that you should try to achieve in the course of using this manual. We hope that you will:

1. Interact with other students and your instructor by asking questions about the laboratory material, by comparing your findings, and, when possible, by presenting your results in class discussions at the end of the laboratory session.

2. Acquire knowledge that will provide a foundation for further scientific study.

3. Apply what you have learned in this course to your daily life, and try to make more informed decisions about such matters as nutrition, medicine, natural resources, endangered species, environmental hazards, and the like.

SAFETY

Experiments in biology laboratories sometimes involve working with potentially dangerous chemicals and expensive equipment that must be used properly. To ensure your personal safety, follow these simple rules:

1. Do not eat in the laboratory.

2. Do not drink in the laboratory.

3. Never smoke in the laboratory.

4. Protect your face and eyes by wearing safety glasses and contact lenses. Tie back long loose hair.

5. Roll up long sleeves when using equipment or open flames.

6. Keep open flames away from flammable chemicals or materials and *yourself!*

7. Report any injury to yourself or another student, no matter how minor, to the instructor.

8. Report any spills to your instructor, and clean up the spills immediately.

9. Determine the shortest exit route from the building, and be prepared to leave the room immediately in case of a fire.

PREPARATION

1. Read the assigned exercise before the laboratory session. Otherwise your time will be spent less productively than it should be.

2. Use your textbook to complement each lab by reading about the key topics listed at the beginning of each topic while the laboratory work is still fresh in your mind. If the material presented in the topic has not yet been discussed in lecture, read the relevant material *before* the laboratory session.

METRIC SYSTEM AND SCIENTIFIC NOTATION

If you are not familiar with the metric system, consult Appendix D at the end of this manual. You will be expected to use the metric system in this course.

Some measurements in biology have very small or very large units, so it is awkward to write them out as decimals. Instead, we use scientific notation in which the decimal point is placed after the first digit and the number is expressed as a multiple of the power of 10. For example, 506 kilograms is expressed as 5.06×10^2 kg, and 1/200 (.005) of a second is expressed as 5×10^{-3} sec. Scientific notation makes it easy to use the metric system. In our second example, 5×10^{-3} sec equals 5 msec because 10^{-3} sec equals 1 msec.

Introductory biology laboratory may be one of your few opportunities to explore firsthand many of the topics covered in this manual. We hope that you will take advantage of this time to interact with your classmates and your instructor as much as possible so that this experience will be both rewarding and enjoyable.

Ithaca, New York
April 1985   C. E.

Biologically Important Molecules

OBJECTIVES

When you have completed this topic, you should be able to:
1. Define the term functional group and give the functional group or groups characteristic of an acid, an amino acid, a carbohydrate, a fatty acid, and an alcohol.
2. Describe how to carry out a simple laboratory test for a monosaccharide, a polysaccharide, a protein, and a fat.
3. Describe how a protein can be broken down into its building blocks—amino acids.
4. Show by thin-layer chromatography that different amino acids have different chemical properties.
5. Explain how chromatography works to separate chemically different substances.

KEY TOPICS

Atoms, bonds, compounds, polarity, chemical reactions, oxidation, reduction, water, carbon chemistry, biological molecules.

INTRODUCTION

An **element** is a particular type of atom that is different from the atoms of all the other elements. The elements most abundant in living material are:

Carbon	= C	Nitrogen	= N
Hydrogen	= H	Sulfur	= S
Oxygen	= O	Phosphorus	= P

These are by far the most important elements in biological systems: they can be combined in enormous variety to make up the chemical molecules on which life is based.

In most biological molecules the atoms are held together by **covalent bonds** in which electrons are shared between adjacent atoms. Ionic bonds, hydrogen bonds, and disulfide bonds are also important. If you are not sure how each of these bonds is formed, refer back to your text and review them.

Fortunately for us, covalent bonds are not very easily broken down under ordinary conditions. Some small molecules are especially stable and are used as the building blocks or **subunits** of very large molecules called **polymers.** A polymer often consists of many similar subunits strung together in a long chain. It is easier to

break down a polymer into its subunits than to break apart the subunits themselves.

Biological molecules can be categorized on the basis of similar parts called **functional groups:**

Carboxyl	Hydroxyl	Amino

$$-C\diagup^{\!\!\!O}_{\diagdown O-H} \qquad -O-H \qquad -N\diagup^{\!H}_{\diagdown H}$$

Aldehyde	Ketone	Sulfhydryl

$$-C\diagup^{\!\!\!O}_{\diagdown H} \qquad \overset{|}{\underset{|}{C}}=O \qquad -S-H$$

Hydrocarbon

$$H-\overset{|}{\underset{|}{C}}-H$$

For example, any molecule that has the carboxyl group

$$-C\diagup^{\!\!\!O}_{\diagdown O-H}$$ is an acid. (Remember that one line represents one covalent bond and two lines represent a double bond.) The term **fatty acid** refers to the group of acids

that have the carboxyl group and several $H-\overset{|}{\underset{|}{C}}-H$ groups besides. An *amino acid* molecule has an amino group and a carboxyl group. A carbohydrate such as a monosaccharide or simple sugar has an aldehyde or ketone group and some hydroxyl groups. (Aldehyde and ketone groups are specific examples of carbonyl compounds which always contain $-\overset{|}{\underset{|}{C}}=O$.)

Amino acid molecules may have additional functional groups (sulfhydryl, additional carboxyl groups, additional hydroxyl groups, and so on), but they all share the functional groups characteristic of an amino acid.

Functional groups can be divided into two groups, depending on whether they contain **polar covalent bonds** or are **ions**.

Polar Functional Groups

$-C\overset{\displaystyle O}{\underset{\displaystyle O-H}{\big<}}$ carboxyl group

$-C\overset{\displaystyle O}{\underset{\displaystyle H}{\big<}}$ aldehyde group

$\overset{|}{\underset{|}{C}}=O$ ketone group

$-O-H$ hydroxyl group

$-N\overset{\displaystyle H}{\underset{\displaystyle H}{\big<}}$ amino group

$-C\overset{\displaystyle O}{\underset{\displaystyle O^-}{\big<}}$ anion (negative charge)

$-\overset{\displaystyle H}{\underset{\displaystyle H}{\overset{|}{\underset{|}{N}}}}-{}^+H$ cation (positive charge)

Non-Polar Functional Groups

$H-\overset{|}{\underset{|}{C}}-H$ hydrocarbon group

$-S-H$ sulfhydryl group

Learn the names and structures of these functional groups in order to understand the chemistry of today's lab.

Polar functional groups interact with each other and with water, another polar substance; they do not interact significantly with non-polar functional groups or with non-polar solvents.

For example, oil does not mix with vinegar, a solution of acetic acid and water. What kind of functional groups must oil therefore contain? _____

IDENTIFICATION OF BIOLOGICAL MOLECULES

Molecules of a certain class have similar chemical properties because they have the same functional groups. A chemical test that is sensitive to these groups can be used to identify molecules that are in that class. Practice the following tests by using them to see what various foods contain. In each test, you will be including a substance that does not react in the test to serve as a **negative control**. A substance known to give a reaction in the test would be a **positive control**.

Please follow the directions carefully, so that your test results are unambiguous. Record your results in Table 1-2, at the end of this topic.

IF YOU ARE USING PIPETS IN THIS LAB, USE 2 mL OF SOLUTION PER CENTIMETER AND OMIT MARKING THE TUBES.

Carbohydrates

$-C\overset{\displaystyle O}{\underset{\displaystyle H}{\big<}}$ $-O-H$

_____   _____

These molecules contain the **aldehyde** and **alcohol** functional groups. Label them correctly.

Certain mono- and disaccharides can be detected because of their aldehyde groups. Some polysaccharides can be detected because of their specific three-dimensional structure. Carbohydrates, which are water soluble or hydrophilic substances, are not detected by their hydroxyl groups.

Can you explain why not?

_____

_____

Benedict's Test

A **reducing sugar** test that depends on a free aldehyde group: $-C\overset{\displaystyle O}{\underset{\displaystyle H}{\big<}}$

Monosaccharides and some disaccharides have a free aldehyde group and consequently will react to give a positive **Benedict's test.** Such a sugar acts as a **reducing agent** and is called **reducing sugar.** The reaction goes like this:

$$\text{BENEDICT'S REAGENT} + R-C\overset{\displaystyle O}{\underset{\displaystyle H}{\big<}} \xrightarrow{\text{heat}}$$

oxidized form   reducing sugar

$$\text{BENEDICT'S REAGENT} + R-C\overset{\displaystyle O}{\underset{\displaystyle O-H}{\big<}}$$

reduced form   acid sugar

This is a typical **oxidation-reduction reaction** in which oxidation of the sugar occurs simultaneously with reduction of the Benedict's reagent. Remember that

> **REDUCTION means removal of oxygen or addition of hydrogen**
> **OXIDATION means addition of oxygen or removal of hydrogen**

In this case, the sugar obviously gained an oxygen during the reaction and therefore the sugar underwent oxidation.

Some disaccharides (e.g. sucrose) and all polysaccharides (e.g. starch) are not reducing sugars because they do not have free aldehyde groups.

Will ordinary table sugar give a positive Benedict's test? _____

You'll use the Benedict's Test to compare the reducing sugar content of onion juice with that of potato juice:

■ Mark 3 test tubes at 1 cm and 3 cm from the bottom.
■ Add onion juice up to the 1-cm mark of tube #1.
■ Add potato juice to the 1-cm mark of tube #2 and water to the 1-cm mark of tube #3.
■ Add Benedict's Reagent to the 3-cm marks of all 3 tubes and mix.
■ Heat the tubes for 3 minutes in a boiling water bath.
■ Remove the tubes using the tongs provided and compare their colors.

A change from clear blue to red or orange indicates an abundance of reducing sugars. A change to green indicates the presence of a smaller amount of reducing sugar.

Which vegetable, potato or onion, has more reducing sugar? _____

What was the purpose of tube #3. _____

Iodine Test

Another test, the **Iodine Test,** can be used to distinguish starch from mono-, di- and other polysaccharides. Starch is a polymer of glucose in which the chains are coiled up in a particular way so that they can interact with the iodine molecules to give a distinctive blue-black color. Other polymers, even those of glucose, lack the precise coiled structure of starch and do not give the dark color. Thus the iodine test is a specific test for **starch** that depends on the precise three-dimensional coiling of this glucose polymer so that it can interact with iodine.

Compare the starch content of onions and potatoes:

■ Mark 3 tubes at 1 cm.
■ Fill one to the mark with onion juice, another with potato juice, and the third with water.
■ Add 3 drops of iodine to each tube and mix.

A positive test will give a blue-black color. A yellow or brown result is negative.

Which vegetable, onion or potato, stores more starch?

_____

Sudan III Test

A fat is a hydrophobic molecule consisting of a glycerol molecule joined to three fatty acids. The important functional groups involved in a fat are these:

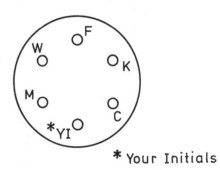

The hydroxyl groups of the glycerol (label the hydroxyl functional group above), react with the carboxyl groups of the fatty acids (label the carboxyl group) in a condensation reaction, so these functional groups are no longer available for a test reaction. Instead, the **Sudan III test** depends on the detection of the hydrocarbon groups remaining. The colored dye, Sudan III, and the hydrocarbon groups are **non-polar** and stick tightly together in their **polar** surroundings. Simple **hydrophobic interaction** is thus the basis for this rather inelegant test.

Since fats are not very soluble in water, extracts of four foods have been made using 95% ethanol (ethanol is the alcohol found in beer and wine, etc.). A fifth tube contained only water and was extracted for the control. Test each of the five tubes for the presence of fat as follows.

■ Using a lead *pencil*, mark a filter paper disc with a "W" (water), "F" (flour), "K" (cream), "C" (coconut), and an "M" (margarine) so that the letters are fairly equally spaced on the filter paper. Draw a small circle next to each letter (see Fig. 1-1). Add your initials somewhere.

Sudan III Test

* Your Initials

Figure 1-1. Filter paper ready for the Sudan III test.

■ Using the proper Pasteur pipet, add a small drop from each tube to the appropriate circled spot on the filter paper. *Use only the dedicated pipet provided with each solution and return the pipet to its proper solution when you are finished with it.*
■ Allow the paper to dry *completely.* Use the blow dryer if necessary.
■ Soak the paper for 3 minutes in the Sudan III solution.
■ Use forceps to remove the paper from the stain.

■ Rinse the paper in the water bath for one minute.*
■ Examine the intensity of staining of the five spots and rate the four foods as 0 = no color, + = faint orange color, + + = definite orange color.

What was the purpose of the "water" spot?

_____

Which foods contain detectable amounts of fat? _____

_____

Which has the highest fat content? _____

Biuret Test

Proteins are polymers of amino acids in which the carboxyl group of one subunit joins head-to-tail with the amino group of its neighbor. In this case, the bound amino group is nevertheless sufficiently reactive to change the **Biuret Test** reagent from blue to violet. Thus the basis of the test is a subtle interaction between the copper ions in the Biuret reagent and the amide bonds in the protein backbone. This test is specific for the **amino group** found in the peptide bonds of proteins:

You'll observe how the blue biuret solution reacts in the presence of protein by comparing the amount of protein in egg white with the amount in chicken soup. The solutions contain one egg white or one cup of chicken broth in equivalent volumes.

■ Mark 3 test tubes at 3 cm and 5 cm from the bottom.
■ Add egg white solution to the 3-cm mark of the first tube, chicken soup solution to the 3-cm mark of the second tube and water to the 3-cm mark of the third tube.
■ Add sodium hydroxide (NaOH) to the 5-cm marks and **mix.** Be careful not to get NaOH on yourself.
■ Add 5 drops of 1% copper sulfate ($CuSO_4$) to each tube and **mix.**

A color change from blue to violet occurs when copper ions react with the amide bonds and such a change indicates the presence of proteins.

Which food contains more protein? _____

* Note: Sudan III stains fats and so it will color the spots on the filter paper orange if those spots have fat. Specifically, it will bind to the hydrocarbon groups in the tails of the fatty acids. The filter paper itself will pick up some of the dye, so the *excess* must be soaked off in order for you to see the spots. Rinse some more if no spots are apparent. You should see at least one spot!

Testing Unknowns

Your instructor will provide each of you with an unknown food. The letter gives you the group of possible unknowns that you might have:

A	B	C
soy flour	corn starch	ground coffee
glucose	honey	instant coffee
powdered milk	table sugar	
enriched flour	egg white	

D	E
Vermont Maid syrup	glucose
Maple syrup	table salt
	potato starch
	gelatin

The compositions of these foods are given in Table 1-1. Low levels of components will probably not show up in these tests.

■ Record the letter and number of the unknown (e.g. A-3) in Table 1-2.
■ Determine the results you would *expect* for each possible food in each of the tests you have used in Table 1-2. For group A, that would be soy flour (−, +, +, +), glucose (+, −, −, −) etc.
■ USING *PART* OF THE UNKNOWN FOR EACH TEST, place a small sample in a clean test tube and then test it for reducing sugar, starch, fat, and protein with the tests you've just used. **Do not add reagents to the entire original unknown.** Test only a small portion of solid unknowns and dissolve them in distilled water when appropriate, as for the Benedict's test. The starch test may also be done in a test tube. Be sure to **mix all components** thoroughly so that you don't get a false negative reaction. Record the results in Table 1-2.
■ **SAVE ALL TUBES SO THAT YOU MAY CHECK YOUR RESULTS WITH YOUR LAB INSTRUCTOR**
■ For each test, decide which, if any, substance on your list of possible unknowns was ruled out and enter it in the table. For example, a positive test for reducing sugar would rule out corn starch (starch must give a negative test). A negative test for reducing sugar would rule out honey (glucose in honey must give a positive test). You may ask your lab instructor about the composition of any of the foods.
■ Identify your unknown and enter the name of the food in the space provided.
■ Ask your lab instructor to check your conclusion on the master key before you leave.
■ If necessary, discuss your results with your instructor and repeat any doubtful tests.

AMINO ACID CHROMATOGRAPHY

If you touch a pen containing washable black ink to a piece of tissue, the ink will spread out on the paper and will separate into red, green, and blue bands. As the liquid in which the colored pigments are dissolved is absorbed by the cellulose fibers of the tissue, the pigments can't keep up: some will move almost as fast as the solvent but some will move very slowly. This is because

TABLE 1-1. COMPOSITION OF FOODS*

Grams per 100 grams edible portion (or %)
AMOUNTS IN PARENTHESES NOT DETECTED IN TESTS

	Water	Calories	% Protein	% Fats	% Carbohydrate
Corn Starch	12	362	(.3)	(trace)	87.6 starch
Egg White	87.6	51	10.9	(trace)	(0.8)
Egg Yolk	51.1	348	16.0	30.6	(0.6)
Enriched flour (white)	12	364	(10.5)	(1.0)	76.1 starch
Gelatin (dry)	13.0	335	85.6	(.1)	(0)
Glucose	9	335	(0)	(0)	91
Ground Coffee	4.1	301	(12.5)	15.4	28.5
Honey	17.2	304	(0.3)	(0)	82.3 glucose + fructose
Instant Coffee	2.6	129	(0)	(0)	35.0
Maple Syrup (estimated)	21.5	299	(0)	(0)	(77) only sucrose
Potato Starch	7.6	351	(8.0)	(0.8)	79.9 starch
Powdered Skim Milk	4	352	35.8	(0.7)	51.6 lactose
Soy Flour (high fat)	8	380	41.2	12.1	33.3
Table Salt	.2	0	(0)	(0)	(0)
Table Sugar	.5	385	(0)	(0)	(99.5)
Vermont Maid Syrup (estimated)	25	286	(0)	(0)	74 glucose + fructose

*Watt, Bernice K. and Annabel L. Merrill. "Composition of Foods. Raw. Processed. Prepared." Agricultural Handbook No. 8. Revised December 1963. Superintendent of Documents, U.S. Govt. Printing Office. Washington, D.C.

each pigment has a tendency to stick or **adsorb** to the cellulose fibers, and those that stick more strongly will be slowed down the most. As a result, each substance will have its own characteristic rate of movement and the pigments will separate from each other. This is the essential principle of **chromatography.**

Chromatography has been adapted to separate all kinds of mixtures into their individual components. The substances do not have to be colored, so long as they can be identified somehow when the chromatography is finished. To make the chromatography reproducible, the mixture is applied in a tiny spot to the **matrix,** or stationary phase, which might be cellulose, silica gel, alumina, or some other inert substance. One end of the matrix is then dipped in a **solvent,** which will rise up the matrix by capillary action. As the solvent is **absorbed** and moves along, it dissolves the substances in the mixture, and allows them to migrate along the matrix. Different substances will migrate different distances. The solvent is carefully formulated so that the substances are not completely soluble in it, or they would move as rapidly as the solvent itself. They must also not be completely insoluble or they would not migrate at all. As they move they tend to adsorb or stick to the matrix to different degrees, so adsorption also helps to separate them. When the solvent has almost reached the edge of the matrix, the chromatography is stopped, and the finished **chromato-**

gram is dried after noting the exact position of the **solvent front** (the leading edge of the area wet by the solvent). Finally the individual substances are identified, and the distance moved by each one from the origin is carefully measured. This distance is compared with the distance traveled by the solvent itself: the ratio of the two is the R_f and is always constant for a given substance in a particular solvent-matrix system:

$$R_f = \frac{\text{distance traveled by substance (cm)}}{\text{distance traveled by solvent (cm)}}$$

When a protein is broken down by hydrolysis into its subunits—amino acids—the result is a mixture of 20 or more individual amino acids.

$$\text{protein} + H_2O \xrightarrow{\text{hydrolysis}} 20 \text{ amino acids}$$

How are proteins broken down during digestion in the body?

_____

_____

_____

The problem is to determine that these subunits are indeed amino acids and identify the ones present. Although each amino acid has its characteristic R_f, when 20 amino acids are involved it isn't practical to try to separate them all in a single chromatography. Instead you will try to separate a mixture of two or three at a time to see how chromatography works. The matrix you will be using is silica gel and the solvent contains butanol, acetic acid, and water. You will be given pure amino acid solutions to use as **standards** from which to calculate their correct R_f values. Then you will also chromatograph unknown solutions, calculate the R_f values of the components, and identify them by comparison with the standard R_f's. You will need three slides to run your chromatograms and will chromatograph two solutions on each slide.

■ To prepare a slide for thin layer chromatography, first stir the slurry of silica gel with the glass rod to mix it well.

■ Then use a pair of forceps to dip the clean slide into the slurry to within 5 mm of the top, gently move it back and forth to make sure it is evenly coated, and carefully withdraw it, holding it in a vertical position as you do so.

■ Let the slide dry in air, choose the most smoothly coated side, and wipe the silica gel off the *other* side with a paper towel. Touch the slide as little as possible so that you do not contaminate it with finger grease.

■ Use a teasing needle to mark the origin: make a small scratch on each edge of the silica gel layer about 1 cm from the bottom so that your slide looks like the one shown in Figure 1-2.

■ Using a separate capillary pipet for each solution as you spot, apply two standard amino acid solutions between the origin marks: touch the gel very quickly with only the end of the pipet or your spot will be too large. After the first drop dries, apply a second drop beside it. The two amino acid spots should be at least 1 cm apart, and the spots must not overlap. (See Figure 1-3.)

■ Let the spots dry thoroughly in air.

■ While your first slide is drying, prepare your second and third slides in the same way: spot two more standard amino acid solutions and two different mixtures of unknown amino acids, unknown mixtures #1 and #2. Your instructor may ask you to substitute unknown amino acids for some of the standards.

■ When you are ready to chromatograph, use forceps to set the slide *with the amino acid spots at the bottom* into a Coplin jar containing the solvent. The level of solvent

Figure 1-3. Chromatography slide after spotting samples.

should be low enough so that your spots are above, not in, the solvent at the start. (Your spots will dissolve in the solvent rather than migrate if they are in the solvent.)

■ Let the solvent move up the gel until it is within 1 cm of the top of the silica gel layer. This takes about 30 min. (See Figure 1-4.)

■ Remove the slide with forceps and immediately make a scratch mark on each edge of the silica gel to show the position of the solvent, the **solvent front.**

■ Allow nothing to touch the silica gel while you let it dry in air.

■ Use forceps to transfer the slide to the box provided for ninhydrin spraying. Ninhydrin reacts with amino acid spots to produce identifiable visible spots.

BE VERY CAREFUL WHEN USING TOXIC NINHYDRIN SPRAY AND WORK IN A FUME HOOD IF AT ALL POSSIBLE.

■ Spray the slide as demonstrated by your instructor.

■ Allow the slides to dry until colored spots appear.

Did your amino acids migrate away from the origin all right? _____

■ For each spot, record the color in Table 1-4 and measure the distance traveled. (The exact distance is the distance from the center of the original spot at the origin to the center of the colored spot.)

■ Measure the exact distance traveled by the solvent in each case, so that you can calculate the R_f values for each amino acid. (See Figure 1-5.)

■ Finally you can now identify the amino acids in your unknown amino acid mixtures by comparing the R_f of each spot with the R_f values for the standard amino acids. Since you determined the R_f values for only four amino acids, you may have to obtain R_f's from other members of the class to identify some of your unknown spots.

Return all materials and solutions and clean up your work area before leaving the laboratory. Hand in your results according to the instructions given.

Figure 1-2. Chromatography slide.

Figure 1-4. Running a chromatogram. Stop the chromatography before the solvent reaches the top of the silica gel.

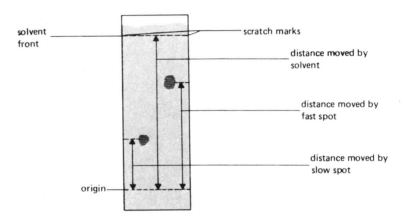

Figure 1-5. Measuring a chromatogram. Measure the distance from the origin to the center of each spot.

EXPLORING FURTHER

Baker, Jeffrey J. W., and Garland E. Allen. *Matter, Energy and Life: An Introduction to Chemical Concepts.* 4th ed. Reading, Mass.: Addison-Wesley, 1981.

Journal Articles

Block, Eric. "The chemistry of garlic and onions." *Scientific American,* 114, March 1985.

Calvin, M. *Organic Chemistry of Life: Readings from Scientific American.* San Francisco: W. H. Freeman, 1973.

Grosser, A. E. "The culinary alchemy of eggs." *American Sci.,* 71, 129–131, 1983.

Scrimshaw, Nevin S., and Lance Taylor. "Food." *Scientific American,* September 1980.

Sharon, Nathan. "Carbohydrates." *Scientific American,* November 1980.

Student Name _____ **Date** _____

TABLE 1-2. RESULTS FROM CHEMICAL TESTS

Record the results from each of the chemical tests.

Benedict's Test: green to red is positive.

Tube	Substance	Color	Reducing sugar present?
1	onion juice		
2	potato juice		
3	water		

Iodine Test: blue to black is positive

Tube	Substance	Color	Starch present?
1	onion juice		
2	potato juice		
3	water		

Sudan III Test: orange spot is positive

Code	Substance	Color of spot	Fat present?
W	water		
F	flour		
K	cream		
C	coconut		
M	margarine		

Biuret test: violet is positive

Tube	Substance	Color	Protein present?
1	egg white		
2	chicken soup		
3	water		

TABLE 1-3. UNKNOWN RESULTS

Unknown Group and Number: _____

Expected results for each possible food in each test (+ or −):

POSSIBLE UNKNOWNS IN MY UNKNOWN GROUP				
Component				
reducing sugar				
starch				
fat				
protein				

Actual results of tests (+ or −):

Test	Test Result (+ or −)	Food(s) Ruled Out
reducing sugar		
starch		
fat		
protein		

Unknown was: _____ **(Check against master key)**

Student Name _____ **Date** _____

TABLE 1-4. RESULTS FROM AMINO ACID CHROMATOGRAPHY

Standard Amino Acids	Color	Distance Moved by Amino Acid	Distance Moved by Solvent	R_f
Alanine				
Arginine				
Asparagine				
Aspartic acid				
Cysteine				
Glutamic acid				
Glutamine				
Glycine				
Histidine				
Isoleucine				
Leucine				
Lysine				
Methionine				
Phenylalanine				
Proline				
Serine				
Threonine				
Tryptophan				
Tyrosine				
Valine				
Unknown Amino Acids				
#1 =				
#2 =				
#3 =				
#4 =				
Unknown Mixture #1				
Unknown Mixture #2				

What amino acids did unknown mixture #1 contain? _____

What amino acids did unknown mixture #2 contain? _____

The Life of Cells: The Microscope

OBJECTIVES

When you have completed this topic, you should be able to:
1. Carry a microscope correctly and place it correctly on your lab desk.
2. Explain the function of each part of the microscope as shown in Figures 2–1 and 2–2.
3. Clean the microscope lenses correctly using lens paper.
4. Prepare the microscope for examining a ready-made (prepared or permanent) slide.
5. Locate the object of interest and focus on it.
6. Switch from low to high power and refocus.
7. View a slide under oil immersion, and remove the oil from the slide and lens afterward.
8. Determine the magnification of the microscope.
9. Measure a tiny object by viewing it in the microscope field at a known magnification.
10. Prepare a wet mount.
11. State the advantages and disadvantages of a compound microscope and stereomicroscope.
12. Store the microscopes properly.

KEY TOPICS

Metric units, light microscope, specimen preparation.

INTRODUCTION

The purpose of a microscope is to see inside of organisms and cells—to see what is invisible to the naked eye. The eye can be aided with a **simple microscope** which is nothing more than a magnifying glass with one lens, or with a **compound microscope** which has two lenses at opposite ends of a tube. The **ocular lens** is the one nearest the eye, and the **objective lens** is nearest the object or specimen. Both of the microscopes that you will be using today are compound and quite a bit more sophisticated than the exquisite simple microscopes with which Anthony van Leeuwenhoek made his discovery of the microbes. A microscope is a precision instrument, and easily damaged. You should not attempt to use it until you have grasped the function of each vital part.

HOW TO USE THE STEREOMICROSCOPE

This microscope has relatively low magnification, usually $4\times$ to $30\times$, and is used for viewing and manipulating larger objects. It is really two microscopes with two oculars so that objects can be viewed with binocular vision in three dimensions. Also, the depth of the field that is in focus at the same time is much greater than with the compound microscope. The light source can be directed down onto the object, in addition to or instead of up through the object, so that you can view objects too thick to transmit light. Otherwise the stereomicroscope is similar to the compound microscope that you have already used except that the magnification may be varied continuously by rotating the "zoom" knob rather than by rotating the objectives.

■ Carrying the stereomicroscope by its arm, place it on the table, and locate the following parts using Figure 2-1 as your guide.

Base with built-in illuminator

Light switch: Turns on the illuminator. Push the switch on the front of the base to turn on the light. If your microscope has a separate light source, turn it on and aim it down onto the stage.

Illumination control knob: Rotates to provide reflection or transmission or, in some microscopes, to combine transmission and reflection.

1. **Transmission:** Light travels up through specimen.
2. **Reflection:** Light is directed down onto the specimen from which it is reflected up into the microscope.
3. **Transmission-reflection:** Combines (1) and (2). Rotate the knob to get the best possible illumination for a particular sample.

Oculars: Move the oculars together or apart until you feel comfortable looking into the microscope. The two fields of view should overlap completely so that you see a single circle of light.

"Zoom" knob: Controls magnification. It is located next to the oculars on the body of the microscope. Turn it until the indicator mark is on 4× or the lowest magnification. Some microscopes have revolving objectives much like a compound microscope.

Stage: Place a small ruler on the stage.

Focus knob: A single knob that you should turn until the ruler is in sharp focus.

How big is the field under the lowest possible magnification? _____ mm

Turn the zoom knob to the highest magnification. How big is the field? _____ mm

Now look at your finger or some other handy object under low power. Is it right side up or upside down?

_____

Move your finger to the right; which way does the image move? _____

Your instructor will provide objects or cultures of biological interest for you to view in the stereomicroscope such as:

insect	*Volvox*
leaf	*Planaria*
fungus	*Hydra*

If you want to look at a liquid culture, place a few drops in a depression slide or small dish.

When you are finished, remove the sample, turn off the light, clean the lenses with lens paper, cover the stereomicroscope, and store it in its box or cabinet.

You can see that this microscope is extremely useful when a small amount of magnification is needed, or when you need to manipulate or dissect things too small to be seen with the naked eye. One task that is greatly facilitated under a stereoscope is removing scratches from a stereo record with a fine needle: the grooves that have been crushed can be easily straightened out again so that the needle no longer skips. Similar microscopes are used in human microsurgery.

Figure 2-1. Stereomicroscope. Your microscope may be similar to the one shown in this diagram. Your instructor may be able to provide a diagram that represents your microscope exactly.

Figure 2-2. Compound microscope. Your microscope is similar to the one shown in this diagram. Some of the parts that may not be present on your microscope are marked (*).

HOW TO USE THE COMPOUND MICROSCOPE

Identifying the Parts

Study figure 2-2 as you locate each of the following:

Arm: Supports the body tube and is the part that you can grasp to carry the microscope. Pick up your microscope by its arm, keeping it upright, and supporting it underneath with your free hand. Set it gently on your lab desk.

Base: Gives the microscope a firm, steady support.

Ocular lens: Magnifies ten times (10×). This lens is often unattached, and thus it may fall out unless the microscope is kept upright.

Objective lens: Magnifies the object by the factor marked on the particular lens. Low power (10×) gives the smallest image, high power (sometimes called high dry) gives a large image (40×), and oil immersion gives the largest image (100×). Sometimes a very low power scan objective (4×) replaces the oil immersion lens. Objective lenses are always used in order: low, high, oil immersion.

Nosepiece: The revolving part to which objectives are attached. It must be firmly clicked into position when the objective is changed. Rough treatment can cause it to snap off.

Body tube: Joins the nosepiece to the ocular lens.

Stage: Supports the slide that is held onto it by **stage clips,** and has a hole so that light can shine up through the specimen. Always center the specimen over this hole.

Course adjustment: Moves the body tube or stage up and down, depending on the design of the microscope, to approximately the right position so that the specimen is in focus. This knob is used only with the **low power** or **scan** (focus finder) **objective.**

Fine adjustment: Moves the body tube (or stage) up and down to precisely the right position so that the specimen is perfectly in focus. Use it to achieve fine focus with the low power objective and for *all focusing* with the high power and oil immersion objectives.

Light source: Usually a small electric light beneath the stage that is controlled by a push-button light switch. Sometimes a mirror is used to reflect light from another source into the microscope.

Iris diaphragm: Regulates how much light and lamp heat go through the specimen. It is controlled by a lever that is moved back and forth.

Condenser: A lens (substage condenser or light director), located above the diaphragm, which concentrates the light before it passes through the specimen. Its position is controlled by a knob on microscopes in which it is adjustable.

Observer: The microscope is useless when the observer *looks* but does not see.

Cleaning the Lenses

Clean lenses are necessary for a clear view of your specimen.

NOTHING SHOULD TOUCH THE MICROSCOPE LENSES EXCEPT THE SPECIAL LENS PAPER AND APPROPRIATE SOLVENT.

Use a clean piece of lens paper to wipe the ocular and objective lenses. Sometimes you may need to moisten the lens paper with alcohol or xylene to remove grease or oil which will blur the image. Follow the directions of your instructor regarding the use of solvent.

> If there's dirt in your microscope scene,
> Use only lens paper to clean,
> If you do it just right,
> Your field will be bright,
> If not, you can try some xylene.

Viewing a Prepared Slide

Develop familiarity with your microscope by looking at a prepared slide of a letter ("e," "k," and so on) or some other object.

■ First click the lowest power objective into position.
■ Then use the coarse adjustment to raise the ocular (or lower the stage) as far as possible.
■ Place the slide (oriented so that you can read the letter "e" properly) on the stage and position the letter over the hole in the stage.
■ Now look through the microscope and adjust the diaphragm lever (and condenser knob) so that enough light is coming through to make the field bright.

In which direction do you move the lever to increase the amount of light? _____

■ View the objective lens *from the side* and turn the coarse adjustment until the lens *almost* touches the slide.

Did you have to turn the knob toward you or away from you? _____

■ Look into the microscope and slowly turn the coarse adjustment in the opposite direction so that the objective lens is moving *away* from the slide.
■ Continue turning until the letter "e" comes into focus.

Remember that the coarse adjustment is used only on low power, so that you should not have to use it again with this slide.

■ Finish focusing with the fine adjustment knob.

Does the object appear normal or upside down?

■ Move the slide a tiny bit away from you while observing the object in the microscope.

Does it move away from you or toward you?

■ Move the slide back and forth and note that the inverted image always moves in the direction opposite to the direction in which the slide is moved.
■ Center the image in the middle of the field of view.
■ Move the high power lens into position, making sure that it clicks in correctly; you may have to focus a little with the fine focus adjustment knob but do *not* touch the coarse focus adjustment; you may also have to increase the amount of light in order to have a clear view.

If you do not see anything in the field, you probably did not have the image properly centered. Return to low power, center the image, and then switch to high power. Only the central portion of the low power field is visible under high power. Ask your instructor for help if you are still having trouble.

■ When you have finished viewing the letter and are ready to go on, return to low power, turn the coarse adjustment knob to move the objective away from the slide, and return the slide to the front desk.

Using Oil Immersion

Learn to use oil immersion by viewing one of the designated slides. In this technique the resolution of the image is increased by filling the space between the oil immersion lens and the slide with oil. It works because oil has a much higher index of refraction than air and contributes to the magnification of the image.

OIL IS USED ONLY WITH THE OIL IMMERSION LENS. DO NOT USE OIL WITH ANY OF THE OTHER LENSES.

■ With your low power lens in position, locate the object and center it in the field.
■ Switch to high power and refocus.
■ Swing the high power lens away from the slide, and place a drop of immersion oil in the center and cover slip and over the specimen.
■ Swing the oil immersion lens into position and refocus using the fine focus only. Note the improved resolution obtained by using immersion oil.
■ When you are finished viewing, swing the immersion lens away, but do not put any other lens into position. Raise the body tube with the coarse adjustment and remove the slide. First wipe most of the oil off with lens paper, then use a piece of lens paper wet with xylene to wipe off the rest of the oil off the lens and the slide. Finally, wipe the lens and slide with dry lens paper.
■ Click the low power lens into position and you are ready to go on.

Computing Magnification

Magnification is a measure of how big an object looks to your eye compared to "life size". Life size images are specified as 1. Magnification is usually written by a number followed by "×," which stands for "times life size" (for example, 10× means 10 times life size). A simple lens like magnifying glass magnifies 3× to 10× or so. A compound light microscope can magnify things up to 1000×. **Resolution,** on the other hand, measures how clearly you can see details in the microscope, and is usually given as the distance between two objects that can just barely be resolved. It depends in part on the quality of the lenses used. Resolution increases with magnification up to a theoretical limit: the maximum resolution in an ordinary light microscope is $1/2$ λ where λ is the wavelength of light used. If λ = 500 nm, as in green light, the resolution is $1/2$ × 500 nm = 250 nm (0.25 μm).* The use of immersion oil will increase the resolving power somewhat to about 0.18μm.

The ocular lens on your microscope gives 10× magnification of the image made by the objective lens. The objective lens magnifies the object 4× or more, so total magnification is the magnification of the first lens *times* the magnification of the second lens. The magnification of the objective lens may be 4×, 10×, 40×, or 100×. Fill in the magnifications of the objective lenses of your microscope and the total magnification:

Ocular	Objective	Total Magnification
10×	_____×	_____×
10×	_____×	_____×
10×	_____×	_____×
10×	_____×	_____×

Measuring Objects in the Microscope

If the field of view is a certain size under the lowest power or magnification, it will be correspondingly *smaller* as the power is increased. If the magnification is known, the relative sizes of the two fields can be calculated.

■ Place a ruler on your stage and measure the size of the field under the lowest magnification:

$$\text{field} = \underline{\hspace{1cm}} \text{ mm (a)}$$

$$\text{lowest total magnification} = \underline{\hspace{1cm}} \times \text{ (b)}$$

■ Switch to another magnification:

$$\text{total magnification} = \underline{\hspace{1cm}} \times \text{ (d)}$$

■ Calculate the field size of the second magnification where:

$$\begin{array}{cccc} \text{(a)} & \text{(b)} & \text{(c)} & \text{(d)} \end{array}$$
$$\text{field 1} \times \text{magnification 1} = \text{field 2} \times \text{magnification 2}$$

$$\text{field 2} = c = \frac{a \times b}{d} = \underline{\hspace{1cm}} \text{ mm}$$

■ Calculate the approximate field sizes in μm for your microscope and enter in the following table:

Objective	Total Magnification	Field size in μm
scan	_____×	_____ μm
low power	_____×	_____ μm
high power	_____×	_____ μm
oil immersion	_____×	_____ μm

Once the size of the field in micrometers is known, it is possible to estimate the size of an object by comparing its size to the size of the field. For example, suppose an object is one-half the diameter of the field under low power. The size of the field is 1500 μm under low power. The size of the object is

$$1/2 \times 1500 \ \mu\text{m} = 750 \ \mu\text{m}$$

■ Obtain a prepared slide containing small organisms.
■ View the slide under low power and determine whether higher magnification is needed to determine the size of the organisms.
■ Switch to higher powers if necessary.
■ Note the size of the organism relative to the diameter of the field, and record the objective lens used, the magnification, and the size of the field in the following chart.
■ Calculate the approximate size of the organism in micrometers.

Organism measured	
Objective lens	
Total magnification	
Size of field (μm)	
Relative size of organism	
Size of organism (μm)	

Preparing a Wet Mount

Wet mounts are used to study fresh, living material. They can be used only for a little while because they will soon dry out, but they are useful for observing qualities such as color, movement, or behavior that cannot be observed on dead, stained material. Follow the steps shown in Figure 2-3 to prepare your wet mount.

■ Obtain a slide, coverslip, and teasing needle from your instructor.
■ Place a drop of the sample on your slide; it will contain some interesting living organisms.
■ Touch the coverslip to one edge of the drop, and gently lower it with the teasing needle, as shown.

---

*Refer to the description of metric units in Appendix D if these terms are unfamiliar to you.

Figure 2-3. Wet mount. Mount your living specimen as shown to avoid trapping air bubbles under the coverslip.

If you have been careful, the slide will not have any bubbles. If not, you will see them as circles of various sizes with very dark edges when you look at your sample.

■ Locate your organism under low power and then switch to high power.
■ Make a sketch of what you see and record the total magnification:

Total magnification = _____ ×

Identify the organism if you can:

_____

_____

_____

■ When you are finished, discard the coverslip and clean the slide.

Studying Biological Organisms

Your instructor will provide cultures of living organisms or prepared slides for you to study in the microscope. Always view the organisms under low power first, then increase the magnification as necessary. You may be asked to sketch and estimate the size of the following organisms:

yeast	*Paramecium caudatum*	*Amoeba*
Volvox	*Paramecium bursaria*	*Euplotes*
Spirogyra	*Chlamydomonas*	*Stentor*

Storing the Microscope

■ Return to the low power objective.
■ Raise the body tube or lower the stage with the coarse adjustment so the lenses can't strike the stage accidentally.
■ Clean all lenses with lens paper and (if you have not already done so) clean the oil immersion lens with xylene.
■ Turn off the light.
■ Cover the microscope, if there is a cover for it.
■ Pick up the microscope by its arm, supporting it under the base, and return it to its storage box or cabinet.

EXPLORING FURTHER

Corrington, Julian D. *Getting Acquainted with the Microscope.* Rochester: Bausch and Lomb, 1969.

Headstrom, Richard. *Adventures with a Microscope.* New York: Dover Publications, 1977.

_____. *Adventures with a Hand Lens.* New York: Dover Publications, 1976.

Leeuwenhoek, Antony van. *Antony van Leeuwenhoek and his Little Animals.* New York: Dover Publications, 1960.

Journal Articles

Fein, Jack M. "Microvascular surgery for stroke." *Scientific American,* April 1978 (#1385).

Quate, Calvin F. "The acoustic microscope." *Scientific American,* October 1979 (#3061).

The Life of Cells: Organization and Reproduction

OBJECTIVES

When you have completed this topic, you should be able to:
1. Describe the structures that you can expect to see in a typical plant cell with the light microscope.
2. Describe the structures that you can expect to see in a typical animal cell with the light microscope.
3. Describe how a bacterial cell looks under the light microscope.
4. Explain how a prokaryotic cell such as a bacterium basically differs from a typical eukaryotic cell.
5. Describe the 4 stages of the cell cycle.
6. Describe what you look for in the microscope during interphase and in each stage of mitosis.
7. Identify in the microscope which stage of mitosis an animal or plant cell has reached.
8. Describe the main differences between mitosis in a plant cell and in an animal cell.

KEY TOPICS

Light microscopy, staining, cell structure, prokaryotic cells, eukaryotic cells, cell cycle, mitosis.

INTRODUCTION

In today's laboratory you will study biology from the viewpoint of the individual cell. Although the cell is considered to be the building block of all organisms, because it can carry on all activities associated with living things, cells differ enormously in shape, size, and capability. **Prokaryotic cells** are less complex, are usually found only in unicellular organisms, and have more limited capabilities than **eukaryotic cells.** Higher organisms are made up of highly integrated aggregations of specialized eukaryotic cells, but some sophisticated organisms consist of a single eukaryotic cell.

No one cell can be considered "typical," so you will be studying several examples. Every cell (with some highly specialized exceptions) has **DNA** or a **nucleus, cytoplasm,** and a **cell membrane.** It also has many organelles, vital to its survival, which are too tiny to be

seen in the light microscope and consequently cannot be studied here.

Cells come into existence through the division of their parent cells, and most cells divide in turn to produce daughter cells. Usually this occurs during **mitosis,** when the genetic material is duplicated, and one copy is passed on to each daughter cell. Mitosis is generally followed by **cytokinesis,** or cytoplasmic division, in which the rest of the cell divides in half to form two new cells. Sometimes cytokinesis does not occur, and a cell with many nuclei may form. In animals such a cell is called a **syncytium,** and in plants it is termed a **coenocyte.**

Mitosis is part of the **cell cycle.** Trace one turn of the cycle in Figure 3-1. During G₁ (first gap) the decision to begin the process of cell division is made. DNA replication occurs in the **S** (synthesis) period. At this time each chromosome doubles so that it consists of two **sister chromatids** joined by the **centromere.** Although

19

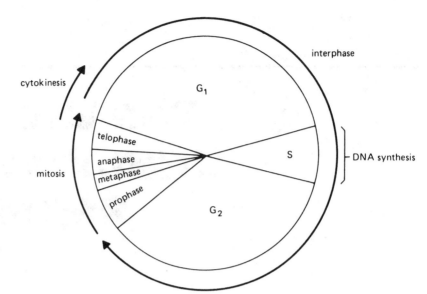

Figure 3-1. The cell cycle. The decision to divide occurs in G_1, the chromosomes are replicated in S, the preparations for cell division are made in G_2, the nucleus divides in mitosis, and the cell cytoplasm divides in cytokinesis.

the chromosomes are uncoiled and therefore invisible in the light microscope at this time, chemical techniques can be used to show that the chromosomes are replicating. The replicated chromosomes that appear at the beginning of mitosis are double-stranded and one strand enters each of the daughter cells. The two daughter cells produced by mitosis are exactly equivalent to the parent cell and can be thought of as carbon copies. The **G_2** period precedes **M** or mitosis, the brief part of the cycle during which discrete chromosomes are visible.

A "TYPICAL" CELL

No one cell will show all the features that a cell might have, so you will instead look at three ordinary cells to see what they are like. The first two have a true nucleus with a nuclear membrane and other characteristics not found in prokaryotes.

Onion Epidermis (Eukaryotic Plant Cell)

■ Break or cut off with a razor blade a piece of a single layer of onion from within the onion (the outermost layer may contain only dead cells). See Figure 3-2.
■ Return the onion to its storage container.

■ Snap the piece in half and then use forceps to peel off a bit of tissuelike transparent epidermis from the inner layer as shown in Figure 3-2.
■ Mount the epidermis in tap water on a slide so that it is flat and not doubled over on itself. Add a coverslip.
■ View the slide under low power.

What is the shape of the cells?

_____

What is the thick layer that surrounds each of the cells?

_____

What does the clear part of each cell contain?

_____

If you are looking at a confusing mix of overlapping cell parts, you probably do not have a good piece of epidermis. Ask your instructor for help. Some cells will not have a **vacuole,** if they are young. Also, the **cell membrane,** which lines the inner surface of the cell wall, is too thin to be seen in the light microscope, but you can see exactly where it must be.

■ Raise the coverslip and add a drop of 45% acetocarmine dye; this will stain the **cytoplasm** and **nucleus** of your cells pink or red.
■ Distinguish between the vacuoles and the cytoplasm. The cytoplasm is within the cell membrane and is "living," whereas the contents of the vacuoles are often inert storage materials.

Figure 3-2. Onion skin. The desired epidermis is extremely thin and transparent.

■ Locate the nucleus, which now should be red.

What kinds of molecules are located in the nucleus?

_____

_____

What is the function of the nucleus?

_____

■ In the space provided in Figure 3-5 (at the end of this topic), make a sketch of the onion cell to show the parts that you saw.

SKETCHES FOR THIS LAB SHOULD BE MADE IN THE SPACES PROVIDED AT THE END OF THE EXERCISE. YOUR INSTRUCTOR MAY ASK THAT THEY BE HANDED IN WHEN YOU LEAVE.

■ When you are finished with each specimen, discard the coverslip and clean the slide for the next specimen. Your instructor will tell you whether you should discard, rather than wash, a slide on which you used stain.

Human Cheek Epithelium (Eukaryotic Animal Cell)

■ Use a clean toothpick to scrape the inside of your cheek gently.
■ Stir the scrapings into a drop of tap water and add a drop of methylene blue dye to stain the cheek cells. Add a coverslip.
■ View your cells under low power and locate some that are spread out rather than bunched up in a big clump.

The cells you are looking for are pale blue and have a very dark blue **nucleus.** You may see some that are folded over so that you can see how flat they are.

■ Switch to high power and take a closer look at one of the cells.

What shape is the cell?

_____

Do you see a vacuole or cell wall?_____

Again, you cannot see the **cell membrane** but can assume it surrounds the **cytoplasm.**

■ Look closely at the **nucleus** and locate the **nucleolus** within it (try another cell if necessary).

What is the function of the nucleolus?

_____

This cell is highly specialized and has a protective function. As a result, it cannot carry out certain functions found in other animal cells.

What are some of these functions?

_____

_____

_____

Bacterium (Prokaryotic Cell)

■ Use a toothpick to place a tiny dab of yogurt on your slide. Add a small drop of tap water and stir the toothpick around to spread out the cells. Add a coverslip.
■ Focus on the slide under low power and then switch to high power.

The swarms of **rod-shaped** organisms that you see are cells of yogurt bacterium *Lactobacillus*. These bacteria are adapted to live on milk sugar (lactose) and are used by human beings to convert ordinary milk into yogurt, which is acidic and keeps much longer than milk.

■ Add a drop of immersion oil to your slide and view the bacteria under oil immersion if your microscope has an oil immersion lens.

Can you see any structure within the cells?

_____

Bacteria have tough **cell walls** but do not have any of the membrane-bound organelles that are found in eukaryotic cells.

What organelle is found in both eukaryotic and prokaryotic cells? _____

If time permits, look at some of your own oral bacteria:

■ Use a clean toothpick to scrape some of the tartar from between your teeth.
■ Smear out the scum on a slide and pass the slide over the small flame of an alcohol lamp or Bunsen burner to fix the cells onto the slide.
■ Add a drop of crystal violet stain and wait 1 min.
■ Wash off the excess dye with a gentle stream of water and blot off the excess water with a tissue, being careful not to touch the spot where the bacteria are.
■ If you have an oil immersion lens, let the slide dry and then add a drop of oil and view under oil immersion.
■ If you do not have oil immersion, add a drop of water and coverslip and view under high power.

The bacteria are tiny and darkly stained. They may be rod-shaped, round, or spiral-shaped, and some may stick together in clumps. Choose some different types and draw what you see in the space in Figure 3-5 at the end of this topic.

■ If a demonstration slide is available, view the three main types of bacteria using oil immersion.

What shapes can you see?_____

_____

_____

MITOSIS IN AN ANIMAL CELL

An animal cell about to undergo mitosis has already replicated its DNA during the S period of interphase.

How many strands does each chromosome have?

_____

What are the strands called?_____

The **centrioles,** pairs of organelles, found only in animal cells, have also replicated. The daughter centrioles

22   TOPIC 3 ■ THE LIFE OF CELLS: ORGANIZATION AND REPRODUCTION

move to the opposite ends or **poles** of the cell, and their position determines how the chromosomes will move during mitosis. The chromosomes always move toward the centrioles, and the cell always divides in a plane perpendicular to a line joining them.

Centrioles have an interesting structure closely related to that of cilia and flagella. They are little cylinders made of nine triplets of microtubules, and each centriole is made of two such cylinders at right angles. They determine the orientation of the **mitotic spindle,** which is also composed of microtubules and extends from one centriole to the other. During mitosis, the chromosomes move along fibers in the mitotic spindle, and gather at the poles of the cell. The position of the centrioles determines the orientation of the **astral rays,** microtubules extending out from the centrioles in all directions. The function of these astral rays is not known.

The centrioles, mitotic spindle, and astral rays are collectively called the **mitotic apparatus,** and take up much of the interior of the cell when it is in mitosis. Mitosis requires a great deal of energy, so there are many mitochondria associated with the mitotic apparatus to provide energy for synthesis and chromosome movement.

■ View a prepared slide of animal cells undergoing mitosis, such as the cells in whitefish embryos, first under low, and then under high power in your microscope.
■ Locate cells that are undergoing mitosis, some of which have large, prominent mitotic spindles and condensed chromosomes.
■ Using the following descriptions and Figure 3-3 as your guide, locate cells which represent interphase, each of the stages of mitosis and cytokinesis.

Interphase (G_1-S-G_2)

During interphase, the genetic material is in the form of greatly extended fibers of DNA that form a tangled mass called **chromatin.** The fibers are too small to be seen in the microscope so the nucleus looks homogeneous. The nucleus is bounded by the double **nuclear membrane,** and contains **nucleoli,** which are centers for the synthesis of RNA. They may not be visible in every cell.

How many nucleoli do you see in the interphase cells?

_____

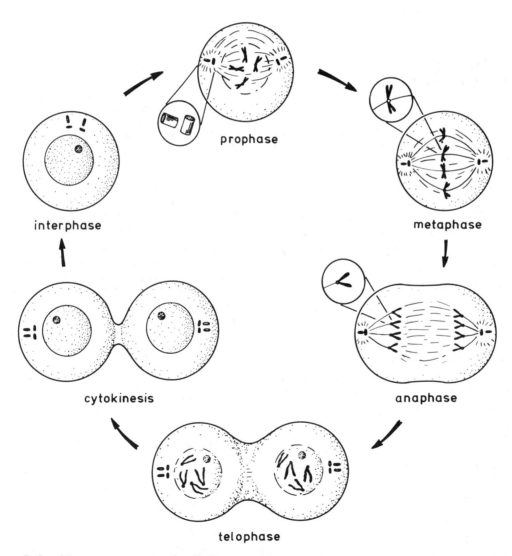

interphase

prophase

metaphase

anaphase

telophase

cytokinesis

Figure 3-3. Mitosis in an animal cell. Since mitosis is a continuous process, each stage blends into the next. Note the centrioles and the astral rays not found in plant cells.

Prophase (M)

As the cell enters prophase, the chromatin starts to condense into discrete chromosomes, the nucleoli disappear, and the nuclear membrane breaks down. By the end of prophase, the centrioles have migrated to opposite poles, the chromosomes are moving to the center of the cell, and the mitotic spindle starts to appear.

Metaphase (M)

The spindle forms, and the chromosomes take up positions on the **metaphase plate,** an imaginary plane in the middle of the cell halfway between the two poles. They are located on the outside of the spindle, so they would be arranged in a circle if you viewed them from one of the poles. Each double-stranded chromosome is attached to a **spindle fiber** at its centromere, and its flexible arms are free to move about.

Anaphase (M)

Metaphase ends and anaphase begins when the centromere of each chromosome divides. Each sister chromatid now has its own centromere, and is called a chromosome, so that there are twice as many chromosomes as there were during metaphase.

If a certain cell has three pairs of chromosomes (N = 3), how many chromosomes does the cell have during metaphase?

_____

How many chromosomes does it have during anaphase?

_____

Spindle fibers, attached to the centromeres, cause chromosomes to move, with the arms of the chromosomes trailing passively behind. A chromosome without a centromere will not move during anaphase, and is randomly left behind in one of the two daughter cells.

Telophase (M)

The chromosomes gather at the poles in telophase, and begin to form the daughter nuclei. Since each original chromosome in the cell contributed a chromosome identical to itself to each new nucleus, the two daughter nuclei will be identical to the nucleus of the parent cell. The nuclear membrane begins to reform, the nucleoli reappear, and the chromosomes begin to unwind and disappear from view. At the end of telophase, the nuclei look like interphase nuclei, and in fact have entered interphase of the next cell cycle.

Cytokinesis (M-G₁)

Cytokinesis, or division of the cytoplasm, usually accompanies telophase. In animal cells the membrane constricts in a ring around the middle of the cell, and eventually pinches the cell in two. In embryos this ring is called the **cleavage furrow.** The cytoplasm and all its constitu-

ents are passively divided so that each cell gets about half the materials and organelles in the cell.

Why couldn't the chromosomes be passively divided when the cell pinches in two?

_____

_____

MITOSIS IN A PLANT CELL

■ View a prepared slide of plant cells undergoing mitosis, such as the root tip cells of an onion, first under low and then under high power. In the onion root tip, look at the cells near, but not at, the very tip of the root in the region marked "X" in Figure 3-4. Avoid the cells in the very center.
■ Locate cells in interphase, each stage of mitosis, and in cytokinesis. If the section does not happen to pass through the nucleus of a cell, that cell will appear to have no nucleus, and should be skipped.
■ Draw an onion cell in one stage of mitosis in Figure 3-5, at the end of this topic.

Note the following differences between mitosis in the plant cells compared with mitosis in the animal cells that you have seen:

1. **Interphase.** The nuclei look similar to the animal cell nuclei, but may have a different number of nucleoli.

How many nucleoli do the onion cells have?

_____

2. **Prophase.** There are no centrioles in plant cells, and you will not see any astral rays. Otherwise the events of prophase are similar.

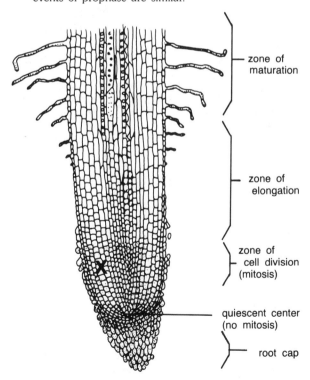

Figure 3-4. Onion root tip. Look at the position marked **X** to find dividing cells.

3. **Metaphase.** Events are similar to those in the animal cell. You will see the spindle but no astral rays.
4. **Anaphase.** Events are similar to those in the animal cell.
5. **Telophase.** Events are similar to those in the animal cell. In plants, telophase cells can be easily distinguished because you will see two nuclei within a cell that is about the same size as the other cells that have only one nucleus. The two new daughter cells together are the same size as the parent cell, and look like mirror images. Growth of the cells will occur later on.
6. **Cytokinesis.** This process is completely different in plant cells. The parent cell does not pinch in or change shape at all. Instead, membrane vesicles form in the metaphase plate, and coalesce to form a cell plate, or **middle lamella,** dividing the two daughter cells. Cellulose is laid down on either side of this plate to eventually form cell walls between the two new cells. Each cell then begins to elongate in its long dimension until it is as big as the parent cell, and can enter another cycle of mitosis.

Working with your partner, determine the stage of mitosis in 100 cells, and record your results in Table 3-1 at the end of this topic.

■ Move your slide until you have the field filled with an area where there are many cells undergoing mitosis (you should be viewing under high power).
■ Place the pointer on a vertical row of cells, or make a mental note as to which row you are going to count.
■ Indicate the stage of each cell in turn to your partner as you go down the row. Do not leave out any cells unless there is no nucleus visible at all.
■ As each cell is staged, your partner should make a check next to that stage in the table.
■ When you have counted about 50 cells, change places, and let your partner stage the rest.
■ Continue until you have counted exactly 100 cells.

It is known that onion root tip cells take about 16 hr to complete the mitotic cycle. By determining the percentage of cells in each stage of mitosis and in interphase, you can calculate the amount of time spent in each stage. For example, if 10 cells out of 100 were found to be in prophase, the percentage of cells in prophase is $10/100 \times 100 = 10\%$. This shows that any one cell spends 10% of the time in prophase, so it

spends 0.10×16 hr or 1.6 hr (1 hr and 36 min, since 0.1 hr = 6 min) in that stage.

■ Calculate the percentage of cells in each stage, and enter the results in Table 3-1. (There is no calculation if you counted exactly 100 cells; just enter the number of cells.) You may be asked to use the combined totals of the class for your calculation.
■ Calculate the hours and minutes spent in each stage, if the entire cell cycle takes 16 hr (0.1 hr = 6 min).

When you have finished, return all of your slides and materials and properly store your microscope.

EXPLORING FURTHER

Brock, Thomas D. et al *Biology of Microorganisms.* 4th ed. Englewood Cliffs, New Jersey: Prentice-Hall, 1984.
DeRobertis, E. D. P., and E. M. F. De Robertis. *Cell and Molecular Biology.* 7th ed. Philadelphia: W. B. Saunders, 1980.
Giese, A. C. *Cell Physiology.* 5th ed. Philadelphia: W. B. Saunders, 1979.
Nester, E. W., C. E. Evans, M. E. Lidstrom, N. N. Pearsall and M. T. Nester. *Microbiology.* 3rd ed. Philadelphia: Saunders College Publishing, 1983.

Journal Articles

Albrecht-Buehler, Guenter. "The tracks of moving cells." *Scientific American,* April 1978 (#1386).
Dustin, Pierre. "Microtubules." *Scientific American,* August, 1980 (#1477).
Lazarides, Elias, and Jean Paul Revel. "The molecular basis of cell movement." *Scientific American,* May 1979 (#1427).
Margulis, Lynn. "The origin of plant and animal cells." *American Scientist 59:*230, 1971.
Mazia, Daniel. "The cell cycle." *Scientific American,* January 1974 (#1288).
Porter, Keith R., and Jonathan B. Tucker. "The ground substance of the living cell." *Scientific American,* March 1981.
Sloboda, Roger D. "The role of microtubules in cell structure and cell division." *American Scientist 68:*290, 1980.

Student Name _____ **Date** _____

Sketch of an onion skin cell.

Sketch of bacteria.

Sketch of an onion root cell in mitosis: stage is _____

Figure 3-5. **Observations.** Note the magnification used in each case.

Student Name _____ **Date** _____

TABLE 3-1. DATA ON MITOTIC STAGES IN PLANT CELLS

Make a check in the appropriate box for each cell staged. Then total the checks.

Number of Cells in Stage	Total	% in Stage	Hr and Min in Stage
Interphase:			
Prophase:			
Metaphase:			
Anaphase:			
Telophase:			

The Life of Cells: Membranes

OBJECTIVES _____

When you have completed this topic, you should be able to:
1. Define solute, solvent, and chemical gradient.
2. Define the following processes and identify the characteristics that distinguish them from one another: diffusion, osmosis, active transport.
3. Give three factors that affect the rate of diffusion and state whether they increase or decrease the rate.
4. Define and use correctly the following terms: osmotic pressure, selectively permeable, hypertonic, isotonic, hypotonic.
5. Describe what happens when an animal cell and a plant cell are put into distilled water; and then describe what happens when they are put into a concentrated salt solution; use the following terms correctly in your answer: turgor pressure, plasmolysis, lysis, hypertonic, hypotonic, osmosis.
6. State the function of the contractile vacuole in protozoans like *Paramecium* and *Amoeba.*
7. State the function of the central vacuole and tonoplast in plant cells.
8. Given any two solutions of different osmotic potentials that are separated by a selectively permeable membrane, state which solution is hypertonic and in which direction there will be a net flow of water.

KEY TOPICS _____

Diffusion, dialysis, osmosis, permeability, active transport, cell membrane.

INTRODUCTION

In this exercise you will study two ways in which substances move into and out of cells: diffusion and active transport.

What kinds of substances must enter a typical human cell?

_____

_____

What kinds of substances must move out of such a cell?

_____

_____

Cell membranes are selectively permeable in that only certain substances may pass through them.

Do hydrophobic or hydrophilic substances pass more readily through a cell membrane?

_____

If you put a high concentration of a solid substance, the **solute,** into a liquid, the **solvent,** the randomly moving molecules of the dissolving solute will spread throughout the liquid. This spontaneous or "downhill" process is called **diffusion** and it does not require any input of energy. As they spread out, the molecules form a **concentration gradient** or **chemical gradient** with the highest concentration near the dissolving solute and the lowest concentration farthest away. The diffusing molecules will tend to move down the concentration gradient from a higher to lower concentration until they reach equilibrium. Then they will be spread out evenly and there will be no further *net* movement. The free en-

27

ergy of the solution will be *lower* and the entropy (disorder) will be *higher* after diffusion has occured.

Diffusion takes place rapidly in a gas, but more slowly in a liquid or solid. You are experiencing both types of diffusion when you smell odors. Diffusion in air is followed by diffusion in a liquid, as the chemical odor reaches your nasal membranes, where it must dissolve before exciting the sensory cells.

When diffusion occurs across a cell membrane, solutes may pass into or out of the cell in the process called **dialysis.** Each solute will move from the side where its concentration is higher to the side with a lower concentration, because the direction of movement by diffusion is always down the concentration gradient. Its movement will be independent of the movement of the other solutes.

In the special case of diffusion where the substance diffusing across the membrane is water, the process is called **osmosis.** During osmosis, water will flow from the side with the most water and lower solute concentration, to the side with the lower water and higher solute concentration.

The solution with the lower solute concentration is **hypotonic** relative to the other solution. Conversely the more concentrated solution is **hypertonic** relative to the first. **Osmotic pressure** is a quantitative measure of the force needed to oppose osmosis from pure water into a solution. It is proportional to the concentration of particles in the solution: The hypotonic solution will have a lower osmotic pressure than the hypertonic one.

PURE WATER HAS AN OSMOTIC PRESSURE OF ZERO AND IS THE MOST HYPOTONIC SOLUTION POSSIBLE.

Cells cannot control the process of osmosis directly since cell membranes are freely permeable to water, and since osmosis is a spontaneous downhill process requiring no energy input. Cells can and must control their water content, however, in order to keep their solutes at the correct concentrations required for life processes to function. They can do this by removing excess water with special structures such as the contractile vacuole of protozoans, or they can increase their solute concentration, permitting water to enter the cell by osmosis.

Many substances are brought into the cell or removed from the cell *against* their chemical gradients in the process of **active transport.** Since this is an uphill process, a biologically active membrane that can utilize energy from cell respiration is required. The process of active transport is highly specific in that each particular substance to be carried across the membrane must be transported by a specific carrier molecule. The carriers are membrane proteins, and their transport function must always be coupled with cell respiration. If there is no cell respiration, or if the integrity of the membrane is destroyed, active transport cannot occur.

DIFFUSION

Diffusion of a Liquid in a Liquid

Since liquids are highly sensitive to convection currents, the success of the experiment depends on not allowing

your setup to be disturbed or jiggled once the experiment is under way.

■ Fill a small beaker with water and set it in a protected place. Wait 10 min.
■ Add a drop of red dye to the surface of the solution as gently as possible. Try not to disturb the surface, but hold the dropper as close to it as you can.
■ Watch the dye spread through the solution from time to time during the lab period.

At the end of period answer the following questions:

Is the **concentration** of the colored part of the solution greater at the beginning or end of the experiment?

_____

Is the **free energy** of the solution greater at the beginning or at the end? _____

Is the **entropy** of the solution greater at the beginning or at the end? _____

What difference would you have seen if you had originally set up the beaker in the refrigerator?

_____

_____

Diffusion in a Solid

The solid you will use is agar, which is clear like jello so you can see what is happening. The substances that will be diffusing are solids that react with each other to give colored compounds. The position of the colored bands shows where the two substances first come in contact. The band will be closer to the substance that diffuses more slowly. The setup for this experiment is shown in Figure 4-1.

■ Take a Petri dish of 1.5% agar and turn it upside down. Make a dot near one edge and label it A. Use a ruler to measure 15 mm from A and make a second dot B. Make dots C and D also exactly 15 mm from A and as evenly spaced as you can.
■ Use a cork borer to make holes in the agar at A, B, C, and D. Work carefully and slowly so you don't damage the agar.

DIFFUSION IN AGAR

Figure 4-1. Diffusion in a solid. A Petri dish of agar has four holes filled with the following solutions. A contains 1 M $AgNO_3$; B contains 1 M NaCl; C contains 1 M KBr; and D contains 1 M $K_3Fe(CN)_6$. Run the experiment in the dark.

■ Use a Pasteur pipet or dropper to add these solutions to the corresponding holes. Be careful *not to overfill the holes* and try to fill them all to about the same level.

A: 1 M AgNO$_3$ silver nitrate
B: 1 M NaCl   sodium chloride
C: 1 M KBr   potassium bromide
D: 1 M K$_3$Fe(CN)$_6$ potassium ferricyanide

■ Place the Petri dish in the dark and check it from time to time until you can see colored bands forming where the solutions meet solution A.

Ag$^+$ will react with negative ions from the other solutions to give colored substances. Record what colors appear in Table 4-1 at the end of this topic.

■ Measure the distance between each hole and the colored band, and record it in the table. Then calculate the ratio of the distance each ion moved from holes B, C, and D versus the distance moved by the Ag$^+$ ion: Cl$^-$ distance/Ag$^+$ distance, and so on. Record these ratios in the table. Since time is constant, the ratio of distances traveled is equal to the ratio of rates.

$$\frac{D_1}{D_2} = \frac{R_1}{R_2}$$

Rank the relative rates of the Cl$^-$, Br$^-$, and Fe(CN)$_6^{\equiv}$ ion as slow, faster, or fastest.

As you might expect, the larger an ion is, the slower it will diffuse through the agar. Given that the molecular weights (MW) of the ions in holes B, C, and D can be ranked Cl$^-$ < Br$^-$ < Fe(CN)$_6^{\equiv}$, which ion should move fastest?

_____

Which should move slowest? _____

Did your results agree with your expectations?

_____

Calculating Diffusion Rates

The diffusion rate is inversely related to the square root of the molecular weight, so the ratio of rates will be

$$\frac{\text{rate}_1 = \dfrac{1}{\sqrt{MW_1}}}{\text{rate}_2 = \dfrac{1}{\sqrt{MW_2}}} \text{ or } \frac{R_1}{R_2} = \sqrt{\frac{MW_2}{MW_1}}$$

■ Given the molecular weights of the ions, calculate the expected ratio of their diffusion rates, and enter your results in Table 4-1.
■ Enter your observed ratios next to your calculated ratios for comparison.

OSMOSIS

Osmosis in a Model Cell

You will use the following system to become familiar with osmosis: Two solutions will be separated by a **selectively permeable membrane** that is permeable to water, glucose, and small molecules, but not to larger

selectively permeable membrane

Figure 4-2. Model cell. A selectively permeable membrane filled with solution A represents the cell. It is placed in solution B to start the experiment.

molecules. Water will diffuse from one to the other in the process of osmosis, and small molecules will diffuse across the membrane in the process of **dialysis.** This setup is shown in Figure 4-2.

■ Obtain a short piece of dialysis tubing (12-15 cm), and soften it by soaking it in distilled water.
■ Fold one end over and tie it tightly with a piece of thin string or strong thread.
■ Fill the bag with solution A, a liquid "meal" containing:

25% glucose
0.5% egg albumin
1% starch

■ Fold over the top, squeeze out all the air, and tie tightly. The bag should be limp.
■ Place the bag in a small beaker and add enough of solution B (distilled water containing a very small amount of iodine) to cover it. Let it stand for an hour or so while you go on.

At the end of your experiment answer the questions in Table 4-2, remembering that the bag is permeable to glucose, iodine, and water but not to starch or protein.

Osmosis in a Living Cell

To watch osmosis across a living membrane, see what happens when a plant cell comes in contact with a hypertonic solution. Note that the plant is kept in an aquarium which contains fresh water that is hypotonic to the plant cell. The cell swells with **turgor pressure** but is prevented from undergoing **lysis** (bursting) because its rigid cellulose walls exert wall pressure on the cell contents. Many animal cells have no such protection against lysis and can exist only in an isotonic solution.

■ Make a wet mount of an *Elodea* leaf and focus on it under high power.
■ Add a drop or two of 10% NaCl solution to the edge of the coverslip.
■ Touch a piece of tissue to the opposite side of the coverslip to pull the solution through and observe.

BEFORE

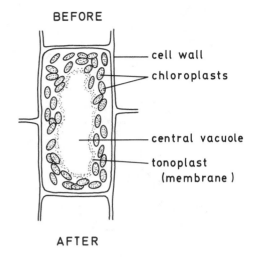

cell wall

chloroplasts

central vacuole

tonoplast
(membrane)

AFTER

Figure 4-3. *Elodea* cell.

Figure 4-3 shows the cell *before;* sketch the cell *after* NaCl in the space provided.

The cell is now (turgid, flaccid) _____ .

The cell has undergone (lysis/plasmolysis/death)

_____ .

■ Now add a few drops of distilled water to the edge of the coverslip and pull it through with tissue while watching the cell.

ACTIVE TRANSPORT

Work in pairs to study active transport in yeast, a fungus (See Figure 4-4). The substance to be transported is neutral red, a dye that is red in a slightly acidic solution and yellow in a basic solution. Sodium carbonate (Na_2CO_3) will be used to make the dye solution basic initially. Conditions inside living yeast cells are relatively acidic. Record your results in Table 4-3.

■ Obtain two 1-g samples of baker's yeast.
■ In a 250-mL Erlenmeyer flask (Flask A) place 1 g of yeast, 25 mL of 0.75% Na_2CO_3 (sodium carbonate), and mix well. Boil this flask gently for 2 min and cool. The cells are now dead.
■ Add 25 mL of 0.02% neutral red. Record the color of the suspension.
■ In a second flask (Flask B) place 25 mL of 0.75% Na_2CO_3 and 25 mL of 0.02% neutral red. Record the color of the solution.

A Boiled
(permeable)

B Living
(selectively permeable)

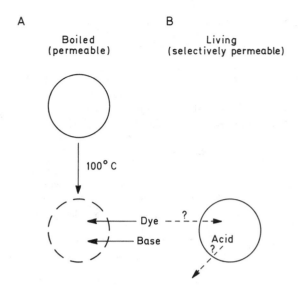

100° C

Dye - - - ?

Base

Acid
?

Figure 4-4. Active transport experiment.
Non-living (A) and living (B) yeast cells are compared.

■ Add 1 g of yeast, swirl the flask, and watch for a color difference compared to Flask A. Record the final color of each flask.

Either the cells in Flask B put out something to change the solution or the dye entered the cells and was changed in the cytoplasm. To test this, compare cells in Flasks A and B:

■ Filter a portion of the contents of Flask A into a test tube. Record the color of the yeast cells and the solution.
■ Filter a portion of the contents of Flask B into a test tube. Record the color of the cells and the solution.
  Think about your observations, then answer the questions in Table 4-3 about Flask B.
■ Add an equal volume of 0.75% acetic acid to the remaining contents of Flask A to acidify the suspension. Record the color of the suspension in Flask A.
■ Filter a portion of the suspension. Record the color of the cells and complete Table 4-3.

When you are finished, wash the glassware that you have used and clean up the lab desk for the next student.

EXPLORING FURTHER

See Topic 3 references.

Journal Articles

Dautry-Varsat, Alice, and Harvey F. Lodish "How receptors bring proteins and particles into cells." *Scientific American,* 52, May 1984.

Lodish, Harvey F., and James E. Rothman. "The assembly of cell membranes." *Scientific American,* January 1979 (#1415).

Rubenstein, Edward. "Diseases caused by impaired communication among cells." *Scientific American,* March 1980 (#1463).

Staehelin, L. Andrew, and Barbara E. Hull. "Junctions between living cells." *Scientific American,* May 1978 (#1388).

Unwin, Nigel, and Richard Henderson. "The structure of proteins in biological membranes." *Scientific American,* February 1984.

Student Name _____   **Date** _____

TABLE 4-1. RESULTS FROM THE DIFFUSION EXPERIMENT

Band	Reaction	Color
AB	$Ag^+ \rightarrow Cl^- = AgCl$	
AC	$Ag^+ \rightarrow Br^- = AgBr$	
AD	$Ag^+ \rightarrow Fe(CN)_6^{\equiv} = Ag_3Fe(CN)_6$	

Ion	Measurement	Distance (mm)	Ratio $D_1/D_2 = R_1/R_2$	Relative Rate
Cl^- Ag^+	B → AB band A → AB band	$D_1 =$ $D_2 =$	$Cl^-/Ag^+ =$	Cl^- moved _____
Br^- Ag^+	C → AC band A → AC band	$D_1 =$ $D_2 =$	$Br^-/Ag^+ =$	Br^- moved _____
$Fe(CN)_6^{\equiv}$ Ag^+	D → AD band A → AD band	$D_1 =$ $D_2 =$	$Fe(CN)_6^{\equiv}/Ag^+ =$	$Fe(CN)_6^{\equiv}$ moved _____

MW_1	MW_2	MW_2/MW_1	$R_1/R_2 = \sqrt{MW_2/MW_1}$	Observed Ratio R_1/R_2
$Cl^- = 35$	$Ag^+ = 108$			$Cl^-/Ag^+ =$
$Br^- = 80$	$Ag^+ = 108$			$Br^-/Ag^+ =$
$Fe(CN)_6^{\equiv} = 212$	$Ag^+ = 108$			$Fe(CN)_6^{\equiv}/Ag^+ =$

TABLE 4-2. RESULTS FROM THE OSMOSIS EXPERIMENT

Which solution was hypertonic (A or B)? _____

Which solution gained water (A or B)? _____

Which solution had the higher osmotic pressure (A or B)? _____

Which substance inside the membrane reacted with the iodine? _____

Which substance(s) moved out through the membrane?

_____

What test that you learned in Topic 1 could you use to test for the presence of glucose outside?

_____

If you swallowed some of solution A, which substance(s) could be absorbed directly by the cells of your gut, assuming that they had the same permeability as the dialysis tubing?

_____

Which substance(s) would have to be further digested?

_____

If your dialysis bag was flaccid or limp at the beginning of the experiment, at the end was it (very flaccid, flaccid, turgid, very turgid)?

_____

Which of the following statements best describes the situation at equilibrium if you let the system stand for a long time? _____

1. No molecules move across the membrane.
2. All molecules cross the membrane equally often in either direction.
3. Molecules to which the membrane is permeable cross equally often in either direction.
4. Only water molecules cross the membrane equally often in either direction.

TABLE 4-3. RESULTS FROM THE ACTIVE TRANSPORT EXPERIMENT

	FLASK A	FLASK B
Initial color of suspension		
Final color of suspension		
Color of cells		
Color of solution		
Is dye inside cells?	XXXXX	
Did Na_2CO_3 enter cells?	XXXXX	
Is the membrane permeable?	XXXXX	
Color of acidified suspension		XXXXX
Color of cells		XXXXX
Did neutral red enter cells?		XXXXX
Did acetic acid enter cells?		XXXXX

What term describes a membrane that is permeable to some substances but not to others? _____

Are dead cells permeable or impermeable to acetic acid? _____

The Life of Cells: Tissues and Organs

OBJECTIVES

When you have completed this topic, you should be able to:
1. Explain why large organisms such as animals and plants must be multicellular.
2. Define the terms tissue and organ.
3. Name four important kinds of animal tissue and give the function of each.
4. Explain how tissues work together in an animal organ such as the intestine.
5. Describe where the main types of epithelial tissue are found.
6. List the main types of connective tissue.
7. Describe the differences between the three main types of muscle tissue.
8. Explain the role of neurons and glial cells in carrying out the function of nervous tissue.
9. Explain the difference between meristematic and permanent tissue.
10. Give the functions of surface, fundamental and vascular tissues.
11. Explain the role of each of the types of permanent tissue in a plant organ such as the leaf.

KEY TOPICS

Epithelial tissue, connective tissue, muscle tissue, nervous tissue, animal organs, meristematic tissue, permanent tissue, surface tissue, vascular tissue, fundamental tissue, plant organs.

INTRODUCTION

Multicellular organisms can grow large in size only because they have specialized tissues and organs to carry out specialized functions. In these organisms, the surface-to-volume ratio becomes much lower than it is in tiny unicellular creatures, so diffusion is no longer adequate to meet the need for obtaining food and oxygen and disposing of wastes. If there is a large number of cells, some of them can be specialized for one purpose and some for another. A **tissue** is one or a few types of closely related cells that efficiently carry out a particular specialized function. Representative examples of different tissue types are illustrated in Color Plates 1, 2, and 3. Several different tissues may be closely associated in an **organ,** to carry out a more general function. For example, the cells in muscle tissue are specialized to contract; muscle tissue is in turn associated with different types of epithelium, connective tissue, and nervous tissue in an organ such as the intestine, which is specialized for

digestion. Some food may still enter the cells of the intestine by simple diffusion, but it reaches these cells rapidly by the mechanical and biochemical action of the digestive **system,** made up of all the organs involved in digestion, and the food is then quickly carried off to the rest of the body by the circulatory system. Thus tissues, organs, and organ systems compensate for the inefficiencies inherent in large size.

The advantages of a larger size have led to the great success of many of these organisms. They may be stronger, faster, have a much greater range of prey, have fewer predators, compete better for sunlight, be less sensitive to drying out, and so forth. In other words, because of their specialized tissues, they can compete better and may become more highly adapted than could a small single-celled organism.

In today's laboratory you will be introduced to some of the important types of animal and plant tissues and then see how these tissues work together in two rather complex organs.

ANIMAL TISSUES AND ORGANS

Epithelial Tissue

Epithelial tissues form a protective layer over the outer and inner surface of the body and they line the body cavity. Since the surfaces are subjected to continual wear, these cells are constantly being sloughed off and must be replaced from an underlying layer where the cells are always dividing. A **basement membrane** is found under this layer. In **simple epithelium** all cells contact this membrane, but in **stratified epithelium** there are additional layers of cells. Certain types of epithelium are further specialized for protection, secretion, absorption, or sensing stimuli. Epithelial cells produce the feathers of a bird, the teeth of a shark, and your own hair and fingernails. Everything that enters into your body proper must pass through a layer of epithelium.

The main types of epithelium are **squamous** (simple or stratified), **cuboidal** (simple or stratified), and **columnar** (simple or pseudostratified). (See Figure 5-1.)

■ If you have not already looked at epithelium from your own cheek, turn back to Topic 3 and do so now. These cells are flattened **stratified squamous epithelium** in which there are many layers. The cells you scrape off have been pushed upward to the surface by the actively dividing cells below.

■ Obtain a prepared slide of a tissue such as the air sacs of the lung where **simple squamous epithelium** can be seen. These cells are also flat, but they are arranged in a single layer.

Why would it be advantageous for these cells to form a very thin layer?

_____

■ Obtain a prepared slide of kidney tissue, showing the tubules in cross section. Note the single layer of **simple cuboidal epithelium** that lines each tubule. This type of epithelium is usually adapted for secretion or absorption and may have tiny projections called **microvilli** to increase the surface area of each cell.

Simple columnar epithelium consists of a single layer of column-shaped cells and will be seen later. Sometimes columnar cells are crowded so tightly that they are of different lengths and appear to be stratified. They are then called **pseudostratified columnar epithelium,** but all of the cells do contact the basement membrane.

Connective Tissue

Connective tissues hold together the other tissues of the body and make up the framework of the organs. **Fibroblasts** are cells that are often found in connective tissue, and they are one of the most common cells in the body. Instead of forming sheets, the cells of connective tissue may be scattered through a semisolid **matrix,** which allows diffusion of molecules through the tissue but prevents the movement of invading bacteria. The tissue derives its strength from **fibers** laid down in the matrix by the cells. These may be made of **collagen,** a strong and tough protein, **elastin,** a stretchy protein, or fine **reticular fibers.** Some of the types of connective tissue are **loose, dense,** and **elastic reticular.** Some additional tissues are also considered to be connective tissue: **adipose tissue** (fat), **cartilage, bone, blood, lymph,** and **blood-generating tissue.** Some representative types of connective tissue are shown in Figure 5-2.

■ Obtain a prepared slide of dense connective tissue and observe it in the compound microscope. If it is the irregular type, there will be bundles of collagen fibers interwoven to resist stress in any direction. Regular dense connective tissue will have all the fibers oriented in one direction to take up stress, as in a tendon.

■ Locate some cells. These are fibroblasts, which are scattered through the tissue.

■ Now obtain and observe a prepared slide of elastic connective tissue, as from a ligament. Here the fibers are made of the protein elastin and, unlike collagen fibers, they can stretch somewhat in response to stress.

■ Finally obtain and observe a prepared slide of adipose tissue. This tissue looks like a honeycomb because each of the tightly packed cells is filled with a droplet of lipid. The nucleus of each cell is flattened and pushed out to one side. Collagen fibers, reticular fibers, and blood capillaries run between the cells.

■ Find the nucleus of one adipocyte.

Adipose tissue not only efficiently stores energy as fat, but also helps cushion the internal organs and insulates the surface of the body against heat loss or gain.

Other types of connective tissue are **cartilage, bone,** and **blood.** You will have a chance to see cells of these tissues in later laboratories. The cells of cartilage are called **chondrocytes** and they secrete an intercellular matrix that includes fibers of modified collagen or elastin and lacks blood vessels. Bone cells are called **osteocytes** and they secrete a matrix, collagen, and calcium minerals. The bulk of the bone consists of cylindrical columns of collagen onto which the calcium minerals

SQUAMOUS

CUBOIDAL

COLUMNAR

Figure 5-1. Epithelial tissue. The main types are squamous, cuboidal, and columnar.

AREOLAR

- macrophage
- fibroblast
- elastic fibers

BONE

- lacunae
- Haversian canal
- matrix

ADIPOSE

- fat

BLOOD

- red blood cells
- white blood cell
- plasma

CARTILAGE

- chondrocyte

LYMPH

- white blood cells
- lymph

Figure 5-2. Connective tissue. There is a great variety of connective tissue types. Here you see loose (areolar), adipose, cartilage, bone, blood, and lymph.

accrete. The minerals make bone hard. Without them the bone would have a rubbery consistency and be of limited use in supporting a large animal such as ourselves. Bone is richly supplied with capillaries and nerves that run through systems of tiny canals, each called a **Haversian system.** Blood is a fluid tissue in which the red blood cells, white blood cells, and platelets are suspended in a liquid plasma. It transports gases and nutrients and has many other vital functions.

Muscle Tissue

The cells of muscle are called muscle **fibers** and their function is to contract. Each cell is packed with the proteins actin and myosin, which shorten the cell when it is stimulated. The three main types of muscle tissue are **skeletal, smooth,** and **cardiac.** They are shown in Figure 5-3.

■ Obtain and observe a slide of skeletal muscle. The striations that you see are the pattern of actin and myo-

sin myofibrils, which are lined up in register. This type of muscle is usually under voluntary control.

Do you see nuclei in skeletal muscle cells?

_____

Cardiac muscle is similar in that it has striations, but its cells connect in a branching network. These cells show a spontaneous, rhythmic contraction, which is involuntary but can be modified by nervous control.

Smooth muscle cells lack striations and are capable of slow, sustained contraction. They are found in internal organs and usually function without voluntary control. One place where smooth muscle is found is in the intestine where its contractions move food through the digestive system automatically.

Nervous Tissue

The function of this tissue is to conduct electrochemical impulses for communication between parts of the body.

SMOOTH   STRIATED   CARDIAC

nuclei   nuclei   disc between cells

Figure 5-3. Muscle tissue. The three types are smooth, skeletal (striated), and cardiac. Only skeletal muscle is under voluntary control.

Neurons and their associated **glial cells** are the main cell types. Some cells themselves have become modified to sense stimuli, for example pain receptors and olfactory receptors in the nose. A motor neuron, which would usually carry impulses to a muscle, is shown in Figure 5-4.

■ Obtain and observe a slide of nervous tissue in which individual neurons can be seen. The motor neurons in the spinal cord are a good example.
■ Note the nucleated cell body and the many branching processes. Impulses may travel along the processes leav-

ing these cells all the way to the hand or foot. The cell shape is clearly adapted for communicating with other cells in the nervous system.

Intestinal Cells

In organs and more complex multicellular organisms, the cells are often very simple. The complexity is created by *combinations* of cells rather than the cells themselves.

(a)

MOTOR NEURON

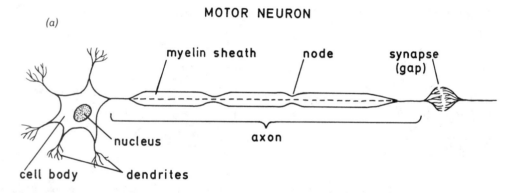

myelin sheath   node   synapse (gap)

nucleus

axon

cell body   dendrites

(b)

Figure 5-4. A motor neuron. This type of neuron is adapted for rapid transmission of impulses over its long axon. Its many dendrites receive impulses from neighboring neurons. In (b) you see the cell bodies of two motor neurons and the nuclei of many glial cells. (From Villee, Solomon, and Davis, *Biology*)

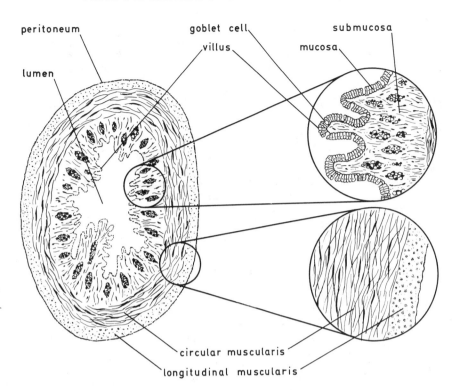

Figure 5-5. Intestine in cross section. The lumen is the hollow interior of the intestine where you would find undigested food. The projections into the lumen are villi, which increase the area for absorption.

Each individual cell tends to lose some functions, such as motility or protection, and to specialize in other functions, such as support, secretion, or contraction.

■ Take a prepared slide of the cross section of intestine and view it under low power.
■ Note the hollow inner space which is the **lumen.** There are five or more layers of different tissues surrounding the lumen. They are organized in sequence from the inner side into the **mucosa, submucosa, muscle,** and the **peritoneum.** Study the cell types in each layer in turn, using Figure 5-5 as your guide.
■ Make a sketch of each of the following cell types in the space provided at the end of this topic (Figure 5-7).

COLUMNAR EPITHELIAL CELLS

These cells make up the inner layer of the mucosa. They follow its highly folded inner surface and secrete mucus, enzymes, and fluid into the lumen of the gut. Their specialty is protection and secretion.

GOBLET CELLS

These are large cuplike spaces facing the lumen of the gut and are filled with mucus secreted by the goblet cells. These cells are highly specialized for secretion.

CONNECTIVE TISSUE CELLS

These cells make up the bulk of the structure of the submucosa. The dense connective tissue cells secrete collagen fibers that support the other cells and the many blood vessels and lymph vessels that pass through this layer. Since blood is a fluid connective tissue itself, the blood cells within the vessels are another type of connective tissue cell specialized for oxygen transport or defense against harmful organisms.

SMOOTH MUSCLE CELLS

These cells are smooth muscle cells and are specialized for contraction. You can see the cell nuclei, which are darkly stained. The muscle cells are in two layers: The cells of the inner layer (closer to the lumen) have a spindle shape. They are oriented as rings so that they are cut in longitudinal section. The cells in the outer layer look like circles. They are also spindle shaped, but are oriented along the length of the intestine and so have been cut in cross section. The two layers of muscle cells counteract each other: If the inner layer contracts, the section of gut will become long and thin, but if the outer layer contracts, the section will become short and fat.

SQUAMOUS EPITHELIAL CELLS

The peritoneum is the outermost layer of cells and is only one cell layer thick. The cells are flattened and serve to protect the outer surface of the intestine. The nuclei may be seen as small elevations. The cells lining the blood vessels are also squamous epithelium.

What type of squamous epithelial cells did you see earlier in this exercise?

PLANT TISSUES AND ORGANS

Plants are quite different from animals in that actively dividing tissue is found only in certain parts of the plant body. This tissue, called **meristem,** occurs at the tips of the roots and of the branches and it allows them to grow in length. Cells that are no longer dividing tend to specialize and are known as **permanent tissues.** The outer cells become **surface tissue** and form a protective covering. Some internal cells become **vascular tis-**

sue, a system of tubes for transport of solutions of minerals and nutrients. The rest of the cells become **fundamental tissue** and carry out plant functions such as photosynthesis, support, and storage.

Meristematic Tissue

■ Obtain an onion root tip and observe it under low power in the compound microscope.
■ Refer to Figure 5-6 and locate the region of dividing cells.
■ Center these cells and switch to high power; note that chromosomes are visible within many of the nuclei. This is the meristematic tissue of the root tip.

Permanent Tissue

■ Switch back to low power and observe the center of the root above the region of cell division. This is where the bundle-like **vascular** tissue is forming.
■ Look at the edge of the root as far up the side as you can (away from the root tip). Notice how the cells have elongated and that some of them have grown long extensions called root hairs. These cells have formed **surface** tissue, which in the root is very important in absorbing water and minerals from the soil. Root hairs are an adaptation for increasing the efficiency of absorption.
■ Note that most of the root's permanent tissue is **fundamental tissue.** These cells give support and firmness to the root and give the growing root tip something to push against as it forces its way through the soil.

The Leaf

Now that you have been introduced to the types of plant tissue, study how these tissues function together in the leaf, an organ specialized for photosynthesis.

■ Obtain a cross section of a leaf and observe it under low, then high power in your microscope.

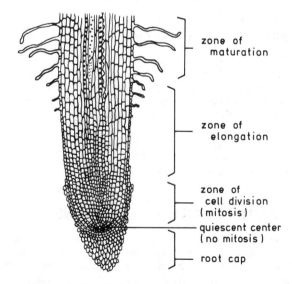

zone of
maturation

zone of
elongation

zone of
cell division
(mitosis)

quiescent center
(no mitosis)

root cap

Figure 5-6. Onion root tissue. Meristematic tissue (dividing cells) is found in a region of active cell division just behind the root cap. Permanent tissue (mature, non-dividing cells) is found in the zone of maturation.

SURFACE TISSUE

■ Find the single layer of cells along the upper surface of the leaf. This is the **epidermis,** which forms a protective layer and secretes a waxy **cuticle.** The waterproof epidermis keeps the leaf from drying out.
■ Note the openings, called **stomata,** in the lower epidermis on the underside of the leaf. The two small cells on either side of each opening are the **guard cells,** specialized epithelial cells that control the passage of gases into and out of the leaf.

VASCULAR TISSUE

This tissue consists of bundles of **xylem** and **phloem** tissue that transport materials into and out of the leaf.

■ Locate oval or round **vascular bundles** in your leaf. They may be stained red.
■ Locate the xylem vessels. They are the large empty-looking structures within the vascular bundles. Xylem cells are dead (no nuclei).
■ Find the spiral thickenings in the walls of xylem vessels. These are easy to see where the vessels run parallel to the cut through the leaf and they usually stain red.

In the stems of woody plants, many xylem vessels are bunched together to make up the woody part. The cell walls are made of cellulose and are greatly thickened to give support to the stems of these large plants and to conduct water and minerals over great distances without collapsing.

■ Locate the phloem cells alongside the xylem vessels; they are smaller, more lightly stained, and may lack a nucleus.

Phloem tissue is also specialized for transport, but has only living cells and controls the substances that travel in them. Phloem conducts food from the leaves to the stem and roots for storage, and then from storage back to the next crop of leaves.

FUNDAMENTAL TISSUE

The simplest fundamental tissue is **parenchyma.** These cells are thin-walled and usually have a large central vacuole. The internal tissue of the leaf is a particular type of parenchyma called **chlorenchyma,** because chloroplasts are present for photosynthesis. The cells that are packed together at the top of the leaf are very active in photosynthesis and are the **palisade mesophyll** cells. Those beneath, where there are many **air spaces,** are the **spongy mesophyll** cells.

■ Notice how gases entering at the guard cells can travel in the air spaces up to the palisade layer.
■ Before leaving this slide, label the important cells types in the drawing of the leaf cross section at the end of this topic (Figure 5-8).

When you are finished with your observations, return the slides and store your microscope properly.

EXPLORING FURTHER

Bold, H. C., C. J. Alexopoulos, and T. Delevoryas. *Morphology of Plants and Fungi.* 4th ed. New York: Harper and Row, 1980.

DeRobertis, E. D. P., and E. M. F. DeRobertis. *Cell and Molecular Biology.* 7th ed. Philadelphia: W. B. Saunders, 1980.

Fawcett, D. W. *The Cell.* 2nd ed. Philadelphia: W. B. Saunders, 1981.

Kessel, Richard G., and Randy H. Kardon. *Tissue and Organs: A Text-Atlas of Scanning Electron Microscopy.* San Francisco: Freeman, 1979.

Leeson, C. P., and T. S. Leeson. *Histology.* 3rd ed. Philadelphia: W. B. Saunders, 1976 (Especially for the four primary tissues.)

Weiss, L., and R. O. Greep. *Histology.* 4th ed. New York: McGraw-Hill, 1977. (Especially for the digestive system.)

Journal Articles

Albersheim, Peter. "The walls of growing plant cells." *Scientific American,* April 1975 (#1320).

Caplan, Arnold I. "Cartilage." *Scientific American,* 84, October 1984.

Epstein, Emanuel. "Roots." *Scientific American,* May 1973 (#1271).

Ross, R., and P. Bornstein. "Elastic fibers in the body." *Scientific American,* June 1971 (#1225).

Sonstegard, David A., Larry S. Matthews, and Herbert Kaufer. "The surgical replacement of the human knee joint." *Scientific American,* January 1978 (#1378).

Student Name _____ **Date** _____

```
┌─────────────────────────────────┐   ┌─────────────────────────────────┐
│    Columnar Epithelial Cells     │   │           Goblet Cells           │
│                                  │   │                                  │
│                                  │   │                                  │
│                                  │   │                                  │
│                                  │   │                                  │
│                                  │   │                                  │
│                                  │   │                                  │
│                                  │   │                                  │
└─────────────────────────────────┘   └─────────────────────────────────┘

┌─────────────────────────────────┐   ┌─────────────────────────────────┐
│     Connective Tissue Cells      │   │        Smooth Muscle Cells       │
│                                  │   │                                  │
│                                  │   │                                  │
│                                  │   │                                  │
│                                  │   │                                  │
│                                  │   │                                  │
│                                  │   │                                  │
└─────────────────────────────────┘   └─────────────────────────────────┘

┌─────────────────────────────────┐
│     Squamous Epithelial Cells    │
│                                  │
│                                  │
│                                  │
│                                  │
│                                  │
│                                  │
│                                  │
└─────────────────────────────────┘
```

Figure 5-7. Sketches of different cell types.

Figure 5-8. **A leaf in cross section.** Label the important cell types.

Enzyme Action

OBJECTIVES

When you have completed this topic, you should be able to:
1. Give the class of macromolecules to which peroxidase belongs and the subunits that comprise it.
2. Name the substrate and products of the peroxidase-catalyzed reaction.
3. Explain the role of guaiacol in this experiment.
4. Define enzyme, activation energy, active site, pH, and denaturation.
5. Distinguish between oxidation/reduction, activation energy/catalysis, substrate/product, and hydrogen peroxide/peroxidase.
6. Define the term optimum with respect to peroxidase activity.
7. Describe how temperature, pH, enzyme concentration, and substrate concentration affect the reaction rate.
8. Explain why peroxidase is a necessary enzyme for all aerobic or oxygen-utilizing cells.

KEY TOPICS

Chemical reactions, catalyst, proteins, enzymes, enzyme-substrate interactions, pH.

INTRODUCTION

A catalyst speeds up a chemical reaction by lowering the **activation energy** required. Enzymes are **biological catalysts** that carry out the thousands of chemical reactions that occur in living cells. They are generally large proteins made up of several hundred amino acids. Some enzymes consist of a protein **apoenzyme** and a small **cofactor,** which might be a metal ion or a **coenzyme,** often a vitamin derivative.

In an enzyme-catalyzed reaction, the substance to be acted upon, or **substrate,** binds to the **active site,** or business end, of the enzyme. The enzyme and substrate are held together in an **enzyme-substrate complex** by hydrophobic interactions, hydrogen bonds, and ionic bonds.

The enzyme then converts the substrate to the reaction products in a process that often requires several chemical steps, and may involve covalent bonds. Finally, the products are released into solution and the enzyme is ready to form another enzyme-substrate complex. As is true of any catalyst, the enzyme is not used up as it carries out the reaction but is recycled over and over. One enzyme molecule can carry out thousands of reaction cycles every minute.

Each enzyme is specific for a certain reaction because its amino acid sequence is unique and causes it to have a unique three-dimensional structure. The active site also has a specific shape so that only one or a few of the thousands of compounds present in the cell can interact with it. If there is a cofactor on the enzyme, it will form part of the active site. Any substance that blocks or changes the shape of the active site will interfere with the activity and efficiency of the enzyme.

If these changes are large enough, the enzyme can no longer act at all, and is said to be **denatured.** There are several factors that are especially important in determining the enzyme's shape, and these are closely regulated both in the living organism and in laboratory experiments to give the **optimum** or most efficient enzyme activity:

1. **Salt concentration.** If the salt concentration is very low or zero, the charged amino acid side chains of the enzyme molecules will stick together. The enzyme will denature and form an inactive precipitate. If, on the other hand, the salt concentration is very high, normal interaction of charged groups will be blocked, new interactions will occur, and again the enzyme will precipitate. An intermediate salt concentration such as that of blood (0.9%) or cytoplasm is the optimum for most enzymes.

2. **pH.** The pH scale, which is logarithmic, measures the acidity or H^+ concentration in a solution. The

scale runs from 0 to 14 with 0 being highest in acidity and 14 lowest. When the pH is in the range of 0–7, a solution is said to be acidic; if the pH is around 7, the solution is neutral; and if the pH is in the range of 7–14, the solution is basic. Amino acid side chains contain groups such as —COOH and —NH₂ that readily gain or lose H⁺ ions. As the pH is lowered, an enzyme will tend to gain H⁺ ions, and eventually enough side chains will be affected so that the enzyme's shape is disrupted. Likewise, as the pH is raised, the enzyme will lose H⁺ ions and eventually lose its active shape. Many enzymes have an optimum in the neutral pH range and are denatured at either extremely high or low pH. Some enzymes, such as those which act in the human stomach where the pH is very low, will have an appropriately low pH optimum. A **buffer** is a compound that will gain or lose H⁺ ions so that the pH changes very little.

3. **Temperature.** All chemical reactions speed up as the temperature is raised. As the temperature increases, more of the reacting molecules have enough kinetic energy to undergo the reaction. Since enzymes are catalysts for chemical reactions, enzyme reactions also tend to go faster with increasing temperature. However, if the temperature of an enzyme-catalyzed reaction is raised still further, a **temperature optimum** is reached: above this point the kinetic energy of the enzyme and water molecules is so great that the structure of the enzyme molecules starts to be disrupted. The positive effect of speeding up the reaction is now more than offset by the negative effect of denaturing more and more enzyme molecules. Many proteins are denatured by temperatures around 40–50°C, but some are still active at 70–80°C, and a few even withstand being boiled.

4. **Small molecules.** Many molecules other than the substrate may interact with an enzyme. If such a molecule increases the rate of the reaction it is an **activator,** and if it decreases the reaction rate it is an **inhibitor.** The cell can use these molecules to regulate how fast the enzyme acts. Any substance that tends to unfold the enzyme, such as an organic solvent or detergent, will act as an inhibitor. Some inhibitors act by reducing the —S—S— bridges that stabilize the enzyme's structure. Many inhibitors act by reacting with side chains in or near the active site to change or block it. Others may damage or remove the cofactor. Many well-known poisons such as potassium cyanide and curare are enzyme inhibitors that interfere with the active site of a critical enzyme.

TURNIP PEROXIDASE

In this experiment you will study the enzyme **peroxidase** from turnips. Peroxidases are widely distributed in plant and animal cells and catalyze the oxidation of organic compounds by hydrogen peroxide as follows:

$$RH + H_2O_2 \xrightarrow{peroxidase} ROH + H_2O$$

What are the substrates in this reaction?

What are the products?

Any cell using molecular oxygen in its metabolism will produce small amounts of H_2O_2 as a highly toxic by-product. It is critical that the H_2O_2 be quickly removed by enzymes such as peroxidase before it can do damage to the cell.

You will use a reducing agent, guaiacol, that changes color when it is oxidized. This change can be easily measured in the spectrophotometer.

$$\underset{\text{(colorless)}}{4 \text{ guaiacol}} + 2H_2O_2 \xrightarrow{peroxidase} \underset{\text{(brown)}}{\text{tetraguaiacol}} + 8H_2O$$

In this reaction, the oxidation of guaiacol is **coupled** to the reduction of which substance? _____

THE SPECTROPHOTOMETER

A colored solution such as oxidized guaiacol solution appears that way because some of the light entering the solution is absorbed by the colored substance. A clear solution will allow almost all of the light to pass through. The amount of **absorbance** can be determined by using a spectrophotometer, which measures quantitatively what fraction of the light passes through a given solution, and indicates on the absorbance scale the amount of light absorbed compared to that absorbed by a clear solution. The darker the solution, the greater its absorbance.

Inside the machine there is a light that shines through a filter (which can be adjusted to control the color, or wavelength, of light), then through the sample and onto a light-sensitive phototube. The phototube produces an electric current proportional to the amount of light striking it. The absorbance meter measures how much light has been blocked by the sample and thereby prevented from striking the phototube. A clear tube of water or other solvent is the **blank** and has zero absorbance. A solution that contains a small amount of a colored substance might show an absorbance of 0.1, a solution with a moderate amount might show an absorbance of 0.4, and so forth. In fact, in the lower portion of the absorbance scale, the amount of substance in solution is directly proportional to the absorbance reading so that a graph of absorbance versus concentration will give a straight line. This very useful relationship is known as **Beer's law.**

When you are ready to read a sample, use Figure 6-1 to follow these steps:

1. Turn on the instrument with the power switch knob. Allow 5 min for warm-up time.
2. Adjust to the desired wavelength (in this case use 470 nm).
3. With the sample chamber *empty* and the cover closed, use the power switch knob on the left to set the meter needle to read **infinity absorbance.** (When the chamber is empty, a shutter blocks all light from the phototube.)

ALWAYS READ FROM THE ABSORBANCE SCALE, NOT THE TRANSMISSION SCALE.

Figure 6-1. Spectronic 20 spectrophotometer. The numbered controls correspond to steps in the operating instructions (see text).

4. Fill a spectrophotometer tube or cuvette halfway with distilled water (or other solvent when water is not the solvent in your experiment) to serve as the blank. Wipe it free of moisture or fingerprints with a lint-free tissue (Kimwipe), and insert it into the sample holder. Line up the etched mark with the raised line on the front of the sample holder, and close the cover.
5. With the right-hand knob, adjust the meter to read **zero absorbance.** Remove the tube, empty it, and shake it as dry as possible. This precaution is essential for accuracy.
6. Fill and insert the sample cuvette.
7. Read the absorbance directly from the meter. Rinse the cuvette with clean water and shake it as dry as possible.
8. It is necessary to reset the machine to infinity absorbance and zero absorbance before each experiment because the settings drift a bit. Whenever the wavelength is changed, the infinity and zero absorbance also must be reset.

EXPERIMENTAL PROCEDURE

Preparation of the Turnip Extract

■ Weigh out 2 g of turnip (the peeled, inner portion).
■ Place it in a blender with 200 mL of distilled water.
■ Blend it thoroughly at the high setting for about 1 min.

This suspension is the **turnip extract,** and contains the enzyme peroxidase. The activity of the turnip extract will vary from day to day, depending on the size and age of the turnip and the extent of blending. You should adjust the turnip suspension to be more dilute or more concentrated so that your absorbance for the **base line** is in the range 0.1-0.2.

Kinetics of the Peroxidase Reaction

Pipets will be used to measure accurately the solutions used in this experiment. Your instructor will demonstrate how to use a pipet correctly.

BE SURE TO USE A DIFFERENT PIPET FOR EACH SOLUTION SO THAT THE REAGENTS ARE NOT RUINED BY CROSS-CONTAMINATION.

■ Label the pipets with a tape or marking pencil so each one can be reused with the proper solution.
■ Obtain two spectrophotometer tubes and label them B (blank) and R (reaction).
■ Obtain three test tubes and label them #1, #2, and #3. (#1 will contain a blank reaction without H_2O_2. The contents of #2 and #3 will be mixed to start the reaction.)
■ Set up the three tubes as follows, and make a record of these additions in Table 6-1 (run 1, base line) at the end of this topic.

Tube #1. (blank tube without H_2O_2). Add 0.1 mL of guaiacol, 1.0 mL of turnip extract, and 8.9 mL of distilled water; mix well.
Tube #2. Add 0.1 mL of guaiacol, 0.2 mL of 0.1% H_2O_2, and 4.7 mL of distilled water.
Tube #3. Add 1.0 mL of turnip extract and 4.0 mL of distilled water.

■ Adjust the Spectronic 20 to zero absorbance using tube B filled with solution from tube #1 and following steps 1-5 in the instructions for its operation.

You have now set up the instrument so that any difference in the meter reading with a change in the sample will reflect a difference in oxidized guaiacol concentration.

■ Obtain a stopwatch, wind it up, and be sure that you understand how to use it correctly.
■ Prepare the sample: have ready spectrophotometer tube R, tissue, and tubes #2 and #3 filled with the solutions given above.

YOU WILL HAVE 30 SEC TO MIX THE CONTENTS OF TUBES #2 AND #3, POUR THE CONTENTS INTO THE CLEAN SPECTROPHOTOMETER TUBE, WIPE THE TUBE, AND TAKE YOUR FIRST READING.

■ When you are completely ready, mix the contents of tubes #2 and #3, pour the contents back and forth two times, and then pour quickly into tube R; start the stopwatch when the tubes are mixed. ($t = 0$ when the tubes are mixed).
■ Wipe the outside of the tube and place it in the spectrophotometer.
■ Take your first reading 30 sec or as soon as possible after the tubes were mixed ($t = 30$ sec).
■ Continue to read the absorbance every 30 sec for 3 min.

Record the readings in Table 6-2, and graph the absorbance versus time in Figure 6-2 (at end of topic).

This curve will represent the **base line** of enzyme activity with which the enzyme activity under varying conditions will be compared. In the following experiments you will vary one condition at a time and compare the results with the base line. Be sure you have already recorded the setup for your base line experiment under run 1 in Table 6-1. Check your graph with your instructor before proceeding with the rest of the experiment.

Since this exercise contains too many projects to be

performed by one pair of students, the instructor will specify how the remaining work will be divided up. Use the experimental setup space in Table 6-1 to record your experiment number and what you put into your tubes; record your data in Table 6-2, and graph your results.

1. Effect of Enzyme Concentration

What happens when you use:

(a) TWICE THE AMOUNT OF ENZYME

Tube #1. Add 0.1 mL of guaiacol, 2.0 mL of turnip extract, and 7.9 mL of distilled water.
Tube #2. Add 0.1 mL of guaiacol, 0.2 mL of 0.1% H_2O_2, and 4.7 mL of distilled water.
Tube #3. Add 2.0 mL of turnip extract and 3.0 mL of distilled water.

(b) HALF THE AMOUNT OF ENZYME

Tube #1. Add 0.1 mL of guaiacol, 0.5 mL of turnip extract, and 9.4 mL of distilled water.
Tube #2. Add 0.1 mL of guaiacol, 0.2 mL of 0.1% H_2O_2, and 4.7 mL of distilled water.
Tube #3. Add 0.5 mL of turnip extract and 4.5 mL of distilled water.

Notice that tube #1 always contains 10 mL and tubes #2 and #3 together total 10 mL. Why is this important?

_____

_____

■ Repeat the procedure for preparing the sample, read it, record the data, and graph your results. How does changing the concentration of enzyme affect the rate of the reaction?

_____

2. Effect of Varying the Substrate Concentration

■ Design and carry out an experiment to determine whether varying the concentration of the substrate H_2O_2 affects the rate of reaction. If substrate is present in excess, there would be little or no effect.
Conclusion:

_____

_____

What would happen to the rate if the concentration of substrate were increased further and further?

_____

3. Effect of Temperature

What is the effect of temperature on enzyme activity?

■ Set up an experiment to show the difference in activity found between 0° and 60°. Use the conditions of your base line experiment, but run the reaction in the water baths at different temperatures that are available to you, such as 4°, 15°, room temperature = about 22°, 30°, 37°, and 55°C.
■ Record the exact temperature for each run.
■ Place tubes #2 and #3 in the water bath to equilibrate for 5 minutes before mixing.
■ Read the absorbance immediately after mixing; then return tube R to the water bath and wait.
■ Read the absorbance again at 3 minutes.
■ Graph your 2 data points for each temperature.
■ Next, set up another run but heat tube #3 in a boiling water bath at 100° for 10 min and test its activity as in Run 1.

Is the boiled enzyme active? _____

Explain what happened during boiling:

_____

_____

_____

_____

_____

At what temperature in the range 0–100° do you see

maximal activity? _____

This temperature is called the enzyme's temperature

_____ .

4. Effect of pH

Measure the effect of pH by using the base line conditions but substituting buffers at pH values between 4 and 9 (4.0, 5.5, 7, and 8.5) for distilled water in Tube #3. Compare each pH rate with the others. (You cannot compare the base line and buffer results, because buffer itself will change the rate.)

At which pH is the enzyme most effective?

_____

Why is this important biologically?

_____

_____

_____

5. Effect of Inhibitors

Hydroxylamine is a small molecule whose structure is similar enough to that of H_2O_2 that it attaches to the iron atom that is part of the peroxidase enzyme. Its inhibition is **reversible** and **competitive.** To test how this substance affects enzyme activity, in Tube #3 substitute 3.0 mL of distilled water and 1.0 mL of 10% hydroxylamine. Mix this tube and wait 1 min. Then measure the activity of the peroxidase as usual.

Is the peroxidase still active? _____

How could you restore activity in the presence of this inhibitor?

_____

_____

Explain the action of hydroxylamine on the enzyme's activity:

_____

_____

_____

_____

_____

When you are finished with your work, wash and thoroughly rinse your glassware, return the reagents, and discard any debris left from your experiment. Rinse thoroughly, but *DO NOT BRUSH* your spectrophotometer tubes.

EXPLORING FURTHER

Barker, R. *Organic Chemistry of Biological Compounds.* Englewood Cliffs, N.J.: Prentice-Hall, 1971.

Calvin, M. *Organic Chemistry of Life: Readings from Scientific American.* San Francisco: W. H. Freeman, 1973.

Dickerson, R.E., and I. Geis. *The Structure and Action of Proteins.* Menlo Park, CA: Benjamin-Cummings, 1969.

Journal Articles

DeDuve, Christian. "Microbodies in the living cell." *Scientific American,* 74, May 1983.

Koshland, D. E., Jr. "Protein shape and biological control." *Scientific American,* October 1973 (#1280).

Levinthal, Cyrus. "Molecular model-building by computer." *Scientific American,* June 1966 (#1043).

Mosbach, Klaus. "Enzymes bound to artifical matrixes." *Scientific American,* March 1971 (#1216).

Student Name _____ **Date** _____

TABLE 6-1. EXPERIMENTAL DESIGN FOR PROJECT # _____ List the contents of each tube.

	Tube #1	Tube #2	Tube #3
Run 1 (Base line)			
Run 2			
Run 3			
Run 4			
Run 5			
Run 6			
Run 7			

TABLE 6-2.   RESULTS FROM TURNIP PEROXIDASE EXPERIMENT

Read absorbance every 30 sec. Read at 30 sec and 180 sec for the temperature experiment.

Time (sec)	Run 1 (Base line)					
30						
60						
90						
120						
150						
180						

Time (sec)						
30						
60						
90						
120						
150						
180						

Student Name _____ **Date** _____

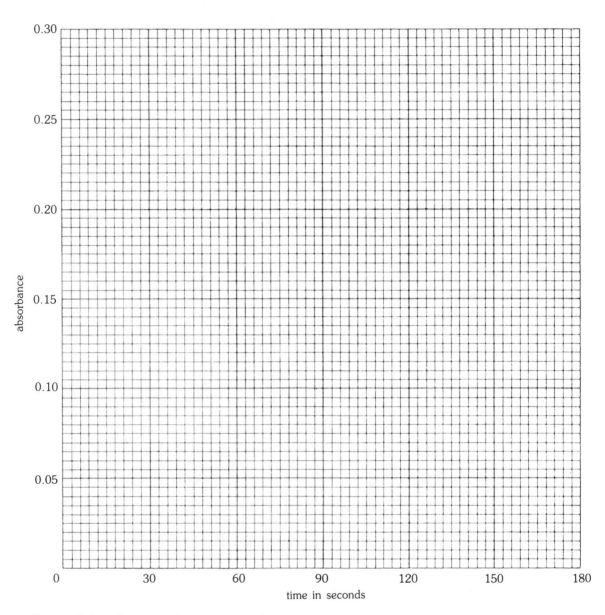

Figure 6-2. Kinetics of turnip peroxidase activity.

Results of experiment # _____
Conclusions:

_____

_____

_____

_____

Student Name _____ **Date** _____

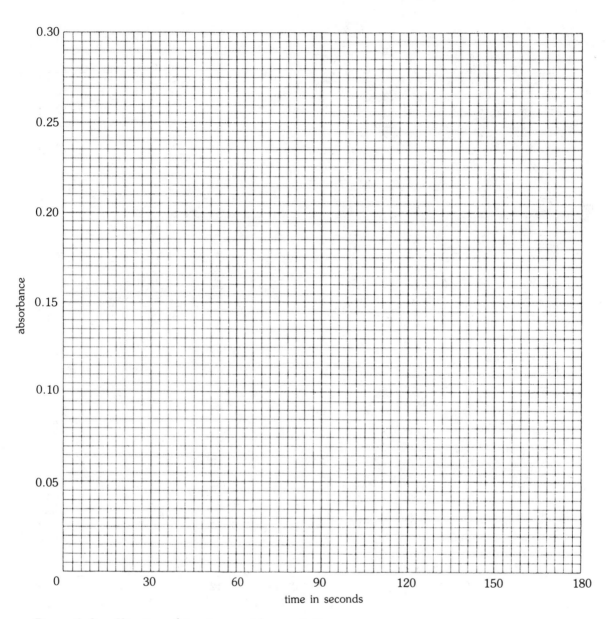

Figure 6-2. **Kinetics of turnip peroxidase activity.**

Results of experiment # _____
Conclusions:

_____

_____

_____

_____

Photosynthesis

OBJECTIVES _____

When you have completed this topic, you should be able to:
1. Identify the pigments involved in photosynthesis by paper chromatography.
2. Give the function of chlorophyll and the accessory pigments.
3. Determine the wavelengths most useful for photosynthesis by determining the absorption spectrum of a pigment extract.
4. Distinguish between the electron transport and carbon fixation reactions of photosynthesis.
5. Demonstrate the effect of changing the level of light on electron transport as measured by O_2 production.
6. Demonstrate the effect of changing the level of light on electron transport by measuring reduction of a dye in the Hill reaction.
7. Explain why stimulating carbon fixation affects electron transport as measured by O_2 production.
8. Describe an experiment designed to measure the extent of carbon fixation as a function of light.

KEY TOPICS _____

Chloroplasts, electromagnetic radiation, photosynthetic pigments, photochemical reactions, photosystems I and II, electron transport, chemiosmosis, photophosphorylation, carbon fixation.

INTRODUCTION

The overall reaction of photosynthesis can be understood as two closely linked processes. The first is called **non-cyclic photophosphorylation** and involves light-driven electron transport. Here electrons flow in a **non-cyclic** fashion from water molecules to **NADP+,** which is reduced to **NADPH.** Electron transport depends directly on light **(photo—)** and permits the synthesis of **ATP (—phosphorylation)** through **chemiosmosis.** At this point light energy has been converted to chemical energy in the form of NADPH and ATP. The second part of photosynthesis is called **carbon fixation.** The energy of NADPH and ATP is used to reduce **CO_2** to **glucose** in a series of reactions known as the **Calvin cycle.** These reactions are light-independent in that they can occur in the absence of light as long as NADPH and ATP are provided. In intact photosynthetic systems, however, light is an absolute necessity, since sufficient NADPH and ATP cannot be provided without it. The relationship of these two tightly coupled processes, non-cyclic photophosphorylation and carbon fixation, is shown in Figure 7-1.

PHOTOSYNTHETIC PIGMENTS: CHROMATOGRAPHY

If you have never carried out chromatography, turn back to Topic 1 and read the description of chromatography. You need to understand the following terms: **adsorption, matrix, chromatogram, origin, solvent front** and **R_f.**

In this experiment the matrix will be the cellulose of Whatman #1 filter paper, and the solvent is petroleum ether:acetone (9:1). Although substances do not have to be colored to be separated by chromatography, it is a little more dramatic when you can actually see the different substances as they pull apart to form distinct spots. Color and R_f are the important characteristics you will use to distinguish the photosynthetic pigments from one another. You will begin by applying a green mixture of **PIGMENT** containing **chlorophylls** and **accessory pigments** to the paper, and will obtain a separation of the mixture into several distinct components at the end of the chromatography.

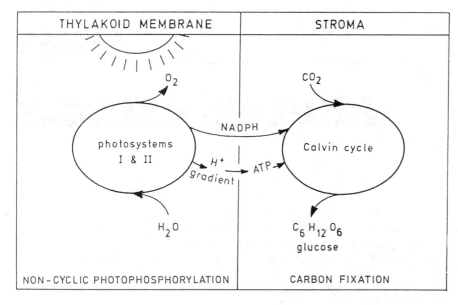

Figure 7-1. Photosynthesis. ATP synthesis by chemiosmosis depends on a hydrogen ion gradient set up as a result of electron transport. The Calvin cycle is tightly coupled to electron flow and quickly stops if light is not available.

Preparing the Chromatogram

A correctly prepared chromatogram is shown in Figure 7-2.

■ Obtain a rectangle of filter paper (about 10 × 15 cm), and lay it on a clean surface, *touching the paper as little as possible* and only at the edges.
■ Use a pencil to mark a straight line 1.5 cm from and parallel to the long edge of the paper; this is the origin.
■ Make three pencil dots on the origin that are at least 3 cm apart.
■ Place a support (such as a pencil) under the top edge of the paper so that the origin doesn't touch the surface.
■ Use a capillary pipet to spot **PIGMENT** onto the dots by touching the pipet to the paper as briefly as possible so that your spots will be quite small.

DO NOT SPOT CHLOROPLASTS OR CHLOROPHYLL EXTRACT ONTO THE PAPER. USE ONLY PIGMENT FOR THIS EXPERIMENT. SMALL SPOTS ARE BETTER THAN BIG SPOTS.

■ Use forceps to hold the paper with three wet spots in front of the blower until the spots are dry, or blow on them yourself. Touch the paper with your fingers as little as possible.

■ Again make a small spot on each dot with the capillary pipet, and dry.
■ Repeat until you have made a minimum of five applications on each dot.
■ Dry the chromatogram thoroughly before starting your chromatography.

Running the Chromatogram

■ Form your dry chromatogram into a cylinder, as shown in Figure 7-3, and staple it at the top and bottom so that the edges are close together but *do not touch or overlap.*
■ Obtain a chromatography jar and cover. Add enough solvent to the jar to just cover the bottom (about 20 mL). Replace the cover on the jar, and close the solvent stock bottle.
■ When the solvent has had a chance to evaporate and saturate the air in the chromatography jar, pick up your chromatogram with forceps, and set it gently in the center of the jar. It should stand up straight and *not touch the sides of the jar.*
■ Cover the jar and leave it undisturbed during the chromatography.
■ Check the jar every few minutes, and note the progress of the solvent as it wets the paper and moves toward the top.

Figure 7-2. Chromatography of photosynthetic pigments. A paper chromatogram after spotting three samples.

Figure 7-3. Chromatography of photosynthetic pigments. A paper chromatogram ready to run has been stapled so that its edges do not touch. The dry chromatogram should be put into the jar so that it does not touch the sides and the origin should be above the level of the solvent. Keep the jar covered.

DO NOT LET THE SOLVENT REACH THE TOP OF THE PAPER.

■ After about 20 min, the solvent will be close to the top of the paper, and you must immediately stop the chromatography. Use the forceps to remove the chromatogram. Replace the cover on the jar.

■ *Immediately* mark the **solvent front** (edge of the part wet by the solvent) with a pencil. You will not be able to calculate any R_f values if you fail to do this before the rapidly drying solvent dries.

■ Dry your chromatogram with the blower, or hang it up with clothespins for a few minutes before analyzing it.

Analyzing the Chromatogram

The number of spots that you observe will depend on the exact condition of the extract that you used. These are the major pigments in the extract:

Chlorophyll *a*: a blue-green pigment
Chlorophyll *b*: a yellow-green pigment
Carotenes: yellow-orange accessory pigments
Xanthophylls: yellow accessory pigments

■ Outline each visible spot with a pencil, and note its color on the chromatogram.

■ Make a dot with your pencil in the center of each spot. If the spot is irregular or band-shaped, use your judgment as to where the approximate center might be if it were a round spot.

■ Take your chromatogram into a dark room, or put it into a darkbox, and view it under long-wavelength ultraviolet light.

NEVER LOOK DIRECTLY AT ULTRAVIOLET LIGHT. IT CAN DAMAGE YOUR EYES.

■ Note the bright pink **fluorescence** of chlorophyll.

■ Use the difference in fluorescence to help distinguish the chlorophylls and any other fluorescent compounds present. Outline the spots with pencil.

■ Note whether there are any dark areas that contain compounds that absorb UV light, but do not show fluorescence. Outline them with pencil.

■ Finally, carefully measure the distance from the origin to the solvent front, and record it in Table 7-2 at the end of this topic.

■ Measure the distance from the origin to the dot in the center of each spot observed in visible or UV light.

■ Record it on the chromatogram and in Table 7-1.

■ Calculate the R_f for each spot, and describe its appearance under visible and under UV light .

■ If you can, identify the major pigments, and record your R_f values for them in the table.

■ Tape the chromatogram into the space provided.

These pigments are located in the thylakoid membranes of the chloroplasts where they normally would absorb light, become chemically excited, and pass electrons to the electron carriers of photosystems I and II. When they are free, however, as they are on the chromatography paper, there are no molecules to accept the electrons, and the UV light-excited molecules release their energy as photons of red light during fluorescence. Only the molecules of certain compounds are able to give up the energy as light. Those of other compounds lose it in the form of heat.

PHOTOSYNTHETIC PIGMENTS: ABSORPTION SPECTRUM

Only the light that is absorbed by chloroplasts can be used in photosynthesis. As you have already seen, the pigments of a green plant look green to the eye because they permit green light to pass through, but absorb the red and blue light. The particular wavelengths of light that are **absorbed** by a certain substance form a pattern called its **absorption spectrum.** The spectrum is determined by illuminating a solution of the substance with each wavelength of light in turn, and measuring the absorption in each case. Using visible light, you will determine the visible spectrum for a mixture of pigments extracted from chlorophasts. The spectrum can then be plotted as a graph of absorbance versus the wavelength or color of light used.

In this experiment you will have to *be careful not to spill the solvent* on or into the spectrophotometer because it will dissolve the plastic.

■ Turn on the Spectronic 20 spectrophotometer to warm up for a few minutes while you turn back to Topic 6 and review the procedure for using this instrument.
■ Fill a spectrophotometer cuvette halfway with 80% acetone to use as your blank.
■ Fill a second tube halfway with diluted **CHLORO-PHYLL EXTRACT.**
■ Set the wavelength at 400 nm, and adjust the needle to ∞ absorbance with the left knob.
■ Insert your blank, and adjust the needle to zero absorbance with the right-hand knob.
■ Insert the tube containing chlorophyll, and take your first reading. It should be in the vicinity of 0.8. If it is not, ask your instructor for help. Record the absorbance in Table 7-3.

The zero and ∞ absorbance will change each time you adjust the wavelength, so you will have to reset the spectrophotometer with and without the blank for each of your readings.

■ Change the wavelength to 405, reset the spectrophotometer, and take your second reading; enter the absorbance in Table 7-3.
■ Continue your readings every 5 nm until the readings have become quite low. Then switch to every 10 or 20 nm.
■ When the absorbance starts to rise, switch back to taking readings every 5nm, and continue until you reach 700 nm.

The purpose of taking the spectrum is to get the shape as accurately as possible, especially around the regions of greatest absorbance (low 400s and high 600s). When the absorbance rises and then falls again, the peak is called the **absorption maximum,** and the wavelength at which it occurs is used as a characteristic for identifying a compound. If you are not sure where at least two maxima are in your spectrum, go back to the regions of high absorbance and take some more readings.

■ Plot your data on the grid provided in Table 7-3, and label each absorbance maximum with its corresponding wavelength.

PHOTOSYNTHESIS IN *ELODEA*

In an intact plant both electron transport and carbon fixation will go on as long as the plant is illuminated, and it is possible to study the effect of light intensity and the concentration of CO_2 on the rate of photosynthesis. A simple way to measure photosynthetic rate is to observe the rate at which oxygen is produced as a result of splitting water. An actively photosynthesizing plant will produce an abundance of oxygen bubbles.

■ Obtain a healthy green sprig of *Elodea,* and measure back about 10 cm from the tip.
■ Wipe a sharp razor blade with alcohol, let it dry, and make a diagonal cut across the stem of the plant as gently as you can. Save the tip.
■ Put the tip into a test tube upside down so that the cut end of the stem is about 3 cm from the top of the tube.
■ Immerse the whole tube in the aquarium, or fill it with tap water until it is completely full and the cut stem is well under the surface of the water.
■ Place the tube 50 cm from the floodlamp, making sure that there is a container of water between the lamp and *Elodea* to act as a heat sink.

Your setup should look like that shown in Figure 7-4.

■ Wait a few minutes for the plant to become adjusted. Bubbles should appear at the cut end of the stem. If there are hardly any bubbles after 15 min, ask your instructor for help.
■ When there are two or more bubbles per minute, begin counting, and record the bubbles produced in a 3-min interval in Table 7-4.
■ Repeat for another 3-min interval. Calculate the average bubbles per minute for the light intensity at 50 cm.

Figure 7-4. Experimental setup to measure oxygen production. *Elodea* can be exposed to different light intensities by moving it toward or away from the light source. The rate of oxygen evolution at different light intensities can be measured by counting the rate of bubble production. The "heat sink" must be used so that the water in the tube doesn't heat up and kill the plant.

Plate 1. Epithelial Tissue

Cuboidal Epithelium

Each individual cell is a short cylinder. This tissue lines the interior of kidneys and glands. It secretes and absorbs. (From Villee, Solomon, and Davis, *Biology*)

Simple Columnar Epithelium

Each cell is like a tall cylinder with the nucleus located in its base. This type of tissue lines the gut and upper respiratory tract. It protects, absorbs, and secretes. Goblet cells are specialized for secretion of mucus, and cilia may be present to move the mucus layer along. (From Villee, Solomon, and Davis, *Biology*)

Stratified Squamous Epithelium

The dividing columnar cells at the basement membrane flatten and eventually die as they are pushed up to the surface. This tissue protects the surface of the body as skin, and lines the mouth and vagina. (From Villee, Solomon, and Davis, *Biology*)

Plate 2. **Connective Tissue**

These are the most common types, with their locations in the vertebrate body.
(From Villee, Solomon, and Davis, *Biology*)

Loose (Areolar) [Beneath the skin]

Collagen fibers

Nuclei of fibroblasts

Adipose [Beneath skin, around organs]

Dense [Tendon, dermis of skin]

Cartilage [Ends of bones, trachea, nose, ear]

Chondrocytes

Lacuna

Intercellular substance

Elastic [Lungs, arteries, ligaments]

Bone [Skeleton]

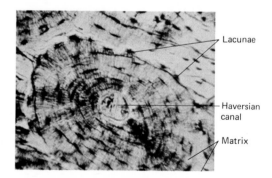

Lacunae

Haversian canal

Matrix

Reticular [Liver, lymph nodes, spleen]

Blood [within circulatory system]

Red blood cells

White blood cell

Plate 3. **Muscle Tissue and Nervous Tissue**

Skeletal Muscle [Striated and under voluntary control]

Cardiac Muscle [Striated, branching, contracts spontaneously, cells joined end-to-end tightly by intercalated discs]

Muscle fibers in cross-section

Nuclei

Muscle fibers in longitudional section

Approximately ×1000

Nuclei

Intercalated disc

Approximately ×900

Smooth Muscle [Lacks striations and its contraction is involuntary]

Neurons [conduct impulses; this type controls muscle contractions; supported by glial cells whose nuclei are visible]

Nuclei

Approximately ×450

(From Villee, Solomon, and Davis, *Biology*)

Cell body of neuron   Nucleus   Neurons

Axon of neuron   Nuclei of glial cells   Dendrites

Plate 4.   Reproduction in Flowering Plants

Imperfect flower of a squash. The staminate flower (left) bears only stamens. The pistillate flower (right) bears only pistils. (J. Robert Waaland, University of Washington/BPS)

Perfect flower of a lily, bearing both stamens and pistils. (R. Humbert/BPS)

Hibiscus flower with stamens and pistils fused into a tube. (E. R. Degginger)

Hibiscus stamen bearing pollen. (From Villee, Solomon, and Davis, *Biology*)

Hibiscus pollen grain showing apertures (arrows) through which the pollen tube emerges. (John A. Lott, McMaster Univ./BPS)

Plate 5. Flowers Adapted to Different Pollinators

Fly. Skunk cabbage with an inconspicuous flower having a carrion-like odor. (Alan R. Bleeker/The Kings College)

Insect. Orchid mimicks a female insect to attract males. (From Villee, Solomon, and Davis, *Biology*)

Bee. Black-eyed Susan with a bull's eye nectar guide. (From Villee, Solomon, and Davis, *Biology*)

WWD. Willow catkin with exposed pistils. (Leo Frandzel)

Moth. Light colored, delicate flowers with scented nectar. (R. Humbert/BPS)

Bat. Fruit plants such as the banana. (Merlin Tuttle/Photo Researchers, Inc.)

Hummingbird. Trumpet-shaped, red flower with no landing platform for insect. (Steve Maslowski/Photo Researchers, Inc.)

Plate 6. **Superficial Human Body Muscles**

(a) Anterior view. (b) Posterior view. Muscles work in antagonistic pairs: Extensors, such as the extensors carpi for the hand or the triceps for the elbow, straighten joints. The corresponding flexors, the flexor carpi and the biceps, bend the same joints.

Orbicularis oculi

Zygomatic

Orbicularis oris

Sternocleidomastoid

Levator scapulae

Scalenes

Clavicle

DELTOID

PECTORALIS MAJOR

BICEPS BRACHII

Serratus anterior

TRICEPS BRACHII

Brachialis

Brachioradialis

Flexor carpi radialis

Palmaris longus

Flexor carpi ulnaris

Tensor fasciae latae

Flexor carpi ulnaris

Palmaris longus

Flexor carpi radialis

Brachioradialis

Platysma

LATISSIMUS DORSI

RECTUS ABDOMINIS

Linea alba

External oblique

Gluteus medius

Iliopsoas

Adductor longus

Gracilis

Sartorius

QUADRICEPS FEMORIS

Patella

Soleus

GASTROCNEMIUS

Peroneus longus

Extensor digitorum longus

Tibialis anterior

Tibia

Flexor digitorum

(a)

Sternocleidomastoid

MASSETER

Splenius capitis

TRAPEZIUS

DELTOID

TRICEPS BRACHII

Brachioradialis

Palmaris longus

Flexor carpi radialis

Flexor carpi ulnaris

Flexor digitorum superficialis

Ulna

Extensor carpi ulnaris

Flexor carpi ulnaris

Extensor digitorum communis

BICEPS BRACHII

Infraspinatus

Teres minor

Teres major

Rhomboideus major

LATISSIMUS DORSI

External oblique

Gluteus medius

GLUTEUS MAXIMUS

Gracilis

Semitendinosus

Biceps femoris

Semimembranosus

GASTROCNEMIUS

ACHILLES TENDON

Peroneus brevis

Calcaneus

(b)

Plate 7. **Blood Cells**

These are the principal types of blood cells circulating in human blood. Photomicrograph (a) shows a lympho-cyte surrounded by red blood cells; (b) shows a neutrophil with a multilobed nucleus; (c) shows an eosinophil.

ERYTHROCTES

7 µm

THROMBOCYTES
(PLATELETS)

1 to 2 µm

LEUKOCYTES

Granulocytes

Agranular leukocytes

Neutrophil

10 to 14 µm

Monocyte

15 to 20 µm

Eosinophil

10 to 14 µm

Lymphocyte

8 to 10 µm

Basophil

10 to 14 µm

(a)

(b)

(c)

(From Villee, Solomon, and Davis, *Biology*)

■ Move the tube to 25 cm, and allow it to adjust. Repeat your measurements and record the results.
■ Now move the plant to 75 cm. Allow it to readjust, and repeat your measurements.

Did you see a different rate of oxygen evolution when the light intensity was increased or decreased?

_____

■ Replace the water in the tube with 0.5% $NaHCO_3$ (sodium bicarbonate, which will act as a source of CO_2 for the plant).
■ Place the plant back at 25 cm, and measure the rate of bubble release for two 3-min intervals.

Does the initial reaction of CO_2 in carbon fixation require

light? _____

Is oxygen produced as a result of carbon fixation or of electron transport?

_____

Can electron transport continue to produce NADPH if there is no CO_2? Why not?

_____

_____

Can the Calvin cycle enzymes continue to fix CO_2 when the light is turned off? Why or why not?

_____

_____

_____

_____

THE HILL REACTION

In 1937 Robin Hill showed that chloroplasts continue to carry out electron flow and oxygen production in the ab-

sence of CO_2 as long as they are provided with an electron acceptor (see Figure 7-5).

What is the fate of the electrons when CO_2 is present?

_____

Hill used a substance that becomes colored as it is reduced, so that the rate of photosynthesis could be measured by observing the rate at which the dye changed color. In this experiment you will use a blue dye nicknamed DCIP (2,6-dichlorophenolindolphenol), which is blue when oxidized, and becomes colorless after it has been reduced:

$$DCIP_{ox} + 2e^- + 2H^+ \rightarrow DCIP \cdot H_{2red}$$

The experimental tube will contain "living" chloroplasts, buffer, and the blue dye, and will be held in the light.

What change will you look for in the experimental tube?

_____

What should the control tube contain?

_____

Should you hold it in the light? _____

The chloroplasts for this experiment are diluted in sucrose buffer so there are 100 μg of chlorophyll per mL, and they should be kept cold until you are ready to use them. Be sure to use the suspension labeled **CHLOROPLASTS.**

■ Set the wavelength of the spectrophotometer at 620 nm.
■ Obtain three spectrophotometer tubes and label them #1, #2, and #3.
■ Add these reagents in the order given (left to right) in Table 7-1.
■ Cover the tubes with Parafilm or stoppers and mix the ingredients by inverting the tube several times.

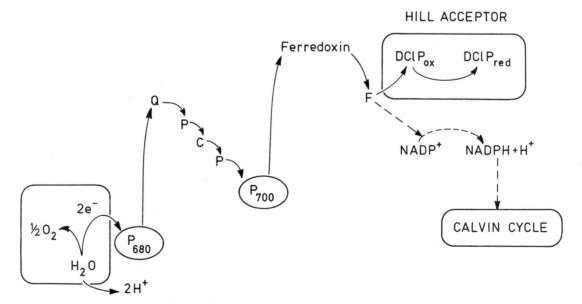

Figure 7-5. The Hill reaction. In the experiment, an electron acceptor, DCIP, is provided to pick up electrons from photosystem I. This allows non-cyclic electron transport to continue in the absence of the Calvin cycle. DCIP is observed to turn blue as it is reduced.

TABLE 7-1. COMPONENTS FOR THE HILL REACTION.

	Chloroplasts	Cold Buffer	Distilled Water	DCIP
Tube #1: blank	0.5 mL	3.0 mL	1.5 mL	—
Tube #2: reaction	0.5 mL	3.0 mL	0.5 mL	1.0 mL
Tube #3: control*	—	3.0 mL	1.0 mL	1.0 mL

*A tube identical to tube #2 but held in the dark would be an equally good control but would use up the chloroplasts.

■ Immediately cover the tubes with aluminum foil, and keep them covered except when they are being measured.
■ Adjust the spectrophotometer to ∞ absorbance, insert tube #1, and adjust the absorbance to 0.
■ Insert tube #2, and record its absorbance in Table 7-5, at the end of this topic. Cover the tube and wait 3 min.
■ Again read the absorbance of tube #2.

Did any change in the dye occur in the dark?

_____

■ Choose one light intensity (1000, 1500, or 2000 footcandles), or take the one assigned to you, and hold your tube at the appropriate position for exactly 30 sec. Cover the tube.
■ Read the absorbance; cover the tube again.
■ Hold the tube in the light for another 30-sec period, and again read the absorbance.
■ Continue until you have 12 readings.
■ Since the experiment is meaningless without the control, read the absorbance of tube #3 (no chloroplasts).
■ Hold the tube for 3 min at the same light intensity that you used in the experiment.
■ Read the absorbance again.
■ Graph your results in Figure 7-6 (at the end of this topic) as percent DCIP reduced as a function of seconds exposed to the light. Label the curve with the light intensity that you used.

    Join forces with students who used the other light intensities available and pool your results for comparison. Work together to answer the questions on the last page of this topic.

CARBON FIXATION

Although carbon fixation can occur in the absence of light, it will quickly slow down and stop because the ATP and NADPH will soon be used up. A leaf or part of the plant that is not illuminated will obtain food from the other parts of the plant, but will not be able to carry on photosynthesis itself. Roots, tree trunks, and the other nongreen parts of plants must routinely obtain carbohydrate from the green photosynthetic parts. In this experiment you will study the effect of depriving part of a green leaf of light. The extent of carbon fixation will be measured as the amount of the storage carbohydrate, starch, that is formed.

■ Fold a pice of black paper in half, and cut out two copies of a small square, rectangle, or some other interesting shape.
■ Stick a label on one of the pieces, and write your initials and the date on it.

■ Use a paper clip to fasten the black shapes to the top and bottom surfaces of a leaf of a plant such as *Coleus* so that they are matched up exactly.
■ Place the plant in sunlight until the next laboratory period.

WAIT ONE WEEK.

■ Remove the leaf that was partially covered and take off the black paper.
■ Drop the leaf into a beaker of boiling 95% alcohol in the hood, and boil it until it turns white.
■ Remove the leaf, and place it in a finger bowl.
■ Flood the leaf with iodine solution, and let it absorb the iodine for a few minutes.
■ Rinse the leaf with tap water, and observe which parts stain darkly.

What happens when the leaf is boiled in alcohol?

_____

_____

What part of the leaf stained dark? _____

What carbohydrate causes the dark staining?

_____

Why does carbon fixation occur only in the light?

_____

_____

If you tested the leaf for glucose, would you expect to find any in the unstained part of the leaf? _____

    When you finish your work, discard any debris, and clean your glassware thoroughly.

EXPLORING FURTHER

Baker, Jeffrey J. W., and Garland E. Allen. *Matter, Energy and Life. An Introduction to Chemical Concepts.* 4th ed. Reading, Mass.: Addison-Wesley, 1981.

Galston, A. W., P. J. Davies, and R. L. Satter. *The Life of the Green Plant.* 3rd. ed. Englewood Cliffs, N.J.: Prentice-Hall, 1980.

Lehninger, A. L. *Biochemistry.* 2nd ed. New York: Worth, 1975.

Lehninger, A. L. *Principles of Biochemistry.* New York: Worth, 1982.

Rawn, J. David. *Biochemistry.* New York: Harper and Row, 1983.

Stryer, Lubert. *Biochemistry.* 2nd ed. San Francisco: W. H. Freeman, 1981.

Journal Articles

Björkman, Olle, and Joseph Barry. "High-efficiency photosynthesis." *Scientific American*, October 1973 (#1281).

Govindjee, and R. Govindjee. "The primary events of photosynthesis." *Scientific American*, December 1974 (#1310).

Miller, Kenneth R. "The photosynthetic membrane." *Scientific American*, October 1979 (#1448).

Stein, William H., and Stanford Moore. "Chromatography." *Scientific American*, March 1951 (#81).

Stoeckenius, Walther. "The purple membrane of salt-loving bacteria." *Scientific American*, June 1976 (#1340).

Waggoner, Paul E. "Agriculture and Carbon Dioxide." *American Scientist 72(2):* 179-184, 1984.

Woodwell, George M. "The carbon dioxide question." *Scientific American*, January 1978 (#1376).

Student Name _____ **Date** _____

Extra space is provided on these data sheets in case some observations are repeated.

TABLE 7-2. DATA FROM CHROMATOGRAPHY

Spot	cm moved	R_f (cm/cm Solvent)	Color (Visible)	Color (UV)	Identification
Solvent front		———	———	———	———
Fastest spot					
Slowest spot					

Chromatogram:

R_f values: carotene (yellow-orange) = _____

xanthophyll (yellow) = _____

chlorophyll *a* (blue-green) = _____

chlorophyll *b* (yellow-green) = _____

TABLE 7-3. ABSORPTION SPECTRUM OF PHOTOSYNTHETIC PIGMENTS

DATA

Wavelength	Absorbance	Wavelength	Absorbance	Wavelength	Absorbance
400 nm					

SPECTRUM

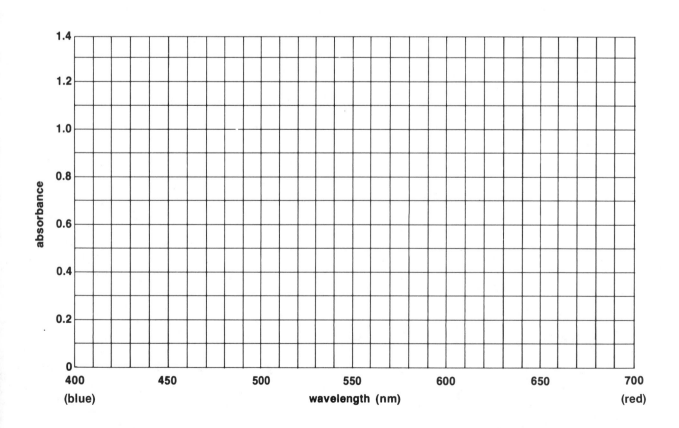

Student Name ⎯⎯⎯⎯⎯⎯⎯⎯⎯⎯⎯⎯⎯⎯ **Date** ⎯⎯⎯⎯⎯⎯⎯⎯⎯

TABLE 7-4. DATA ON OXYGEN EVOLUTION BY *ELODEA*

TAP WATER

Distance	Bubbles/3 min	Avg. Bubbles/min

NaHCO₃

Distance	Bubbles/3 min	Avg. Bubbles/min

SUMMARY

Treatment	Distance	Avg. Bubbles/min
None	75 cm	
None	50 cm	
NaHCO₃	25 cm	
None	25 cm	

What effect did decreasing light (increasing distance) have on the rate of photosynthesis?

⎯⎯⎯⎯⎯⎯⎯⎯⎯⎯⎯⎯⎯⎯⎯⎯⎯⎯⎯⎯⎯⎯⎯⎯⎯⎯⎯

What effect did increasing CO₂ (NaHCO₃) have on the rate of photosynthesis?

⎯⎯⎯⎯⎯⎯⎯⎯⎯⎯⎯⎯⎯⎯⎯⎯⎯⎯⎯⎯⎯⎯⎯⎯⎯⎯⎯

TABLE 7-5. DATA FROM THE HILL REACTION

1. The average initial absorbance of tube #2 was _____.

2. Calculate the change from this value for each reading by subtracting the **new** absorbance from the **initial** absorbance.

3. Calculate the % DCIP reduced = (change × 100)/initial.

TUBE #2 REACTION (extra space provided)

Seconds of Light	(1) Absorbance	(2) Change in Absorbance	(3) % DCIP Reduced
0 (initial)		0	0
0 (3 min dark)			
30			
60			

TUBE #3 CONTROL

Seconds of Light	(1) Absorbance	(2) Change in Absorbance	(3) % DCIP Reduced
0		0	0
180			

Student Name _____ **Date** _____

HILL REACTION AT A LIGHT INTENSITY OF _____ FOOT-CANDLES

Figure 7-6. Hill reaction. Plot the percent DCIP reduced as a function of seconds exposed to light. Be sure to label both axes of your graph. Answer the questions on the next page.

Compare your curve with those of other class members who used different light intensities. Your instructor may ask you to draw additional curves on your own graph.

Did the rate of dye reduction depend on the intensity of the light? _____

Did the lowest light intensity used still show more dye reduction than seen in the control? _____

If the light intensity could be increased even more without heating up the chloroplasts, would the rate of photosynthesis keep increasing indefinitely? Explain your answer.

_____

_____

_____

_____

_____

Cellular Respiration

OBJECTIVES _____

When you have completed this topic, you should be able to:
1. Distinguish anaerobic from aerobic cellular respiration in terms of ATP, oxygen and chemiosmosis.
2. Define fermentation and give its starting materials and end products.
3. Measure CO_2 production by fermenting yeast.
4. List the starting materials and end products of each of the following processes: glycolysis, citric acid cycle, electron transport system.
5. Describe an experiment to measure the respiration rate of a living plant or animal.
6. State the importance of the electron transport system and the role of O_2 in it.
7. Describe an experiment that will measure the reaction of oxygen with an enzyme of the electron transport system.
8. Describe an experiment that will show the effect of an inhibitor on the electron transport system.

KEY TOPICS _____

Energy, ATP, oxidation reduction reactions, coenzymes, glycolysis, citric acid cycle, electron transport system, chemiosmosis, fermentation.

INTRODUCTION

Heterotrophs obtain energy by oxidizing organic molecules and coupling the oxidation reactions to the synthesis of ATP. The ATP is then used to carry out metabolic reactions necessary to maintain the organism's physical integrity, and to support all its other activities.

Some organisms are able to exist in the absence of molecular oxygen, and may even be harmed by the presence of oxygen. They still carry out oxidation reactions but do not use molecular oxygen itself.

Define **oxidation:**_____

_____

_____

Anaerobic respiration in the absence of oxygen is called **fermentation**. It begins with an energy-rich substance such as glucose, utilizes the enzymes of **glycolysis**, and finally produces ethanol and CO_2, or a mixture of organic acids and other compounds. There is a net gain of only two molecules of ATP for each molecule of glucose oxidized in fermentation. These ATP molecules are formed by substrate level phosphorylation.

Most organisms use oxygen in the process of **cellular respiration**. Pyruvic acid, produced by the reactions of glycolysis, loses a molecule of CO_2, then enters another set of reactions, the citric acid cycle (tricarboxylic acid cycle) in which the carbon skeleton is completely oxidized to CO_2. The hydrogen carriers, NAD^+ and FAD, are reduced by the reactions of glycolysis and the citric acid cycle. NADH and $FADH_2$ then transfer their hydrogen atoms to a third set of proteins called the **electron transport chain**. The flow of electrons through this system is coupled to the synthesis of ATP. The very last protein carrier in the chain, **cytochrome oxidase,** reacts directly with molecular oxygen to produce water. This step is the point where the oxygen that organisms take in is used and where **metabolic water** is produced. The purpose of the oxygen is to return the cytochrome oxidase to an oxidized form so that it can pick up more electrons from its neighboring electron carrier. Aerobic respiration of a molecule of glucose usually gives a net yield of 36 molecules of ATP.

As in photosynthesis, the coupling of electron flow to ATP synthesis is explained by the **chemiosmotic hypothesis**. A proton gradient is set up as electron flow pumps H^+ ions into the compartment between the inner and outer mitochondrial membranes. Proton flow back through special channels in the inner membrane, from the higher to lower H^+ concentration, provides the energy for ATP synthesis. Of the 36 ATPs produced by the complete aerobic respiration of one glucose molecule, 32 come from chemiosmosis.

FERMENTATION IN YEAST

Yeasts are eukaryotic fungi that are commercially very important. They are necessary for the production of beer, wine, bread, and industrial chemicals. In this experiment you will study the production of CO_2 during the fermentation of various carbohydrates by yeast cells.

What molecule is split in the fermentation reaction that produces the CO_2?

_____

When carbohydrate is fermented by yeast, only one-third of the carbons are released in the form of CO_2. The rest of the carbon is released as molecules of

_____ .

Why is it advantageous for an organism to be able to carry on fermentation?

_____

_____

Study the experiment shown in Figure 8-1 for measuring fermentation under anaerobic conditions. Work with a partner.

■ Obtain or start an actively fermenting yeast culture (yeast dissolved in a molasses solution).
■ Obtain a test tube rack, four clean, dry test tubes, four graduated pipets, four Pasteur pipets, and pieces of Parafilm or clay.
■ Label the tubes #1–#4.
■ Fill the tubes as follows:

Tube #1: 1 mL of sucrose + 1 mL of yeast suspension.
Tube #2: 1 mL of galactose + 1 mL of yeast suspension.

Tube #3: 1 mL of molasses + 1 mL of yeast suspension.
Tube #4: 1 mL of water + 1 mL of yeast suspension.

■ Mix the solution in tube #1, then draw it up in a graduated pipet, and place your finger over the top of the pipet.
■ Seal the opposite end of the pipet with a piece of Parafilm or clay.
■ Using the Pasteur pipet, completely fill the graduated pipet to overflowing with solution from tube #1.
■ Place the pipet *upside down* in tube #1, and set the tube back in the rack.
■ Repeat for the other test tubes.

As gas forms during the fermentation, it will rise in the pipet and collect at the plugged end. Note the exact level of the gas in each pipet every minute for about 20 min, and record your readings in Table 8-1 at the end of this topic.

Did the type of carbohydrate being fermented affect the rate of gas formation? _____

Which carbohydrate supported the fastest rate of fermentation?_____

Your instructor may ask you to vary this basic experiment by using different concentrations of carbohydrate or yeast, or by adding inhibitors. Ethyl alcohol itself will eventually inhibit yeast fermentation.

RESPIRATION IN PLANTS AND ANIMALS: CO_2 PRODUCTION

In aerobic respiration the carbon skeleton of glucose is completely broken down to CO_2. The CO_2 must be quickly removed via the transport and gas exchange systems, so that it does not build up and make the body fluids so acidic that the organism cannot function.

pipet filled with yeast suspension

clay or parafilm

Tube #1   Tube #2   Tube #3   Tube #4

Figure 8-1. Fermentation experiment. Fermentation by yeast within the pipet produces CO_2. The pipet must be completely filled with yeast suspension at the beginning of the experiment.

In which reactions is CO_2 released during aerobic respiration?

_____

_____

_____

_____

Why does CO_2 make the tissues acidic?

_____

_____

_____

_____

In this experiment you will measure the rate of CO_2 production in several organisms. This rate is an indicator of the respiration rate, or metabolic rate. A diagram of the experiment is shown in Figure 8-2.

Record your results in Table 8-2.

■ Obtain five 100-mL beakers, and label them #1–#5.
■ Set up the beakers as follows:

	Phenolphthalein	**Organism**
Beaker #1	25 mL	1 fish
Beaker #2	25 mL	2 snails
Beaker #3	25 mL	5 cm of *Elodea*
Beaker #4	25 mL	5 cm of *Elodea*
Beaker #5	25 mL	None

■ Cap beakers #1, #2, #3 and #5 with aluminum foil, and note the time.
■ Completely cover beaker #4 with aluminum foil so that the *Elodea* is kept dark, and do not open this beaker until the end of the experiment.
■ At the end of 30 min, return the living organisms to the proper containers on the instructor's desk.
■ Add NaOH (0.0025 M) drop by drop to beaker #1 until the solution definitely turns color. Thoroughly mix the solution after each drop is added, and record the total number of drops needed or the volume of acid used from the buret.
■ Repeat for beakers #2, #3, #4, and #5.
■ If you counted drops, convert the number of drops to milliliters by dividing by 20.

As CO_2 is produced, the pH of the solution will slowly decrease. This change can be measured using the pH indicator, phenolphthalein. The addition of a certain number of drops of NaOH will raise the pH sufficiently so that it becomes pink (above pH 9.2). If CO_2 has been produced, the H_2CO_3 in the solution will increase the number of drops of base needed to turn the solution pink. The more CO_2 produced, the more NaOH needed.

Before calculating the CO_2 production of your organisms, you will need to know their approximate volumes.

■ Obtain a 25-mL graduated cylinder, and fill it with water exactly to the 20-mL mark using a Pasteur pipet.
■ Place one fish in the water so that it is completely below the surface. (If they are very small, use several fish, and then divide the volume by the number of fish.)
■ Note exactly how far above the 20-mL mark the water rose. The difference in water level with and without the organism in the water is the approximate volume.
■ Repeat for the other organisms.
■ If an empty snail shell is available, measure the volume of this nonliving part of the snail, and subtract it from the total volume to determine the volume of the living organism more accurately.

Use the following equation to calculate the CO_2 production in $\mu M/mL/hr$:

$$\frac{[mL\ NaOH\ (exptl.) - mL\ NaOH\ (control)]}{\times\ 2.5\ \mu M\ NaOH/mL}{volume\ of\ organism\ (mL) \times time\ (hr)}$$

Which organism had the highest metabolic rate?

_____

Which one had the lowest rate? _____

Explain your results with *Elodea* in the dark versus in the light:

_____

_____

Which *Elodea* experiment was a better measure of the metabolic rate? _____

Why?

_____

_____

_____

_____

Figure 8-2. Respiration experiment. These aquatic organisms produce CO_2. Each 100-mL beaker contains 25 mL of phenolphthalein solution and its top is covered with aluminum foil. Beaker #4 is completely covered with foil to exclude light.

THE ELECTRON TRANSPORT CHAIN: CYTOCHROME OXIDASE

Most of the ATP in a cell is made in the electron transport system by **oxidative phosphorylation**. The last protein carrier, **cytochrome oxidase**, donates its electrons to catalyze the conversion of molecular oxygen to water:

$$2e^- + 2H^+ + \tfrac{1}{2}O_2 \xrightarrow{\text{cytochrome oxidase}} H_2O$$

The water produced in this way is called **metabolic water** because it is formed by the organism's metabolism, and not taken in from its environment.

If oxygen is removed from the electron transport system, all of the component enzymes will remain in their reduced forms, and electron flow will cease. No ATP can be synthesized by chemiosmosis, and the organism must rely on anaerobic respiration (glycolysis and fermentation) only. Many organisms cannot survive without a functioning electron transport system. Therefore substances such as potassium cyanide or sodium azide, that block these enzymes of the chain are lethal poisons.

Where in the cell are enzymes of the electron transport system located?

_____

In this experiment you will study cytochrome oxidase from beans. The enzyme will be in the form of a crude extract from bean seedlings. Record your results in Table 8-3, at the end of this topic.

■ Obtain four test tubes and label them #1-#4.
■ Add the following reagents to the tubes:

	Bean Extract (Cytochrome Oxidase)	**Sucrose**	**Sodium Azide**
Tube #1	—	4 mL	—
Tube #2	2 mL	2 mL	—
Tube #3	2 mL	1.8 mL	5 drops (.02 mL)
Tube #4	2 mL boiled*	2 mL	—

*Use boiled enzyme if it is available; otherwise, add 2 mL bean extract to the tube, and then hold it in a boiling water bath for 10 min before adding the other reagents.

■ Add 5 drops (0.2 mL) of Nadi reagent A to each tube. Mix.
■ Add 5 drops (0.2 mL) of Nadi reagent B to each tube. Mix.
■ Observe the tubes every 10 min for 30 min, and note the color changes.

The two components of the Nadi reagent will reduce the cytochrome c present in the bean extract. If the cytochrome oxidase is active, it will oxidize cytochrome c, and pass the electrons to oxygen. More of the reagent will then be used to keep the cytochrome c reduced. When the reagent becomes oxidized during this reaction, it turns blue. The electrons are flowing from the dye to oxygen. (See Figure 8-3.)

Sodium azide is a potent inhibitor of cytochrome oxidase, and will block the reaction of this enzyme with molecular oxygen.

Did inhibition of cytochrome oxidase block the reaction of cytochrome c with the Nadi reagent?

_____

If the electron transport system were blocked at an early step, but oxygen and active cytochrome oxidase were present, would the reaction of the Nadi reagent continue in the absence of electron flow from the other cytochromes? Explain your answer.

_____
_____
_____
_____

When you are finished with your work, return all animals and materials, and wash your glassware.

EXPLORING FURTHER

Baker, Jeffrey J. W., and Garland E. Allen. *Matter, Energy and Life. An introduction to Chemical Concepts.* 4th ed. Reading, Mass: Addison-Wesley, 1981.
Lehninger, A. L. *Biochemistry.* 2nd ed. New York: Worth, 1975.

Figure 8-3. Cytochrome oxidase experiment. Colorless Nadi dye$_{red}$ donates electrons to reduce cytochrome c. Cytochrome c in turn passes the electrons to cytochrome oxidase and then to oxygen. Blue Nadi dye$_{ox}$ accumulates as long as electrons flow.

Lehninger, A. L. *Bioenergetics: The Molecular Basis of Biological Energy Transformations.* 2nd ed. Menlo Park, Calif.: Benjamin/Cummings, 1971.

Lehninger, A. L. *Principles of Biochemistry.* New York: Worth, 1982.

Rawn, J. David. *Biochemistry.* New York: Harper and Row, 1983.

Stryer, Lubert. *Biochemistry.* 2nd ed. San Francisco: W. H. Freeman, 1981.

Journal Articles

Amerine, Maynard A. "Wine." *Scientific American*, August 1964 (#190).

Dickerson, Richard E. "Cytochrome c and the evolution of energy metabolism." *Scientific American*, March 1980 (#1464).

Hinkle, Peter C., and Richard E. McCarty. "How cells make ATP." *Scientific American*, March 1978 (#1383).

Revelle, Roger. "Carbon dioxide and the world climate." *Scientific American*, 35, August 1982.

Waggoner, Paul E. "Agriculture and carbon dioxide." *American Scientist* 72(2): 179-184, 1984.

Student Name _____ **Date** _____

TABLE 8-1. FERMENTATION IN YEAST

Note the exact level of the gas in the pipet above the yeast suspension every minute.

Time (min)	Tube #1	Tube #2	Tube #3	Tube #4
0				
1				
2				
3				
4				
5				
6				
7				
8				
9				
10				
11				
12				
13				
14				
15				
16				
17				
18				
19				
20				
Total CO_2 in mL/hr:				

TABLE 8-2. CO_2 PRODUCTION IN PLANTS AND ANIMALS

Record the number of drops or mL (20 drops = 1 mL) needed to change color. Calculate CO_2 production in each case.

Beaker	Organism	NaOH		Volume of Organism (mL)	μM CO_2* mL/hr
		drops	mL		
#1	Fish				
#2	Snail				
#3	Elodea (light)				
#4	Elodea (dark)				
#5	None (control)				

$$*\frac{[\text{mL NaOH (exptl.)} - \text{mL NaOH (control)}] \times 2.5 \ \mu\text{M NaOH/mL}}{\text{volume of organism (mL)} \times \text{time (hr)}}$$

TABLE 8-3. ACTIVITY OF CYTOCHROME OXIDASE Record the color of each tube.

Time (min)	Tube #1	Tube #2	Tube #3	Tube #4
0				
10				
20				
30				

Meiosis and Heredity

OBJECTIVES _____

When you have completed this topic, you should be able to:
1. Draw the structure of a chromosome before replication and after replication.
2. Distinguish between sister chromatids and homologous chromosomes.
3. Distinguish between sexual reproduction and asexual reproduction.
4. State when and in which tissues meiosis occurs.
5. Use models to show how meiosis differs from mitosis in terms of chromosome movement.
6. Explain in terms of DNA synthesis, synapsis, crossing over, and cytokinesis how meiosis differs from mitosis.
7. Identify the haploid and diploid stages of meiosis in a diploid organism such as yourself.

KEY TOPICS _____

Chromosomes, haploid and diploid cells, mitosis, meiosis, crossing over, spermatogenesis, oogenesis, fertilization.

INTRODUCTION

Meiosis is a special type of cell divison by which animals produce **gametes** and by which plants and fungi produce **spores.** This process is necessary whenever *two parental organisms* cooperate in producing offspring by **sexual reproduction.** In animals and plants that reproduce sexually, two sex cells or gametes fuse during fertilization to produce the **zygote.** The zygote will thus always have twice as much genetic material as the gamete. Therefore, at some stage before the next fertilization, the genetic material must be reduced by half, so that the amount of nuclear material stays the same from one generation to the next. This reduction in nuclear material occurs through the process of meiosis. Only specialized germ cells carry out meiosis. The gametes or spores resulting from this process contain only one half of the genetic material of their parent cells.

There are two very important terms associated with meiosis that you will need to understand from the outset:

haploid: A haploid cell contains one unique set of genetic information. It includes one chromosome of each type found in a particular organism and it has the same set of chromosomes that would be found in a gamete or spore from that organism.

diploid: A diploid cell contains two sets of genetic information. It includes two chromosomes of each type found in a particular organism, and it has the same set of chromosomes that would be found in the ordinary body cells of an animal or plant.

With these two terms, we can restate the concept very simply: Meiosis is the process by which diploid cells are converted to haploid cells.

In animals, the haploid gametes usually fuse soon after they form, to produce a diploid zygote. Development of the zygote into a mature animal involves thousands of mitotic divisions to produce diploid cells genetically identical to the zygote. In plants, the spores produced by meiosis usually develop into haploid plants which themselves produce the gametes. This process will be studied later. (See Topics 17 and 23.)

Many organisms can carry out **asexual reproduction** as well as sexual reproduction. Asexual reproduction always involves mitosis rather than meiosis and the offspring are genetically identical to the *single parent.*

In this exercise you will review mitosis in an example of asexual reproduction and compare mitosis with meiosis. It is essential that you thoroughly understand both processes and the differences between them before undertaking the topic of genetics.

MITOSIS IN YEAST

This unicellular organism belongs to Kingdom Fungi because it is an absorptive heterotroph and has many features in common with other fungi. Some more typical fungi in fact may assume a unicellular form when they grow in the sugar solutions favored by yeast. Asexual reproduction involves the budding off of daughter cells and is the more common type. Sexual reproduction can occur when two cells of opposite mating types fuse and undergo meiosis. Four haploid **ascospores** are produced. These processes are shown in Figure 9-1.

■ Make a wet mount of a drop of an actively dividing yeast culture, and observe the cells in the microscope under high power.
■ Note the cells that are producing smaller buds or short chains of buds.

If a yeast cell contains 10 chromosomes, how many chromosomes would there be in a bud nucleus?

_____ In a daughter produced by budding?

_____

If a yeast cell is haploid, is the daughter produced by

budding haploid or diploid? _____

Yeasts are important in the baking and brewing industries and are used to produce important industrial chemicals. Such processes depend on asexual reproduction and fermentation by the yeast cells.

What by-product of yeast fermentation is important in

baking? _____

What by-product is important in brewing? _____

_____

Which of these products is produced in both aerobic and

anaerobic respiration? _____

MECHANICS OF MITOSIS AND MEIOSIS

To clarify the difference in chromosome movement during mitosis and meiosis, you will use pipe cleaners of various lengths to represent the sister chromatids of the chromosomes, and beads to represent the centromeres. A given chromosome may have one or two chromatids, depending on whether it has replicated. The number of chromatids does not affect the fact that it is a single chromosome. A given chromosome may have one or two chromatids, depending on whether it has replicated. The number of chromatids does not affect the fact that it is a single chromosome. The chromatids are not considered complete chromosomes in their own right until they have have separated from each other and *each possesses an unshared centromere.*

The number of complete chromosomes found in a haploid cell is the **haploid number** or **N.** The number of complete chromosomes found in a diploid cell is the **diploid number** or **2N.** In Figure 9-2 you see a diploid cell with four chromosomes (2N = 4) undergoing mitosis compared with another cell containing four chromosomes undergoing meiosis. In each case the chromosomes are first replicated in S phase so that they are double. The number of chromosomes in each cell after

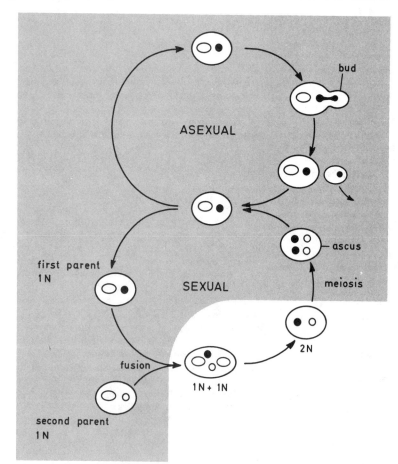

Figure 9-1. The life cycle of a yeast, *Saccharomyces cerevisiae*. Bakers yeast will reproduce in dough asexually by budding. The cells that fuse in sexual reproduction are of two different mating types.

MITOSIS

MEIOSIS

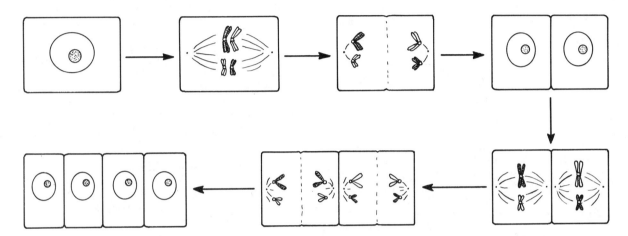

Figure 9-2. Mitosis and meiosis compared. A cell with 2 chromosomes (2N = 2) undergoes mitosis and meiosis very differently. Mitosis produces two daughter cells that are identical to the diploid parent, whereas meiosis produces four haploid cells that are genetically different from the parent cell.

replication is still four. Note that in meiosis the chromosomes do not act independently as they do in mitosis, but join together in **homologous pairs** during meiosis I, the first meiotic division. In a cell with many chromosomes, all of them would join in homologous pairs. During the first meiotic division, the two members of the pair separate, but the chromosomes do not split in half as they do in mitosis, and they remain double-stranded. Thus there is no need for DNA synthesis before meiosis II. The two sister chromatids of each chromosome separate in meiosis II; so that each daughter cell receives one single-stranded chromosome. The four daughter cells produced when a cell undergoes meiosis are usually not identical, in contrast to the carbon-copy daughters produced during mitosis. These four daughter cells are haploid (N) rather than diploid (2N), and contain only one set of the genetic material.

■ Insert two identical pipe cleaners into a bead to construct a chromosome that has already replicated.

■ Make a second, **homologous chromosome** from pipe cleaners the same length as those in the first chromosome. The second chromosome does not need to be the same color as the first, but it must be the same length, and its sister chromatids must be identical to each other (they are carbon copies).

■ Turn to Figure 9-6 at the end of this topic, or use a similar poster that shows parent and daughter cells in metaphase, and place each chromosome on a *separate* spindle fiber, as it would appear in mitosis.

■ Take another bead for each chromosome to represent its second centromere.

■ Separate the sister chromatids and give each one a centromere so that it is a new full-fledged chromosome.

■ Separate the two daughter chromosomes, placing one in each daughter cell, and repeat the process for the second homologous chromosome. Mitosis is complete.

Are the chromosomes in the daughter cells genetically identical to those that you started with except that they have not yet replicated? _____

If not, ask your instructor for help!

During mitosis, each chromosome acts independently, and there is never any pairing of homologous chromosomes. During meiosis, there is **pairing of homologous chromosomes** and the daughter cells formed are *not identical to the parent cell*.

■ Form a homologous pair of replicated chromosomes that are the same length, but different colors. The sister chromatids of each chromosome must be identical in length *and* color.

■ Place the chromosomes in the center of the spindle side by side on the same spindle fiber. The two chromosomes are in **synapsis,** which is a close side-by-side position, and their four strands form a **tetrad** or four-stranded structure. Synapsis is the key event in meiosis and will result in **genetic variation** in the daughter cells.

■ Move one whole chromosome to each of the daughter cells. You do not need more beads because the chromatids **do not separate** during the first meiotic division.

How many chromosomes does each daughter cell have?

_____

■ Separate the sister chromatids of one chromosome, and give each one a bead to represent its centromere. The new chromosomes can now move apart into the daughter cells formed in meiosis II. Note that there was *no chromosome replication* before meiosis II. Otherwise, meiosis II is exactly like mitosis.
■ Repeat the division for the other daughter cell so that you have formed the four daughter cells that result from meiosis II.

How many chromosomes are there in each cell resulting

from meiosis? _____

Are these cells haploid or diploid? _____

What process will restore the diploid number of chromo-

somes in the next generation? _____

■ Starting with four replicated chromosomes, carry out a mitotic division.
■ Starting with four replicated chromosomes, in which the homologous pairs are different colors, and in which one pair is longer so that you can tell the pairs apart, carry out the two meiotic divisions. Make a note of the chromosomes found in each of the four daughter cells.
■ Arrange the chromosomes differently on the spindle in meiosis I so that the products after meiosis II will now be different than before.

How many different types of daughter cells can you create using both arrangements?

_____

■ In Figure 9-6 draw in the chromosomes of a cell undergoing meiosis. Start with four chromosomes (2N = 4), two long and two short, and draw one member of each homologous pair with dotted lines for chromatids, and the other with solid lines. Use pencils of different colors if they are available.

MEIOSIS IN AN ANIMAL CELL

In animals, meiosis occurs only in the gonads.
Where does meiosis occur in a woman?

_____

What is this process called?

_____

Where does meiosis occur in a man? _____
What is this process called?

_____

In males, the sperm are formed much as you illustrated in the section on mechanics. Each cell undergoing **spermatogenesis** will produce four sperm cells. Note that each sperm will have a genetically identical twin. In **oogenesis,** however, a single, large egg cell is produced which carries the energy stores for the development of the zygote after fertilization. Nuclear division oc-

curs in the same way, but cytoplasmic division is very unequal. A nucleus with a small amount of membrane and cytoplasm is discarded after meiosis I as the **first polar body.** A **second polar body** is discarded after meiosis II. If the first polar body undergoes division, there may be two or three polar bodies stuck onto the outside of the **ovum,** or egg cell. Thus, in the female, meiosis gives rise to a single gamete, the ovum, and to polar bodies that have no function and degenerate. Figure 9-3 illustrates the processes of oogenesis and spermatogenesis.

The roundworm *Ascaris* has large, easily removed ovaries in which the stages of meiosis can be seen. This parasitic organism is easily obtained from the intestine of horses. (Another species of *Ascaris* is a common human parasite in warm climates, and it is a serious human pest that sometimes causes intestinal blockage and lung infection.)

In *Ascaris,* as in many organisms, meiosis is not completed until after fertilization. Then meiosis I occurs, followed by meiosis II, fusion of the egg and sperm nuclei, and the first division of the zygote. Cells in progressively later stages of meiosis and early development are found in sections of the oviduct and uterus farther and farther from the ovary (see Figure 9-4).

OOGENESIS

SPERMATOGENESIS

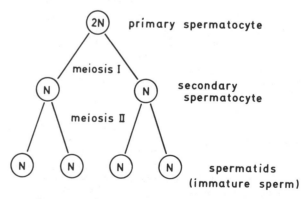

Figure 9-3. Oogenesis and spermatogenesis compared. Oogenesis produces one ovum or egg cell but spermatogenesis produces four sperm cells for each cell entering meiosis.

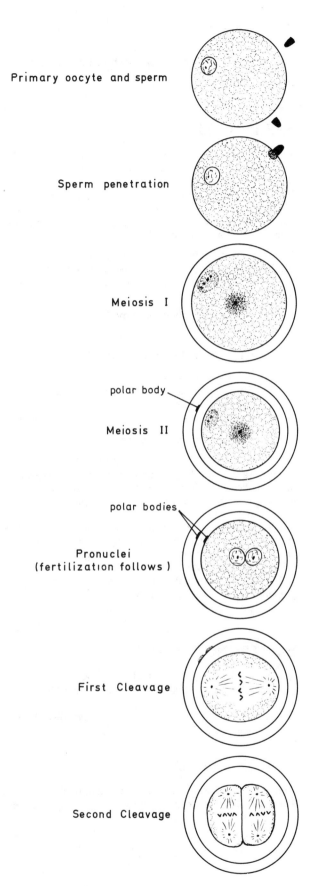

Primary oocyte and sperm

Sperm penetration

Meiosis I

polar body

Meiosis II

polar bodies

Pronuclei
(fertilization follows)

First Cleavage

Second Cleavage

Figure 9-4. Meiosis in *Ascaris*. Fertilization precedes meiosis in this species.

■ Study meiosis in the prepared slide, noting that the earlier stages will be found in the sections at the top of the slide, which are from the part of the oviduct closer to the ovary. A set of slides rather than a single slide may be provided for your study of meiosis.

Sperm Cell

These triangular-shaped cells are small in relation to the egg cells of the female. The top of the sperm cell must enter the egg cell before meiosis can begin. *Ascaris* sperm lack flagella and reach the ova by amoeboid motion.

■ Locate a free sperm cell.

Primary Oocyte (or Future Egg Cell)

This is the cell that will undergo meiosis after the sperm cell penetrates. It is a diploid cell, and has no shell around it.

■ Locate a primary oocyte.
■ Locate a primary oocyte into which a sperm has penetrated. The sperm head becomes modified into a sphere once it enters the oocyte.

Meiosis I

In *Ascaris* there are four chromosomes (2N = 4). How many pairs of chromosomes will there be in meiosis I?

———————————

Each pair of chromosomes forms a **tetrad** as the homologous chromosomes undergo **synapsis.** The tetrads move to one edge of the cell where the spindle forms during prophase I and metaphase I. This is the only time during the entire life cycle of a sexually reproducing organism that the members of a homologous pair of chromosomes come together. While the chromosomes are in synapsis, and the four sister chromatids are close together in the tetrad, sister chromatids of the two chromosomes may exchange parts of their arms in the process of **crossing over.** There is no gain or loss of genetic material, but the genes on one chromatid are exchanged one-for-one with those on the other chromatid. The shuffling of genes during crossing over results in more variety among the gametes than would otherwise occur. When crossing over is going on, there will be crosslike structures visible in the microscope, called **chiasmata.** Special techniques are required in order to see them.

■ Locate a cell in prophase I in which there are prominent tetrads. The sperm nucleus may or may not be visible in the section of cell that you are viewing, but there cannot be a polar body on the cell surface.

The pairs of chromosomes assemble on the equator at metaphase I, and the two daughter nuclei form during telophase I.

Cytokinesis I

During this process, a piece of membrane enclosing one daughter nucleus pinches off to form the first polar body. The large cell is now called the **secondary oocyte.**

■ Locate a secondary oocyte that has a polar body attached to its surface.

Interkinesis

The cell prepares for meiosis II, and there is *no replication* of the chromosomes during this special interphase.

Meiosis II

The secondary oocyte enters prophase II during which the chromosomes become visible and the nuclear membrane, if it has reformed, disappears. In metaphase II the spindle forms at the cell surface, and the chromosomes line up at the metaphase plate. The sister chromatids separate and become chromosomes as the centromeres divide in anaphase II. Daughter nuclei re-form in telophase II.

Cytokinesis II

One daughter nucleus is pinched off to form the second polar body, and the large cell remaining is called the egg cell, or ovum.

■ Locate an ovum with two polar bodies on its surface.

How many chromosomes does the nucleus of an *Ascaris* ovum have? _____

Fusion of the Pronuclei

The haploid egg nucleus and sperm nucleus are called **pronuclei.** They become large and clear, and move toward each other.

■ Locate an ovum in which there are two large pronuclei.

The pronuclei finally fuse to form the zygote.

■ Locate a zygote with one large nucleus.

First Cleavage Division

The zygote begins the process of mitotic division, or **cleavage,** in which it begins to form the multicellular *Ascaris* embryo. After the first division there will be two daughter cells, after the second division four, and so on.

■ Locate a zygote that has divided to form two cells of equal size with large nuclei.

How many chromosomes does each of these cells have?

_____

SPERM CELLS

Your instructor will indicate the source of the living sperm that you will study. It may be from a bull, frog, or another source.

If frog sperm is used, you may be asked to remove the testes from the frog. Instructions for pithing the frog are given in Topic 27 and a diagram of the internal organs can be found in Topic 21.

■ Make a wet mount of sperm suspension or a bit of tissue from the frog testis teased apart in Ringer's solution, and examine it under low, then high power in the microscope.

Are the sperm cells motile or immotile?

_____

What is the shape of the sperm cells?

_____

Why does a sperm cell contain many mitochondria?

_____

_____

_____

Sperm are produced by maturation of spermatids within the seminiferous tubules of the testis. In spermatogenesis, haploid spermatids are produced from diploid spermatocytes (see Figure 9-3).

Turn to Figure 9-5 at the end of this topic and review sexual reproduction by labeling it with these terms: chromosome, chromatid, haploid, 1N, diploid, 2N, meiosis, gamete, fertilization, and zygote.

When you are finished with your work, return all prepared slides, clean up your work area, and store your microscope.

EXPLORING FURTHER

Alberts, B., D. Bray, J. Lewis, M. Raff, K. Roberts, and J. D. Watson. *Molecular Biology of the Cell.* New York: Garland, 1983.

Giese, A. C. *Cell Physiology.* 5th ed. Philadelphia: W. B. Saunders, 1979.

Journal Articles

Sloboda, Roger D. "The role of microtubules in cell structure and cell division." *American Scientist* 68:290, 1980.

Student Name _____ **Date** _____

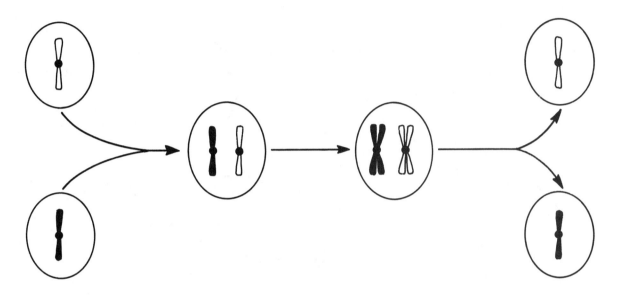

Figure 9-5. Sexual reproduction. Use the terms chromosome, chromatid, haploid, 1N, diploid, 2N, meiosis, gamete, fertilization and zygote to label this diagram.

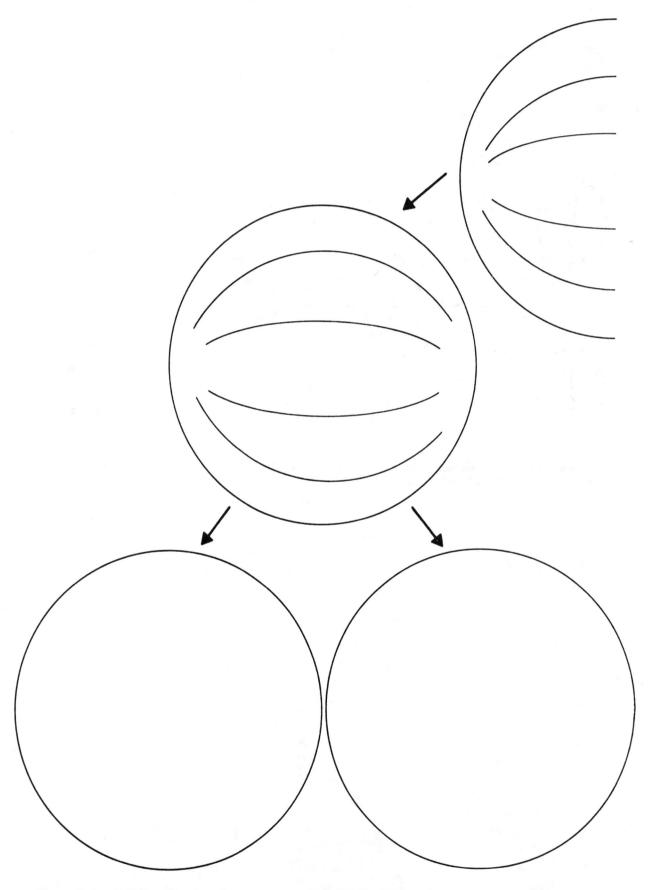

Figure 9-6. Cell reproduction. Diagram meiosis when N = 2.

Student Name _____ **Date** _____

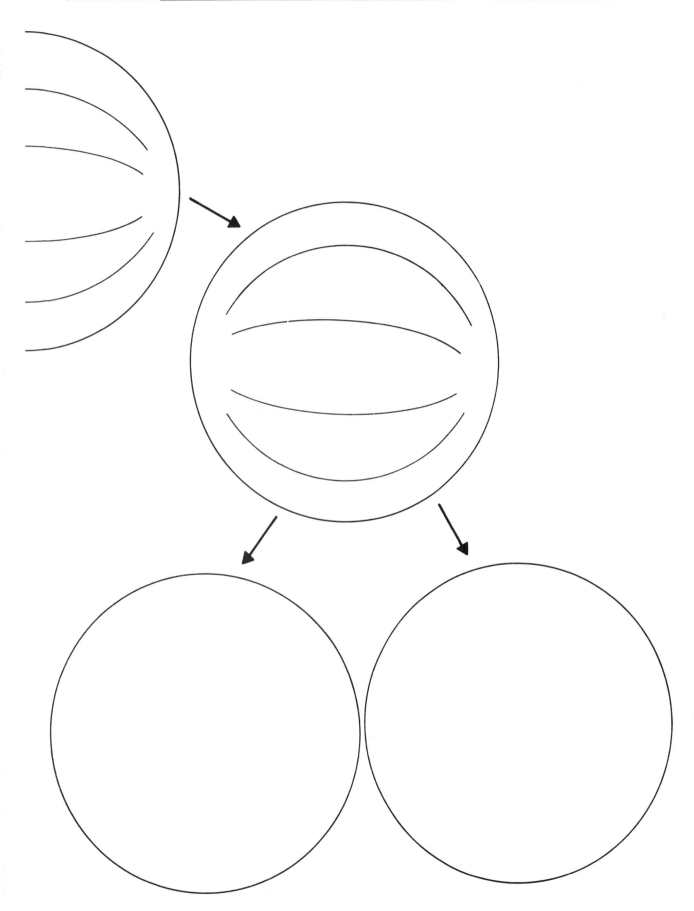

Mendelian Genetics and the Analysis of Data

OBJECTIVES

When you have completed this topic, you should be able to:
1. Explain why *Drosophila* is a good experimental animal for genetic experiments.
2. Describe the morphology of or recognize each stage of the *Drosophila* life history, including the adult male and female.
3. Define the following terms: parental (P_1) generation, first filial (F_1) generation, second filial (F_2) generation, dominant, recessive, allele, homozygous, heterozygous, monohybrid cross, dihybrid cross, segregation, and independent assortment.
4. Use a Punnett square to describe a monohybrid cross and a dihybrid cross in which the two genes show independent assortment; give the genotypic and phenotypic ratios expected in each case.
5. Define linkage, and describe a dihybrid cross in which the two genes are completely linked; give the expected genotypic and phenotypic ratios for the offspring.
6. Define sex linkage; use a Punnett square to describe a cross of a homozygous female with a mutant male, and give the expected phenotype and genotype of the offspring.
7. Give the reciprocal cross and explain why the reciprocal cross is necessary when the mutation might be either dominant or recessive.
8. Given the results from a cross of homozygous wild type and mutant files, determine the mode of transmission of the genes involved.
9. Analyze the results using the chi-square test to see how closely they fit Mendel's laws.

KEY TOPICS

Insects, metamorphosis, Mendelian genetics, dominance, law of segregation, law of independent assortment, mutation, sex determination, sex linkage.

INTRODUCTION

In this laboratory you will have the opportunity to work with the fruit fly, *Drosophila melanogaster*. This tiny fly is one of the most important organisms used by geneticists in studying the mechanism of inheritance. The advantages of using *Drosophila* as an experimental animal are:

1. It has a short life cycle (10 days at 25°C).
2. A single healthy female can produce several hundred offspring.
3. It is easily cultured in the laboratory in small bottles on simple culture media.
4. It is small.
5. There are many different easily recognized variations of *Drosophila*.
6. It has a small number of chromosomes (2N = 8). In addition, the cells of the salivary glands of the larva possess enlarged chromosomes which have been important in mapping the location of certain genes.

In this exercise you will study the life history and morphology of *Drosophila melanogaster*, and analyze the results of a genetic cross in which two different types of *Drosophila* were mated.

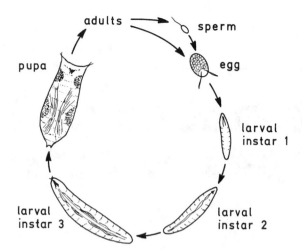

Figure 10-1. Life History of *Drosophila*. At room temperature the cycle from when the egg is laid to hatching (eclosion) of the adult from the pupa takes about 14 days.

LIFE HISTORY

The fruit fly is an insect of the order Diptera (two-winged flies). The Diptera all undergo complete metamorphosis, which means that the immature forms bear no resemblance to the adult. The flies and other insects that undergo complete metamorphosis show four different stages in their life histories (see Figure 10-1):

1. The **egg** is laid by the adult female (♀) on the food surface, and develops into the wormlike larva.
2. The white wormlike **larva,** or maggot, is characterized by its voracious appetite and rapid growth. During the course of its growth the larva will **molt,** or shed its skin, two times. The periods between molts are called **instars.** The third instar ends as the outer skin darkens and hardens, forming the pupal case.
3. During the **pupal** stage, the larval tissue breaks down, and the new winged adult is formed.
4. The **adult** fly that emerges from the pupal case is light-colored and elongated with unexpanded wings. The wings must expand, dry in the air, and stiffen before they can be used for flight.

The adult stage is the reproductive stage, and the adults will mate about 6 hr after emergence. The female (♀) receives about 4000 sperm from the male (♂), and stores these in special sacs. The sperm are released gradually as the eggs are produced. Up to a thousand eggs may be produced by a healthy female.

■ Examine a bottle containing a *Drosophila* culture, and find an example of the larva, pupa, and adult.

MORPHOLOGY
Handling the Flies

Because the fruit fly is small, it will be necessary to immobilize the flies so they can be observed with the stereomicroscope. Ether will be used to anesthetize them. Ether is highly explosive if ignited.

LIGHTING MATCHES OR LIGHTERS AND SMOKING IN THIS LABORATORY ARE FORBIDDEN.

■ Obtain an anesthetizer, re-etherizer (glass Petri dish), ether, camel hair brush, thumper (rubber pad), dissecting needle, and a 3 × 5 in. card or filter paper.
■ Take a vial of wild type (+ +) flies provided by the instructor. Note that + is the symbol used for a normal or wild type trait, so + + means a strain of flies with all normal traits.
■ Etherize the flies exactly as follows, so that you do not overetherize and kill them. (See Figure 10-2.)

1. Add ether to the anesthetizer bottle by putting a few drops of ether on the cotton or foam until it is moist but not wet. Recap the ether bottle immediately.
2. Close the cover on the anesthetizer bottle.
3. Remove the small cap from the cone-shaped part of the anesthetizer bottle.
4. Shake the flies down into the bottom of the glass vial by tapping it lightly on the thumper.
5. Working quickly, remove the plug from the glass vial.
6. Cover the vial with the cone-shaped part of the anesthetizer.
7. Invert the vial and anesthetizer.
8. Shake the flies into the anesthetizer by tapping it lightly on the thumper as shown in Figure 10-2. **DO NOT POUND HEAVILY** because that will loosen the food and let it drop onto the flies.
9. After the flies have all been shaken into the anesthetizer, remove the empty glass vial.
10. Working quickly, replace the small cap in the funnel and wait for the ether to take effect. Watch the flies closely because they will slow down and stop moving in about 30 sec.
11. After most of the flies have stopped moving, count to five slowly. Then remove the cap and pour the flies out onto the 3 × 5 in. card. It is important to follow this procedure exactly because overetherizing will kill the flies. You can tell if you have overetherized them by the position of the wings: Dead flies have their wings extended at right angles to their bodies.
12. Prepare the re-etherizer by adding a few drops of ether to the pad in the Petri dish and setting the dish on the table with the pad side down.
13. The flies will remain immobilized for 5 to 10 min. When the flies begin to move, they must be re-etherized by covering them with the re-etherizing plate. Wait for them to stop moving, and resume your observations.

DO NOT ALLOW REVIVING FLIES TO ESCAPE AND INFEST THE LABORATORY. DISPOSE OF ALL UNWANTED FLIES IN THE MORGUE PROVIDED (A PAN OF MOTOR OIL).

■ Now put the card containing the flies under the dissecting microscope. It is helpful to draw a line halfway across the card, and label the halves male (♂) and female (♀). After you learn to sex the flies, you can brush them onto the appropriate half of the card.
■ Use Figure 10-3 as your guide in identifying your male and female flies.

1. add ether
2. close cover
3. remove cap

4. tap vial

5. remove
   plug

6. cover vial
   with etherizer
7. invert vial

8. tap gently

9. remove vial
10. replace cap
    and wait

11. remove cap, pour
    out etherized flies

Figure 10-2. Etherizing *Drosophila*.

The Head

The members of the class Insecta have three divisions of the body: head, thorax, and abdomen.

■ Examine the head. The eyes of *Drosophila* are of two types, simple and compound. The **compound eyes** are large and made up of many different facets called ommatidia, which form a honeycomb type of arrangement. Pay particular attention to the color: This is the normal dull red or wild type (+) color (remember that the symbol for any normal characteristic is +). Two types of pigment, red and brown, occur in *Drosophila*, and together give the eye the normal color. Mutations affect the amount of each of these pigments and their distribution; many different possible eye color mutants result. The three simple eyes are called **ocelli,** and form a triangle on the top of the head between the two compound eyes. These apparently act to increase the brain's sensitivity to light, but they do not function in the formation of a visual image. Notice the **antennae.** Each antenna has a fleshy base and a featherlike **arista.** Exam-

ine the head from a side view, and look at the mouth parts. In the flies they have been modified to form a tubular **proboscis,** through which food is sucked up. If you press on the side of the head gently, the fly will usually protrude its proboscis.

The Thorax

The thorax consists of three fused segments, each bearing a pair of legs. Examine the legs. From the body outward each leg consists of the **coxa,** the very small **trochanter,** the **femur** (the largest part), the **tibia,** and the five-segmented **tarsi** (singular, **tarsus**). Using the highest magnification on your microscope, look closely at the first tarsal segment of the foreleg. In the male there is a clump of enlarged black bristles. This so-called **sex comb** is found only in the male, and is an important characteristic used in differentiating the sex of the flies. Keep looking until you locate the sex comb. (*Hint:* males are smaller than females.)

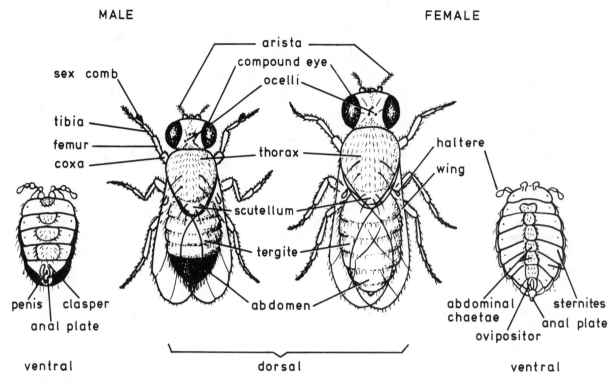

Figure 10-3.   Male and female *Drosophila*. The sex comb of the male and the shape and color of the abdomen can be used to distinguish the male and female.

■ Examine the **wings** of the flies, and notice the veins, which give support to the filamentous wings. Many insects have two pairs of wings that function in flight. The flies, however, have only one pair of functional wings; the second pair is represented by the **halteres,** a pair of small bulbous structures located in back of the base of the functional wings. If you press lightly on the side of the thorax with a dissecting needle and remove the needle, the wings will become erect, and you can easily locate these rudimentary wings. The halteres probably function as stabilizers in flight.

■ Look down on the dorsal (or top) surface of the fly's thorax, and identify the shield-shaped posterior part, or **scutellum,** with its four large scutellar bristles.

There are many genetically defined variations of the thorax. Some important variations are differences in color of the thorax, shortness or absence of scutellar bristles, and altered wing structure.

The Abdomen

Abdomens of male and female flies show several differences that are important in distinguishing between the sexes. Sexing the flies may seem difficult at first, but with practice you will find it quite easy. Some *Drosophila* research workers can supposedly sex flies on the wing! While you are not expected to gain such proficiency, you will have to learn to sex the flies accurately. Here are the differences to look for (in addition to the male sex comb, which you have already seen):

1. **Claspers.** The male has dark-colored claspers on the underside of the abdomen which are not present in the female.

2. **Size.** The male is smaller than the female.
3. **Shape.** The male has a blunt and rounded posterior, whereas that of the female is longer and pointed.
4. **Color.** The entire rear portion of the male abdomen is black, whereas in the female the alternating light and dark bands continue to the tip.

■ First examine the abdomen of a female more closely. On the dorsal (or top) surface the segmented plates, or **tergites,** will be seen as seven bands. The last segment of the abdomen is modified by the presence of the **anus** and the **ovipositor,** which forms the pointed posterior mentioned in (3) above. On the ventral surface find the small **sternites,** the midventral plates (one per segment). The tergites and sternites form a protective armor for the abdomen. Note that the tip of the female's abdomen is pointed and very light in color underneath.

■ Now examine the abdomen of a male fly. Notice that the male has six tergites, compared with the female's seven. The last segments are modified to form the genitalia. Brush the male fly onto his back to observe the genitalia. Just in front of the anus, find the **claspers,** hooklike appendages on the anal plate that aid in copulation. If you press lightly on the abdomen with a needle, you may be able to see the **penis** protruding between the claspers.

THE DARK, BLUNT ABDOMEN, WITH ITS DARK-COLORED CLASPERS UNDERNEATH IN THE MALE, IS THE BEST TRAIT TO USE IN DISTINGUISHING MALE FROM FEMALE FLIES.

■ After you have finished examining the wild type (normal + +) flies, obtain a vial of mutant flies from your instructor. It is helpful to examine the mutant and wild type side by side so the differences can be more clearly seen.

When you are ready to return the flies to the vial (if they are to be saved), do the following:

■ Bend the 3 × 5 in. card slightly, and brush the flies gently onto the glass of the *horizontal* vial as shown in Figure 10-4. Use a creased paper funnel if possible (Figure 10-4).

LEAVE THE VIAL ON ITS SIDE UNTIL THE FLIES RECOVER BEFORE MOVING THE VIAL.

This precaution is important because the surface of the food source is moist, and the flies may stick to the food and suffocate.

If the flies are dead, or if they are not to be saved, dispose of them in the morgue (a pan of motor oil).

THE GENETICS EXPERIMENT

The purpose of this experiment is to determine whether the mutant alleles are dominant or recessive, and how they are inherited.

You will be asked to study either cross A or cross B. These are **reciprocal crosses,** in which the mutations in the mutant parent are exactly the same, but the mutant parent is male in one case and female in the other.

Cross A: virgin wild type (+ +) females × mutant males
Cross B: virgin mutant females × wild type males (+ +)

Why must the female flies be virgin?

_____

_____

Remember that all parent flies used in this experiment are true-breeding, i.e., homozygous for all of their genes. The wild type parents are homozygous for normal alleles, and the mutant stock is homozygous mutant for two genes. Your instructor will give you information concerning the mutant traits you will be studying.

The procedure for setting crosses is as follows:

1. Remove all flies from stock bottles of wild type and mutant flies. Discard these flies because they have already mated.
2. Within the next 8 hr, collect and etherize the flies that have emerged. The females collected within 8 hr

of emerging will by physiologically incapable of mating, and will be virgin.

3. Sex the flies, and separate the males from the females. Store them in separate vials if they are not to be used immediately.
4. Place three virgin females and three males of the type called for in the cross into a horizontal food vial, and label the vial with the cross, the date, and your initials.
5. Wait until all of the flies have recovered from the ether, and then incubate the vial at 24-26°C for two weeks.

If you are going to set the cross yourself, your instructor will provide you with stock bottles of the parental flies and instructions as to when you will collect the virgins and set the cross. Cooperate with students doing the other cross so that you do not waste the flies that you do not need.

If the cross has been done for you, your instructor will give you a bottle or vial containing the adult flies resulting from a cross made two weeks ago. These flies represent the F_1 generation from the homozygous wild type and mutant parents.

Your first task will be to examine these offspring (the F_1), and decide whether the mutant traits are dominant or recessive to wild type. When the wild type and mutant stocks are mated, the offspring will receive one copy of each gene from each parent. If the offspring look like the mutant parent, the mutation is **dominant;** if the offspring look like the wild type parent, the mutation is **recessive:**

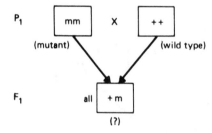

You will consider each mutation in turn, and decide whether it is dominant or recessive.

The second part of the experiment is to determine the mode of inheritance of these genes. In *Drosophila* there are three pairs of **autosomes** and a pair of **sex chromosomes** (2N = 8). If the mutation is located on one of the autosomal chromosomes, it will show auto-

Figure 10-4. Returning flies to the vial. Sleeping flies must never come in contact with the sticky food, so keep the vial horizontal.

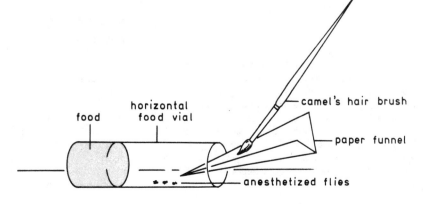

somal inheritance, and it will not matter which parent passed the mutation to the F_1 offspring. Cross A and cross B will give identical results.

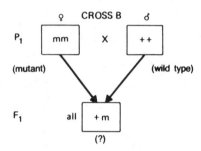

If, on the other hand, the mutation is **sex-linked** and located on a sex chromosome, it *does* matter which parent carried the mutation, and **cross A and cross B will give different results:**

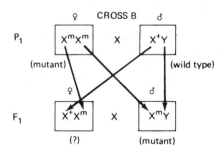

Suppose the mutation is dominant. Then F_1 females, but not F_1 males from cross A will show the mutation. In cross B, on the other hand, all offspring will show the mutation. Cross A will therefore allow the detection of sex linkage when the mutation in question is dominant.

Now suppose the mutation is recessive. F_1 males but not F_1 females from cross B will show it. None of the offspring in cross A will show it. Cross B will therefore allow the detection of sex linkage when the mutation in question is recessive.

Unless you know in advance whether the mutation is dominant or recessive, it is necessary to do both reciprocal crosses to be sure of detecting sex linkage.

What are the possible arrangements of the two mutant genes on the chromosomes?

1. Both of the mutant genes are on the same autosome, so they are inherited together, and are said to be **linked.** Any fly that inherits one mutant allele will also inherit the second one.
2. Both of the mutant genes are on the X chromosome. These traits are sex-linked, and must show the pattern of sex-linked inheritance.
3. The mutant genes are on different autosomes. They are inherited independently of each other, and neither shows the sex-linked pattern of inheritance.
4. One of the mutant genes is on the X chromosome, and the second is on an autosome. The genes will be inherited independently of one another, and will show different patterns of inheritance.

You are to examine the F_1 and determine from the data the dominance relationships and which of the above possibilities is the correct one. Remember that, as a class, you will analyze reciprocal crosses. The information from both crosses will be necessary to determine whether or not sex linkage is involved. Cross A will identify a dominant mutation as sex-linked, while cross B will identify a recessive mutation that is sex-linked.

ANALYZING THE CROSSES

■ Anesthetize the flies, and examine them under the dissecting microscope.
■ Brush the flies onto the center line on the card, and sex them one by one, pushing them to the proper side of the card as you determine the sex. Are all the males similar? Are all the females alike? Do the males resemble the females? Do the offspring resemble the mutant or wild type parents for each mutant trait?
■ Record your observations of the F_1 sample under cross A or cross B (whichever applies) in the analysis chart at the end of this topic. Put a check in the appropriate column for each fly, and total the classes.
■ **Check the results with your instructor before you discard the flies.**
■ When you are satisfied with your results, follow instructions for disposing of the flies, and put your work place and equipment back in order. Before starting your analysis, consult with the students who did the reciprocal cross, and record these data also.
■ Analyze your data by answering the questions in the analysis chart. Diagram your cross for both traits.

REPORT AND STATISTICAL ANALYSIS

Your instructor may ask you to prepare a formal report on your results. Follow the instructions in Appendix A for preparing this report.

The data that you obtained may be tabulated for the class as a whole, and statistically analyzed to see how well they fit the results expected from the most likely pattern of transmission. Instructions for using the chi-square test are given in Appendix B. In your report, show that you understand this test by applying it to the data for at least one trait in the cross that you studied.

EXPLORING FURTHER

Buchsbaum, R. *Animals without Backbones.* 2nd rev ed. Chicago: University of Chicago Press, 1975.

Goodenough, Ursula. *Genetics,* 3rd ed., Philadelphia: W. B. Saunders, 1984.

Srb, A. M., R. D. Owen, and R. S. Edgar. *General Genetics.* 2nd ed. San Francisco: W. H. Freeman, 1965.

Journal Articles

Beadle, George W. "The ancestry of corn." *Scientific American,* January 1980 (#1458).

Bennet-Clark, H. C., and A. W. Ewing. "The love song of the fruit fly." *Scientific American,* July 1970 (#1183).

Benzer, S. "Genetic dissection of behavior." *Scientific American,* December 1973 (#1285).

Crow, James F. "Genes that violate Mendel's rules." *Scientific American,* February 1979 (#1418).

Hadorn. "Fractionating the fruit fly." *Scientific American,* April 1962 (#1166).

Kornberg, Roger D., and Aaron Klug. "The nucleosome." *Scientific American,* February 1981.

Prokopy, Ronald J., and Bernard D. Roitberg. "Foraging behavior of true fruit flies." *American Scientist* 72 *(1)* 44-49 (1984).

Student Name _____ **Date** _____

ANALYSIS CHART

Record the results from your cross and from the reciprocal cross in the following tables; then analyze the results by completing the rest of the form.

CROSS A

Data from a cross of wild type females × _____ males.

Phenotype	Females	Males	Totals
Totals			

CROSS B

Data from the reciprocal cross which was _____ females × wild type males.

Phenotype	Females	Males	Totals
Totals			

Now, keeping in mind the information about the parental generation and your F_1 data from both crosses, draw your conclusions concerning the dominance and mode of transmission of the mutant genes you are studying. To guide you in your analysis, ask yourself the following questions.

TRAIT 1

Trait 1 = _____

Is the mutant dominant or recessive to wild type? _____

Did the mutant show a sex difference in either cross? _____

If so, in which cross? _____

This trait is inherited as

(a) autosomal dominant _____

(b) autosomal recessive _____

(c) sex-linked dominant _____

(d) sex-linked recessive _____

TRAIT 2

Trait 2 = _____

Is the mutant dominant or recessive to wild type? _____

Did the mutant show a sex difference in either cross? _____

If so, in which cross? _____

This trait is inherited as

(a) autosomal dominant _____

(b) autosomal recessive _____

(c) sex-linked dominant _____

(d) sex-linked recessive _____

ARRANGEMENT ON CHROMOSOMES

Your data may allow you to tell whether these two mutations are linked, that is, carried on the same chromosome.

Do both mutations show sex-linked inheritance? _____

If so, they must both be on the X chromosome, and are therefore linked to each other.

Does one but not the other show sex-linked inheritance? _____

If so, they must be unlinked because one is on the X chromosome, and the other is on an autosome.

To decide whether the two mutant traits are always inherited together in an autosomal pattern, you must do another cross.

What kind of cross should this be?

_____

If so, they are located on the same autosomal chromosome.

Which conclusion(s) can you draw from your data?

(a) the mutations are linked and are on the X chromosome _____

(b) the mutations are unlinked because one is on the X chromosome _____

(c) the mutations are linked and are on an autosomal chromosome _____

(d) the mutations are unlinked and neither one is sex-linked _____

(Conclusions (c) and (d) cannot be distinguished on the basis of your F_1 results alone.)

Student Name _____ **Date** _____

CROSS DIAGRAMS

When you have decided on the mode of inheritance for each of the two mutant genes, assign symbols for each gene, and diagram your cross (A or B) below. Show your work in the Punnett square.

What types of progeny would be expected?

_____

_____

Why do you have to do the reciprocal cross?

_____

_____

If you knew ahead of time that the mutation was recessive, which cross (A or B) would you do to decide whether the mutation was sex-linked or not? _____

DIAGRAM OF CROSS (A or B) _____

Trait #1: _____

Type of inheritance for Trait #1: _____

Symbol for mutant allele: _____

Symbol for normal allele: _____

P_1 ♀   ♂

   Genotype

   Phenotype   ×

F_1 ♀   ♂

   Genotype

   Phenotype   +

Trait #2: _____

Type of inheritance for Trait #2: _____

Symbol for mutant allele: _____

Symbol for normal allele: _____

P_1 ♀   ♂

   Genotype

   Phenotype   ×

F_1 ♀   ♂

   Genotype

   Phenotype   +

Human Genetics

OBJECTIVES

When you have completed this topic, you should be able to:
1. Determine your own possible genotypes for several physical traits.
2. Define antigen, antibody, and antiserum.
3. Give the possible genotypes of persons with the following blood types: A, B, AB, O, Rh+, Rh−.
4. Give the blood types that would be compatible in a transfusion with each of the blood types in Objective 3.
5. Describe a Barr body and explain why it is found only in normal female somatic cells.
6. Explain why sex-linked recessive traits in mammals occur much more frequently in males than in females.
7. Define karyotype, centromere, long arm, and short arm.
8. Use diagrams to explain how nondisjunction in the male or in the female can lead to the following karyotypes: XO, XXY, XXX, XYY.
9. Analyze an unknown karyotype and determine whether it represents a normal male, a normal female, or an abnormal genotype.

KEY TOPICS

Sickle-cell anemia, metabolic defects, multiple alleles, human blood groups, human sex chromosomes, nondisjunction, karyotype.

INTRODUCTION

Humans may be of much more interest to the average person than fruit flies, but it is not easy to study variation in human genes by conventional methods. There are problems in finding traits that are controlled by a single gene because it is unethical to deliberately mutagenize human populations. There are also problems in finding the appropriate matings, reciprocal crosses, and so forth. Few are eager to donate blood, tissues, or information about their families and themselves in order to push back the frontiers of human genetics. Much of the early work in this field depended, therefore, on the painstaking analysis of **pedigrees** in which the pattern of appearance of a certain trait in several generations of a family showed how the allele for that trait was inherited. Family photographs, diaries, and the recollections of older family members were used to identify the phenotypes of as many family members as possible. If enough information existed, it was possible to determine the pattern of inheritance of the allele by eliminating those patterns not consistent with the pedigree.

A human pedigree is illustrated in Figure 11-1.

Males are indicated by the squares and females by the circles. Open symbols are used for individuals with a normal phenotype and filled symbols for individuals who show the trait phenotypically. A T connecting the symbols for a man and woman represents their marriage and offspring. Use what you have learned about Mendelian genetics to determine whether this trait is inherited as a dominant or recessive and whether or not it is sex-linked. One approach is to check each possiblity in turn, one at a time, until you either reach an inconsistent result or show that your choice is consistent with the entire pedigree. Repeat for each of the other possibilities. Record your conclusion on the answer sheet at the end of this topic.

It is now known that in addition to many physical characteristics, single genes control many biochemical traits such as blood type and the presence of certain enzymes. More than 150 human diseases are known to be caused by mutant alleles for important proteins and enzymes. Some familiar examples are sickle-cell anemia, hemophilia, and phenylketonuria (PKU).

Now that the genetic basis of these diseases is understood, it is sometimes possible to design tests to deter-

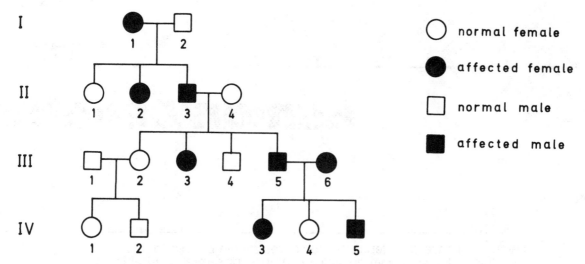

Figure 11-1. A human pedigree. Open symbols represent individuals with a normal phenotype and solid symbols represent affected individuals.

mine whether prospective parents carry mutant alleles that can cause a genetic disease in their child. If there is a risk of genetic disease, the parents may ask for genetic counseling to maximize their chances of having a normal child. In some cases **amniocentesis** may be done during pregnancy. In this procedure some of the amniotic fluid is withdrawn to obtain a sample of fetal cells. The chromosomes from the amniotic sac surrounding the fetus can be studied by **karyotype analysis** to see whether there is a normal complement of chromosomes and whether the fetus is male or female. If the disease is known to be caused by a sex-linked recessive allele, males will have a much greater risk of having the disease than females. If the child is male, a single mutant allele on the X chromosome will cause the child to be affected. If the child is female, however, a single mutant allele will be recessive, and the child's phenotype will be normal. A female must have the recessive mutation on both X chromosomes in order to have the disease, and that is not very likely to happen. The cells can also be grown in culture and tested for **biochemical genetic defects.** If there is a serious untreatable or fatal genetic defect, the parents may decide to terminate that pregnancy. Some genetic diseases can be cured or controlled by medical treatment, but many cannot.

PHYSICAL GENETIC TRAITS

Many human physical traits are genetically controlled. The genes on the chromosomes of males seem to determine that the child will become male, and other genes determine eye color, hair color, height, skin color, and many other traits that distinguish individuals from one another. Several characteristics are known to be controlled by single gene differences. Some of these are listed below and illustrated in Figure 11-2.

1. **Pigmented iris:** The P allele for a pigmented iris (green, hazel, brown, or black eyes) is dominant over the p allele for lack of pigment (gray or blue eyes).
2. **Tongue rolling:** The R allele for the ability to roll the tongue into a U shape is dominant over the r allele for lack of this ability.

3. **Bent little finger:** The B allele for a bent little finger is dominant over the b allele for a straight little finger.
4. **Widow's peak:** The W allele for a widow's peak is dominant over the w allele for a straight hairline.
5. **Thumb crossing:** The C allele for crossing the left thumb over the right thumb when you interlace your fingers is dominant over the c allele for crossing the right thumb over the left.
6. **Attached ear lobes:** The a allele for attached ear lobes is recessive to the A allele for unattached ear lobes.
7. **Hitchhiker's thumb:** the h allele for the ability to bend the last joint of the thumb back at an angle of 60° or more is recesssive to the H allele for the lack of ability to bend the thumb back this far.

■ Determine your own phenotype for each of the above characteristics and record your phenotypes in Table 11-3 at the end of this topic.
■ Fill in your possible genotypes for each of the traits.

If you have the trait determined by the recessive allele, there is only one possible genotype. If your trait is determined by the dominant allele, you should list both possible genotypes, unless one of your parents is homozygous recessive. In that case you are heterozygous.

HUMAN BLOOD GROUPS

The first chemical trait in humans to be understood was the determination of the ABO antigens on red blood cells. Any substance that causes the immune system to produce **antibodies** is an **antigen** or **anti**body-**gen**erating substance. Many different types of substances can be antigens. When a foreign antigen enters the body, antibodies corresponding specifically to the antigen will rapidly increase. Antibodies are proteins that are specific for one particular antigen and bind molecules of the antigen together into clumps. If the antigens are attached to red blood cells, as are the ABO antigens, the red blood cells will clump in the presence of the antibody:

A antigen will clump with anti-A antibodies.
B antigen will clump with anti-B antibodies.

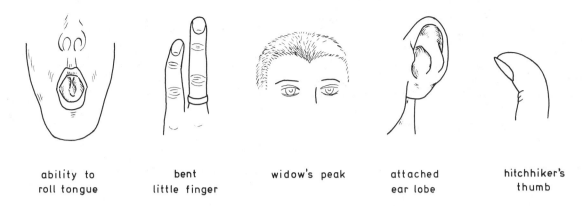

| | ability to roll tongue | bent little finger | widow's peak | attached ear lobe | hitchhiker's thumb |

Figure 11-2. Human genetic traits. These traits are each controlled by a single gene.

AB antigen will clump with both anti-A and anti-B antibodies.

O antigen clumps with neither anti-A nor anti-B antibodies.

Another antigen, which is also present on red blood cells, is called the Rh antigen. Blood cells with this antigen are Rh⁺, and those without it are Rh⁻.

Rh⁺ cells will clump with anti-Rh antibodies.
Rh⁻ cells will not clump with anti-Rh antibodies.

There are many other antigens on red blood cells that are also genetically determined.

Because it is easy to obtain a small sample of blood from a large number of people, the genetic basis of blood groups was soon well understood. The type of antigens of the ABO group that are present are determined by **multiple alleles,** any one of which may occur at a particular locus, or position, on a chromosome. Instead of just two possible alleles at this locus, there are three—namely, I^A, I^B, and i. The I^A allele determines the A antigen, the I^B allele determines the B antigen, the i allele determines neither antigen. Any individual has two alleles for ABO blood groups and could have any of the following genotypes.

Genotype	Blood Type (Phenotype)	Antigen Present	Antibodies in the Blood
$I^A I^A$	A	A	Anti-B
$I^A i$	A	A	Anti-B
$I^B I^B$	B	B	Anti-A
$I^B i$	B	B	Anti-A
$I^A I^B$	AB	A and B	None
ii	O	None	Anti-A, Anti-B

Because a normal person never makes antibodies against his own antigens, the antibodies present in the blood never react with the antigens present on the red blood cells. A person with A antigen on his red blood cells will have anti-B antibodies but never anti-A antibodies. Otherwise the red blood cells would clump together.

Blood groups are medically important because only compatible blood can be used during a blood transfu-

sion. The transfusion will be incompatible if the red blood cells of the donor can clump by reacting with the antibodies of the recipient. The safest type of transfusion is between individuals of the same blood type. In this case, the red blood cell antigens and the antibodies are identical, and there is no possibility of a clumping reaction. If the donor's red blood cells contain any antigen, however, the blood can be given only to individuals who lack the corresponding antibodies. Type A blood, for example, can be given only to persons with type A blood or type AB blood. If the recipient's blood were of type B or type O, there would be anti-A antibodies in it that would clump the donor red blood cells. The antibodies of the donor are greatly diluted during a transfusion and can be ignored.

Use the following procedure to determine your ABO blood type. The anti-A serum that you will use contains anti-A antibodies and will clump or agglutinate red blood cells that have A antigen. The anti-B antiserum contains anti-B antibodies and will clump cells that have B antigen.

DO NOT PRICK YOUR FINGER IF YOU HAVE A BLOOD CLOTTING DISORDER OR HAVE BEEN EXPOSED TO HEPATITIS. TO AVOID THE RISK OF SERUM HEPATITIS, DO NOT TOUCH ANY MATERIALS THAT MIGHT BE CONTAMINATED WITH ANOTHER PERSON'S BLOOD. NEVER USE A BLOOD LANCET ALREADY USED BY ANOTHER PERSON.

If you are unable or unwilling to volunteer to have your finger pricked, work with a partner who doesn't mind doing it. Work quickly so your blood doesn't clot during the test.

■ Obtain a clean slide. Mark it with two circles labeled A and B.
■ Squeeze one of your fingers to increase the circulation, and wipe it with sterile cotton moistened with 70% ethanol.
■ Without touching the "sterile" finger, open a sterile lancet packet from the correct end, and prick your finger or have someone prick it for you.
■ Squeeze out a drop of blood onto each of the circles on your slide.
■ Obtain a toothpick and the anti-A antiserum. Add one drop of antiserum to the blood drop in the circle marked A without touching the dropper to the blood, and stir the drop with the toothpick.

■ Obtain another toothpick and the anti-B antiserum. Add one drop of antiserum to the circle marked B, and stir the second drop with the toothpick.

If there is a positive reaction, the blood cells will form large clumps within 1-2 min, and the drop will appear speckled. If the reaction is negative, the drop will remain cloudy, without clumps.

Did your red blood cells react with the anti-A antiserum?

_____

Did they react with anti-B antiserum? _____

What is your ABO blood type? _____

Another antigen that may be present on red blood cells is the Rh antigen. There are several dominant alleles *(Rh)* that determine the presence of this antigen and a recessive allele *(rh)* that determines the absence of the antigen. Persons normally do not have anti-Rh antibodies whether they have the antigen or not. These are the possible genotypes and blood groups:

Genotype	Blood Group (Phenotype)	Antigen Present	Antibodies in the Blood
Rh/Rh	Rh⁺	Rh	None
Rh/rh	Rh⁺	Rh	None
rh/rh	Rh⁻	None	None

If an Rh⁻ person comes in contact with Rh⁺ blood cells, the immune system will begin producing anti-Rh antibodies. This might happen after a blood transfusion or after a pregnancy in which an Rh⁻ mother carries an Rh⁺ child. If the person then comes in contact with Rh⁺ blood cells a second time, the antibodies will cause the cells to clump. This might happen during a second pregnancy of an Rh⁻ woman carrying a second Rh⁺ child. The antibodies of the mother might enter the circulation of the baby and cause a disease called **erythroblastosis fetalis.** The baby must have an immediate transfusion of antibody-free blood when it is born to stop the clumping reaction.

Determine your Rh blood type using anti-Rh antiserum, which clumps red blood cells containing Rh antigen.

■ Obtain a clean slide.
■ Prick your finger as you did before, or use the same finger, and squeeze a drop of blood onto the slide.
■ Obtain the anti-Rh antiserum and a toothpick.
■ Add 1 drop of the serum to the blood without touching it, and stir the drop with a toothpick.
■ Note whether there is a clumping reaction.

Did your blood clump with anti-Rh antiserum?

_____

What is your Rh blood type?_____

When you are finished with these tests, dispose of all lancets, slides and debris in the container marked **BLOOD TEST WASTES.**

SICKLE-CELL ANEMIA

The presence of normal beta chains in hemoglobin A is determined by the *A* allele. The mutant allele at this locus that causes sickle-cell anemia is called *S.* The mutant hemoglobin S molecules have a greater tendency to aggregate when the concentration of oxygen is low. The aggregates that form distort the shape of the red blood cells and cause them to block capillaries in the joints and internal organs (see Figure 11-3). The lack of circulation that results causes a painful **sickle-cell-crisis,** which can be dangerous and even fatal. The disease of sickle-cell anemia, which occurs mainly in people of African descent, can be controlled to a certain extent by medical treatment, but there is no cure at the present time.

The allele that causes this disease shows incomplete dominance with the normal allele so that a person who is heterozygous has both hemoglobin A and hemoglobin S in his red blood cells. The heterozygous person is a **carrier** for the disease, but usually does not have any symptoms. The normal hemoglobin can apparently compensate for the abnormal hemoglobin S except under certain conditions of extreme stress. A person who is homozygous for the *S* allele is **affected** and has **sickle-cell anemia.** Until recent advances in medical treatment became available, most homozygous children would die in early childhood.

If two persons heterozygous for the *S* allele marry, what is the chance of their child having sickle-cell anemia?

_____

■ Examine the prepared slide of normal blood cells and cells from a person with sickle-cell anemia.
■ Draw a few of the abnormal cells in the space provided at the end of this topic.

Figure 11-3. Sickled red blood cells. Cells containing hemoglobin S will assume bizarre shapes when they are deprived of oxygen. As a result, capillaries will become blocked and cause painful symptoms in the patient. (Photo by Carolina Biological Supply Company)

HUMAN SEX CHROMOSOMES

In humans, sex and other traits are determined by the sex chromosomes. Males have one X chromosome and a tiny Y chromosome which contains very few genes. Females have two X chromosomes. However, early in the development of a female embryo, one of the X chromosomes becomes inactive in each cell, so that only one of the two X chromosomes is actually active. The inactive chromosome becomes condensed, but is still replicated and passed on to all the daughter cells. The condensed X chromosome can be seen in certain cells as a **Barr body.** In epithelium, for example, many of the cells will show the Barr body as a darkly staining mass just inside the nuclear membrane. In other cells, such as certain white blood cells, the condensed chromosome forms a **drumstick,** which protrudes from the nucleus.

Preparations of epithelial cells from the oral cavity are easy to obtain and can be used to screen for chromosomal abnormalities in the sex chromosomes. If a person is a normal female there will be one Barr body in many of the cells. There should be no Barr bodies in a normal male. If there is an extra X chromosome, it will be condensed because there is always only a single active X chromosome in human cells. An abnormal male with an extra X chromosome will have one Barr body, and an abnormal female with an extra X chromosome will have two Barr bodies.

How many Barr bodies would you expect to find in a person with four X chromosomes (XXXX)?

_____

Determine whether your epithelial cells contain Barr bodies using this procedure. About 35% of the cells should have visible Barr bodies if you are female.

■ Obtain a clean slide and a tongue depressor or clean toothpick.
■ Add a drop of methylene blue dye to the slide.
■ Scrape the inside of your cheek with the tongue depressor or toothpick, and stir the cells into the dye.
■ Add a coverslip and examine the cells under high power in the microscope.

Do your cells have Barr bodies?_____

■ Exchange slides with someone of the opposite sex, and note whether Barr bodies are present.

Draw a cell with a visible Barr body and one with no Barr body in the space provided at the end of this topic.

This type of test is used to determine whether athletes competing in certain important sporting events such as the Olympic games are genetically of the appropriate sex for the events they are entering. Persons are usually not allowed to compete in women's events unless they are genetically female.

HUMAN KARYOTYPES

A **karyotype** is the display of a person's chromosomes. Because each cell is supposed to have the same set of chromosomes, in theory, a karyotype could be made from any cell in metaphase. Karyotypes from adults can be made easily from cheek cells or white blood cells. The karyotype can also be determined during fetal development by studying cells removed from the amniotic fluid during amniocentesis. In that case, care must be taken not to confuse cells of the mother with cells from the fetus.

After the cells have been stained and squashed, the individual chromosomes are apparent and can be photographed. The chromosomes are cut out, matched in pairs, and arranged in a chart according to size and shape. The karyotype of a normal male is shown in Figure 11-4.

The pairs of chromosomes are first sorted into groups of about the same shape and size. Note that each of these metaphase chromosomes consists of two sister chromatids joined in the region of the **centromere.** The position of the centromere divides the chromosome into two **long arms** and two **short arms.** Sometimes the arms are almost equal in length, and sometimes the long arms are much longer than the short arms. The pairs are then arranged within the groups in order of decreasing size. The X chromosome is a large chromosome, about as large as pairs 6-7, with arms of about equal length. It is placed over the X in the chart. The Y chromosome is the smallest one, even smaller than those in group G, and it is placed over the Y. A normal female would have two X chromosomes and no Y chromosome. Note that the pairs within a group are very similar and cannot be told apart easily. The exact order of the pairs within the group doesn't matter much in karyotype analysis, but the chromosomes must be placed in the correct group according to their size and the relative lengths of their arms.

Karyotype analysis is often used to determine whether a particular disease or syndrome is due to an abnormal complement of chromosomes. In the course of studies carried out for this purpose, or **medical genetics,** it has become apparent that there is a lot of variation among apparently normal people in the exact arrangement of their chromosomes. This discovery has opened up the field of **somatic cell genetics,** in which the complexity of the interactions of normal human genes is being investigated.

In 1959 Lejeune[*] discovered that children with Down's syndrome (Mongolism) have three copies of chromosome #21. Since then many human genetic disorders have been traced to an abnormal chromosome complement. It has also been found that up to 40% of spontaneously aborted fetuses have abnormal chromosomes, with the XO karyotype (Turner's syndrome) being particularly common.[**] The physical and mental defects associated with these karyotypes are shown in Table 11-1.

An abnormal number of chromosomes in an individual is often the result of an error in meiosis during which an egg or sperm cell with an incorrect number of chromosomes is produced. When the homologous chromosomes pair during meiosis I, it is possible that the members of the pair fail to separate properly during metaphase I, and so both members of the pair eventually end up in the same gamete. The failure of the chromosomes to separate is called **nondisjunction,** and it will result in gametes with extra or missing chromosomes. When the gametes are fertilized, the offspring will have extra or missing chromosomes also. Suppose, for example, that the X chromosomes stayed together during meiosis I in a female. The resulting egg might have two X chromosomes. After fertilization of such an egg, the zy-

_____

[*]Lejeune, Turpin, and Gautier, *Ann. de Genet.* 1, 1959.
[**]C. Stern, *Principles of Human Genetics*, 3rd ed. San Francisco: W. H. Freeman, 1973, p. 131.

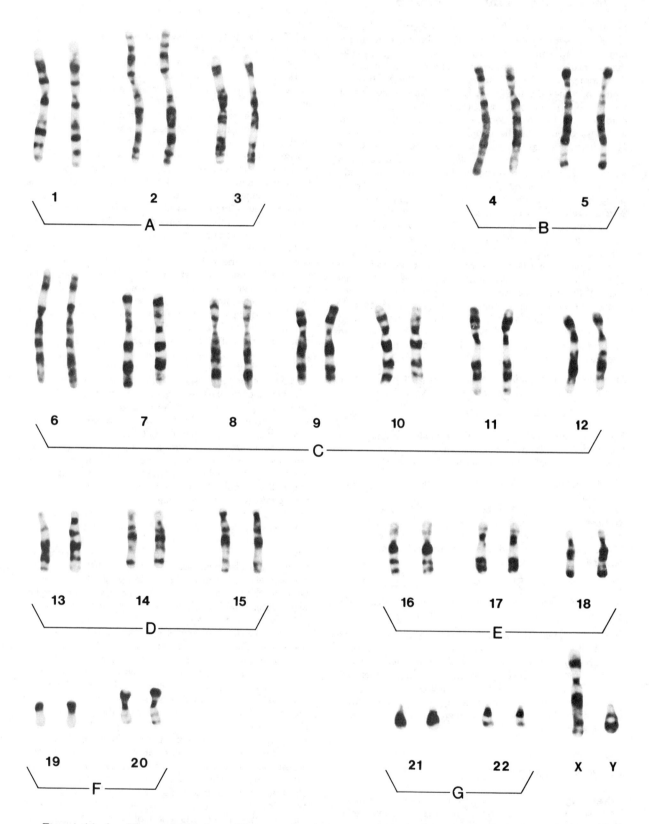

Figure 11-4. **Human karyotype.** These are the chromosomes found in each cell of a normal male. (Courtesy of Jorge J. Yunis, M.D., Medical Genetics Division, University of Minnesota Medical School)

TABLE 11-1. CHARACTERISTICS ASSOCIATED WITH DEFECTIVE KARYOTYPES

Syndrome	Karyotype	Characteristics
Klinefelter's male	XXY	Unusual body proportions and sterility; subnormal mental ability
Turner's female	XO	Short stature; webbing of the neck; may have low mental ability and sterility
Super female	XXX	May have low mental ability; fertile
"Cri du chat"	defective #5	Catlike cry; severe physical and mental abnormalities; nonlethal
Patau's syndrome	extra #13	Physical abnormalities; lethal soon after birth
Edward's syndrome	extra #18	Unusual features of the head and fingers; often dies in infancy
Down's syndrome	extra #21	Characterisic facial features; low mental ability; stocky build; sometimes heart defects

gote would have either three X chromosomes or two X chromosomes and one Y chromosome, depending on the type of sperm that fertilized the egg. Alternatively, the egg might have no X chromosomes after nondisjunction.

What types of zygotes could such an egg form?

■ Obtain from your instructor a copy of a chromosome squash of a human cell.
■ Record the number of this squash in Table 11-4, at the end of this topic.

The karyotype of the cell corresponds to one of the following patterns:

TABLE 11-2. HUMAN KARYOTYPES

Phenotype	Karyotype	Number	✔
Normal male	XY	46	
Normal female	XX	46	
Klinefelter's male	XXY		
Turner's female	XO		
Super female	XXX		
"Cri du chat" male	Partial deletion of short arm of #5		
Patau's female	3 copies of #13		
Edward's female	3 copies of #18		
Down's male	3 copies of #21		

Normal males and females have 46 chromosomes in each cell. There are 22 pairs of autosomes and either a pair of X chromosomes or one X and one Y.

■ Determine the number of chromosomes that you would find in cells of persons with the chromosomal defects listed, and enter the numbers in Table 11-2.
■ Count the number of chromosomes in your chromosome squash and record the number in Table 11-4.

■ Check off the karyotypes that the squash might represent in Table 11-2.
■ Cut out the chromosomes and arrange them in order of decreasing size. Use a ruler, if possible, to accurately determine the relative lengths of the chromosomes.
■ Match up pairs of similarly shaped chromosomes and place them in the correct groups of Table 11-4.
■ Rearrange the pairs of autosomes and the sex chromosomes until you have a reasonably good version of one of the karyotypes that you have checked off in Table 11-2. The order of chromosomes within each group is not important, but the chromosomes within a group must have the same general shape with respect to the position of the centromere and must be of approximately the same size. A chromosome in group B, for example, must be larger than any in group C, smaller than any in group A, and its centromere located towards the top rather than in the middle.

NOTE THAT THE SEX OF EACH KARYOTYPE LISTED IS SPECIFIED.

■ Determine the sex of your karyotype and check that you have arrived at one of the possible phenotypes.
■ Tape the chromosomes in place on the chart.
■ Ask your instructor to check your work, or hand in your chart before you leave.

EXPLORING FURTHER

Bodmer, W. F., and L. L. Cavalli-Sforza. *Genetics, Evolution and Man.* San Francisco: W. H. Freeman, 1976.

deGrouchy, J., and C Turleau. *Clinical Atlas of Human Chromosomes.* 2nd ed. New York: John Wiley and Sons, 1984.

McKusick, Victor A. *Medelian Inheritance in Man: Catalogs of Autosomal Dominant, Autosomal Recessive and X-linked Phenotypes.* 6th ed. Baltimore: Johns Hopkins, 1983.

Saxen, L, and J. Rapola. *Congenital Defects.* New York: Holt, Rinehart and Winston, 1975.

Stern, C. *Principles of Human Genetics.* 3rd ed. San Francisco: W. H. Freeman, 1973.

Sutton, H. E. *An Introduction to Human Genetics.* 2nd ed. New York: Holt, Rinehart and Winston, 1975.

Winchester, A. M. *Heredity, Evolution and Humankind.* St. Paul, Minn.: West, 1976.

Journal Articles

Anderson, W. French, and Elaine G. Diakurnakos. "Genetic engineering in mammalian cells." *Scientific American,* July 1981.

Bishop, J. M. "Oncogenes." *Scientific American,* 80, March 1982.

Brady, R. O. "Hereditary fat metabolism diseases." *Scientific American,* August 1973.

Cerami, Anthony, and Charles M. Peterson. "Cyanate and sickle-cell disease." *Scientific American,* April 1975 (#1319).

Clarke, C. A. "The prevention of rhesus babies." *Scientific American,* November 1968 (#1126).

Croce, Carlo M., and George Klein. "Chromosomal translocations and human cancer." *Scientific American,* 54, March 1985.

Croce, Carlo M., and Hilary Koprowski. "The genetics of human cancer." *Scientific American,* February 1978 (#1381).

D'Eustachio, Peter. "Gene mapping and oncogenes." *American Scientist 72(1):* 32, January-February, 1984.

Friedman, Milton J., and William Trager. "The biochemistry of resistance to malaria." *Scientific American,* March 1981.

Fuchs, Fritz. "Genetic amniocentesis." *Scientific American,* June 1980 (#1471).

Glass, H. Bentley. "The genetics of the Dunkers." *Scientific American,* August 1953 (#1062).

Kolata, G. "Fetal hemoglobin genes turned on in adults." *Science 218:* 1295, 24 December 1982. (Sickle cell anemia treatment.)

Macalpine, Ida, and Richard Hunter. "Porphyria and King George III." *Scientific American,* July 1969 (#1149).

Patau, K. "The identification of individual chromosomes, especially in man." *Am. J. Human Genetics* 12: 250, 1960.

Pines, M. "In the shadow of Huntington's." *Science 84,* 32, May 1984.

Roth, E. F., Jr., *et al.* "Sickling rates of human AS red cells infected in vitro with *Plasmodium falciparum* malaria." *Science* 202: 650-652, 1978.

Ruddle, Frank H., and Raju S. Kucherlapati. "Hybrid cells and human genes." *Scientific American,* July 1974 (#1300).

Trost, C. "The blue people of Troublesome Creek." *Science 82,* 35, November 1982.

Weinberg, R. A. "A molecular basis of cancer." *Scientific American,* 126, November 1983.

Student Name _____ **Date** _____

TABLE 11-3. HUMAN PHYSICAL GENETIC TRAITS

Determine your phenotypes and genotypes for the traits listed in the following table.

Trait	Dominant Allele	Your Phenotype	Your Genotype(s)
Pigmented iris	P = pigment present		
Tongue roller	R = ability to roll		
Bent little finger	B = bent little finger		
Widow's peak	W = widow's peak present		
Thumb crossing	C = left over right		
Attached ear lobes	A = unattached ear lobes		
Hitchhiker's thumb	H = < 60° angle of the thumb		

In the spaces below, draw red blood cells in sickle-cell anemia, a cell with a Barr body, and a cell without a Barr body.

red blood cells in sickle-cell anemia   **cell with Barr body**   **cell without Barr body**

TABLE 11-4. KARYOTYPE ANALYSIS CHART

Chromosome squash # _____

Karyotype of the squash: _____

Corresponding phenotype: _____

Characteristics of phenotype: _____

_____

Population Genetics

OBJECTIVES

When you have completed this topic, you should be able to:
1. State the Hardy-Weinberg Law and the conditions under which it applies.
2. Determine the homozygous frequency of a recessive allele in a sample assumed to be in Hardy-Weinberg equilibrium and calculate the approximate numbers of heterozygous and homozygous dominant members expected in the sample.
3. Define evolution.
4. Describe a model experiment with two alleles in which the selection against the alleles is different and predict the change in frequency of the less advantageous allele.

KEY TOPICS

Hardy-Weinberg Law, natural selection, genetic counseling, negative eugenics

INTRODUCTION

Hardy and Weinberg discovered that sexual reproduction alone will do nothing to change the frequencies of alleles in a population provided that certain conditions are met:

1. There must be no natural selection against either allele (or no difference in natural selection).
2. The population must be large and **panmictic.** Mating between members of the population must be random (panmictic). The population must be large enough in size so that each generation represents a random sample.
3. There must be no net mutation of one allele to the other.
4. There must be no gene flow due to individuals entering or leaving the population through emigration and immigration.

If these conditions are perfectly met, the frequency of each allele will remain exactly the same from generation to generation. Furthermore, the frequencies of the dominant and recessive phenotypes can be determined if the frequency of either phenotype or of either allele is known.

Suppose that the frequency of the A allele is X, and there are two alleles for this gene. The frequency of the second allele, a, has to be equal to $1 - X$ because the sum of the two alleles must be 100%, or a frequency of 1. The chance of getting the genotype AA is the chance of getting one A allele times the chance of getting a second or X^2. To avoid confusion, the frequency of the AA genotype is p^2.

The chance of getting the aa genotype is the chance of getting one a allele times the chance of getting the second. The frequency of the recessive allele is called q, so the chance of the aa genotype is q^2. A heterozygote can be formed by getting a recessive, then a dominant allele $(q \times p)$; or by getting a dominant, then a recessive allele $(p \times q)$. Therefore the chance of ending up with the Aa genotype is $qp + pq$ or $2pq$. In summary, the frequencies of genotypes in each and every generation of a population meeting Hardy-Weinberg conditions can be predicted, once p and q are known, as follows:

$$\text{Frequency: } p^2 + 2pq + q^2$$
$$\text{Genotype: } AA \quad Aa \quad aa$$

Note that the frequency terms represent the terms of the binomial expansion $(p + q)^2$. If more than two alleles are involved, more unknowns can be added, and each term will represent the frequency of a corresponding genotype.

The frequency of phenotypes can then be stated once the frequencies of the genotypes are known:

Dominant phenotype $(A-) = AA + Aa = p^2 + 2pq$
Recessive phenotype $(aa) = aa = q^2$

Because the frequencies of the dominant and recessive phenotypes must add up to 1, the second frequency is known as soon as one or the other is calculated.

107

TASTE TEST

In actual populations it is usually not possible to tell the genotypes of all the individuals. If the *A* allele for a certain trait is dominant over the *a* allele, the *AA* and *Aa* genotypes will have the same phenotype. The **phenotype** is what can be easily observed or measured. If the frequency of the recessive phenotype *(aa)* is measured *(aa = q²)*, q^2 is known. If the frequency of the dominant phenotype is known *(AA + Aa = p² + 2pq)*, q^2 can be calculated because the dominant and recessive phenotypes must add up to 1.

$$q^2 = 1 - (p^2 + 2\,pq)$$
$$aa = 1 - (AA + Aa)$$

This means that the recessive phenotype frequency is equal to 1 minus the dominant phenotype frequency.

In this experiment you will determine your phenotype for a certain trait and use the results from the entire class to calculate the approximate number of individuals in the class who are homozygous dominant or heterozygous for the trait, assuming the class is a population meeting the Hardy-Weinberg conditions.

Phenylthiocarbamide (PTC) is a chemical that tastes bitter to some people (tasters) but not to others (nontasters).

■ Place a piece of PTC-impregnated paper on your tongue and moisten it.

Do you detect a bitter taste other than the taste of the paper itself? _____

■ Chew the paper a bit and roll it around on your tongue.

■ Classify yourself as a taster or nontaster, and record the results of this test in Table 12-2 at the end of this topic.

■ Also record the class results and the total number of students in the class.

The ability to taste PTC is genetically determined by the dominant alleles T^e (early tasters) and T^l (late tasters). (Late tasters can detect PTC only after chewing the paper slightly.) These dominant alleles will be lumped together as *T*. Those people homozygous for the recessive allele *t* are nontasters. Assume that your class is a reasonably accurate sample of an ideal randomly mating population, and use the Hardy-Weinberg Law to calculate the frequencies of *t* and *T* in the class. Once you know *t* and *T*, calculate the percentage of *TT* and *Tt* genotypes in the class.

How many individuals are expected to be homozygous dominant *(TT)*? _____

How many are heterozygous *(Tt)*? _____

■ Record your results in Table 12-2.

Sodium benzoate (SB) is another chemical that only some people can taste. Its taste may seem sour, sweet, or bitter. Repeat the test with a piece of paper impregnated with sodium benzoate.

Are you a taster for sodium benzoate?

_____

Which type of taste did you detect, if you are a taster?

_____

■ Record your observation and the class results in Table 12-2.

What is the frequency of the *t* allele, assuming *t* is a recessive allele for nontaster? _____

Is this frequency different from that of *t* for PTC tasting?

_____

Variation in the ability to taste PTC and sodium benzoate has no obvious survival value today, and yet there is ethnic variation in allele frequencies between different groups. For instance, 63% of Arabs are tasters for PTC, whereas 98% of Native Americans can taste it. At least one condition for the Hardy-Weinberg Law was not met with respect to this gene in the world population.

How do you think this ethnic variation came about?

_____

_____

_____

_____

How could this variation in allele frequency be associated with survival potential for the ability to detect a bitter taste?

_____

_____

_____

_____

Assuming there was no selective advantage for this trait, what other factor might account for the ethnic differences?

_____

NATURAL SELECTION

Evolution is defined as a change in gene (allele) frequency. As you have seen, if a population meets the Hardy-Weinberg conditions, it is in genetic equilibrium, so there will be no change in gene frequency and therefore no evolution. The usefulness of the concept of genetic equilibrium is that we can measure changes in gene frequency that do occur and try to discover which of the stipulated conditions has been altered in order to give that change. Is the observed change in gene frequency over a period of time or in different populations due to mutation, small population size, selective mating, migrating individuals, or natural selection? For most genes, **natural selection** is almost always by far the most important factor in bringing about changes in gene frequency.

In many cases, natural selection will mean that one of two or more possible phenotypes will have a slightly better chance of producing fertile offspring and will therefore have a greater contribution to the gene pool in the next generation. In cases of more severe selection, the less advantageous allele may be lethal or prevent reproduction altogether. In that case there will always be genetic death of individuals with the deleterious phenotype.

In human beings, **cystic fibrosis** is an inherited disease due to an autosomal recessive gene. Affected individuals carry two of the recessive alleles for the disease (genotype *ff*) and as a result form extremely thick mucus in their respiratory systems and elsewhere in the body. Their lungs are susceptible to frequent infections and the disease is progressive and eventually fatal. Usually the victims die in their teens or early twenties, and so do not reproduce. Among whites, one person in twenty is a carrier, i.e. heterozygote, for cystic fibrosis.

Severe natural selection has operated on the gene pool for the cystic fibrosis *(f)* and normal alleles *(F)* over the centuries: The affected individuals do not reproduce and do not pass on their genes. New cases arise only when both parents are heterozygous.

What is the chance that two heterozygotes will produce an affected child? _____

If there were a test for the presence of the gene in a heterozygote, some persons with the *f* allele might refrain from reproducing, particularly if their partner was also a carrier. In that case, their alleles would not be passed on to the next generation and the frequency of the *f* allele would be expected to decline. This type of selection against the apparently harmful *f* allele is an example of **negative eugenics,** or a deliberate attempt to reduce the perpetuation of a harmful allele.

In the following exercise you will compare the effects of natural selection alone and natural selection plus negative eugenics on the frequency of the *f* allele in a model system. Among the children of marriages between heterozygous carriers of the *f* allele and genetically normal individuals, the frequency of the *f* allele should be 25%, the same as in the parents. We will use that frequency at the start of both this and the following experiments.

First Round

In this experiment there will be complete selection against the recessive genotype that is expressed as the affected cystic fibrosis phenotype. The homozygous *FF* and the heterozygous *Ff* genotypes both have the normal phenotype and are not selected against. Both will therefore contribute to the next generation.

■ Obtain a small plastic bag with 75 light beans and 25 dark beans. These 100 beans represent your **initial gene pool.** This is the gene pool that would be generated by marriages between heterozygous carriers and homozygous normal individuals.

■ Shake up the beans to simulate random mixing of the gametes during the first generation of reproduction.

■ Reach into the bag and (without looking!) take out two beans: This is the first individual.

■ Set these beans aside and repeat 49 times until you have used up all the beans, arranging the *FF, Ff* and *ff* genotypes in groups as you draw.

■ Select against the *ff* individuals by removing all of their alleles from the pool. You will be left with the *FF* and *Ff* individuals.

■ Count up the number of light and dark beans left in the pool and calculate the percentage and frequency of each.

■ Enter the results in Table 12-3 under Generation 1.

If you are not confident about how to do this, follow the example in Table 12-1.

Second Round

■ Begin the second round by replenishing your beans so that you have 100 beans with the same percentages of light and dark beans that you had at the end of Round 1. In the example, the new percentages were 80% light and 20% dark, so you would add beans to give 80 light and 20 dark.

■ Shake up the beans.

■ Select 50 individuals.

■ Remove all of the *ff* individuals.

■ Calculate the percentages and frequencies of light and dark beans left after selection, and enter the results in the table under Generation 2.

TABLE 12-1.   SAMPLE CALCULATION FOR ROUND 1. Follow these steps for each round. Enter your results in the tables at the boxed steps. Always round off to the nearest percent.

		F		*f*		TOTAL	
Initial gene pool:		75	alleles	25	alleles	100	alleles
		75%		25%		100%	
		.75		.25		1.00	
First draw:	28FF	+	19Ff		+	3ff	100	alleles
Selection:	-0FF		-0Ff			-3ff	-6	alleles
Survivors:	28FF	+	19Ff			0ff	94	alleles
Selected gene pool:		75	alleles	19	alleles	94	alleles
		80%		20%		100%	
		.80		.20		1.00	
Add in:		+5		+1		+6	
Replenished gene pool with new frequencies:		80	alleles	20	alleles	100	alleles
Second draw:				YOU ARE NOW READY FOR THE SECOND DRAW			

Third Round etc.

■ Begin the third round by replenishing your beans so that you have the new percentages and repeat as described under the second round until you have drawn and selected against the fifth generation.

When you have finished five rounds, you will be tired of drawing beans, but you will have enough data to make a meaningful graph of the decline in the frequency of the *f* allele over five generations.

■ Use the grid in Table 12-3 to plot the *frequency of f* against the number of generations.

NEGATIVE EUGENICS

In this experiment you will assume that affected individuals with the *ff* genotype will not reproduce. Also assume that one half of the heterozygous individuals will refrain from reproducing. The remaining heterozygotes and homozygotes for the normal allele will contribute to the next generation.

■ Obtain a small plastic bag with 75 light beans and 25 dark beans. You may also need a coin to flip. These 100 beans represent your **initial gene pool.** This is the gene pool that would be generated by marriages between heterozygous carriers and homozygous normal individuals.
■ Shake up the beans to simulate random mixing of the gametes during the first generation of reproduction.
■ Reach into the bag and (without looking!) take out two beans: This is the first individual.
■ Set these beans aside and repeat 49 times until you have used up all the beans, arranging *FF, Ff* and *ff* genotypes in groups as you draw.
■ Select against the *ff* individuals by removing all of their alleles from the gene pool; select against the *Ff* individuals by removing one half of them from the gene pool. If you have an odd number of heterozygotes, flip a coin to decide whether to remove the last one. You will be left with one half of the *Ff* individuals and all of the *FF* individuals.
■ Count up the number of light and dark beans left in the pool and calculate the percentage and frequency of each.
■ Enter the results in Table 12-4 under Generation 1.

Second Round

■ Begin the second round by replenishing your beans so that you have 100 beans with the same percentages of light and dark alleles that you had at the end of Round 1. In the example, the new percentages were 80% light and 20% dark, so you would add beans to give 80 light and 20 dark.
■ Shake up the beans.
■ Select 50 individuals.
■ Remove all of the *ff* individuals and one half of the *Ff* individuals.
■ Calculate the percentages of light and dark beans left after selection, and enter the results in the table under Generation 2.

Third Round

■ Begin the third round by replenishing your beans so that you have the new percentages and repeat the procedure described in the second round until you have drawn and selected against five generations.

When you have finished five rounds, you will be tired of drawing beans, but will have enough data so that your graph can be meaningfully compared with the graph for natural selection.

■ Use the grid in Table 12-4 to plot the *frequency of f* against the *number of generations.*

Did you see a rapid effect of natural selection alone on the frequency of the *f* allele in the first experiment?

_____

Did negative eugenics cause the frequency of the *f* allele to decline more rapidly in the second experiment?

_____

In some diseases, the affected individual has the ability to reproduce. Suppose there was a genetic counseling program that was attempting to lower the frequency of such a disease through negative eugenics. Would you advise the counseling program to concentrate its efforts on the affected individuals, or should both the carriers and affected individuals receive counseling? Explain your answer.

_____

_____

_____

_____

Please return your lab materials and discard all debris before leaving your laboratory.

EXPLORING FURTHER

Jansen, J. D. *Child in a White Fog.* New York: Vantage Press, 1975. (Impact of cystic fibrosis).
Stern, C. *Principles of Human Genetics.* San Francisco: W. H. Freeman, 1973.
Wilson, E. O., and W. H. Bossert. *Primer of Population Biology.* Sunderland, Mass.: Sinauer, 1971.

Journal Articles

Scientific American, September 1978: This issue is devoted to Evolution.
Allison, A. C. "Sickle cells and evolution." *Scientific American,* August 1956 (#1065).
Ayala, F. J. "The mechanisms of evolution." *Scientific American,* September 1978 (#1407).
Eckhardt, Robert B. "Population genetics and human origins." *Scientific American,* January 1972 (#676).
Kimura, Motoo. "The neutral theory of molecular evolution." *Scientific American,* November 1979 (#1451).
Lewontin, Richard C. "Adaptation." *Scientific American,* September 1978 (#1408).
Mayr, Ernst. "Darwin and natural selection." *Am. Scientist* 65: 321, May 1977.
Mayr, Ernst. "Evolution." *Scientific American,* September 1978 (#1400).
Wills, C. "Genetic load." *Scientific American,* March 1971 (#1172)

Student Name _____ **Date** _____

TABLE 12-2.   DATA ON PTC AND SB TASTING

Data from the PTC Test

Individual results: Taster _____   Nontaster _____

Class results:

Number of tasters _____ = _____ % tasters ($TT + Tt$)

Number of nontasters _____ = _____ % nontasters (tt)

Total _____

q^2 = _____ ; q = _____ ; frequency of t allele = _____

$1 - q = p$ = frequency of T allele = _____

p^2 = genotype of TT = _____ % of the class

$2pq$ = genotype of Tt = _____ % of the class

If class member is known to be a taster, what is the chance that he or she is homozygous for the T allele?
% $TT \times 100/(\% TT + \% Tt)$ = _____ %

Data from the SB Test

Individual results: Taster _____   Nontaster _____

Class results:

Number of tasters _____ = _____ % tasters ($TT + Tt$)

Number of nontasters _____ = _____ % nontasters (tt)

Total _____

q^2 = _____ ; q = _____ ; frequency of t allele = _____

$1 - q = p$ = frequency of T allele = _____

p^2 = genotype of TT = _____ % of the class

$2pq$ = genotype of Tt = _____ % of the class

If class member is known to be a taster, what is the chance that he or she is a carrier for the t allele?
% $Tt \times 100/(\% TT + \% Tt)$ = _____ %

TABLE 12-3. FLUCTUATION IN FREQUENCY OF *f* ALLELE DUE TO INCREASED
SELECTION AGAINST IT

Rounds	F			f		
	#	%	Frequency	#	%	Frequency
Initial	75	75	.75	25	25	.25
Generation 1						
Generation 2						
Generation 3						
Generation 4						
Generation 5						

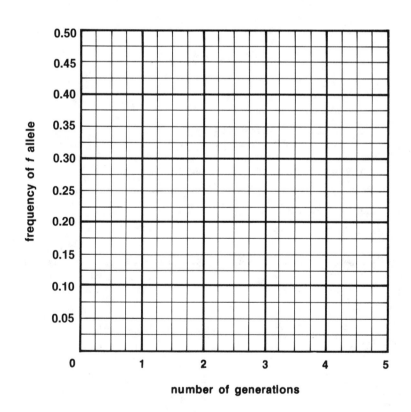

Student Name ———————————————————————— **Date** ————————————

TABLE 12-4. FLUCTUATION IN FREQUENCY OF *f* ALLELE DUE TO GENETIC DRIFT

Rounds	F			f		
	#	%	Frequency	#	%	Frequency
Initial	25	25	.25	25	25	.25
Generation 1						
Generation 2						
Generation 3						
Generation 4						
Generation 5						

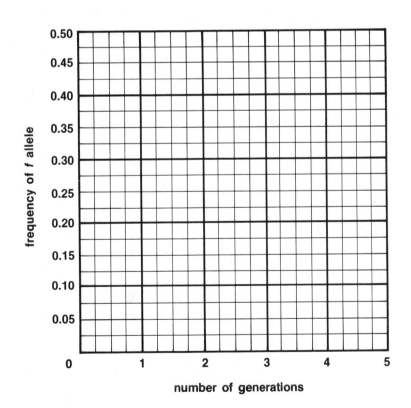

DNA: The Secret of Life

OBJECTIVES

When you have completed this topic, you should be able to:
1. Describe the structure of a deoxyribonucleotide.
2. Explain how nucleotides are arranged in a molecule of DNA.
3. Describe the role of the bases and base pairing in the structure, function, and replication of DNA.
4. Explain the structure of giant salivary gland chromosomes in flies and cite evidence that these chromosomes are active in RNA transcription.
5. Define regulation, induction, and repression.
6. Name the genes of the lactose operon and their products, if any.
7. Explain the effect of lactose on the genes of the lactose operon.

KEY TOPICS

DNA structure, deoxyribonucleotides, base pairing, giant salivary gland chromosomes, gene regulation, lactose operon.

INTRODUCTION

DNA is the macromolecule that contains the blueprints for life. In prokaryotes it is a small circle with a single copy in each cell. In eukaryotes, each chromosome contains a very long DNA molecule associated with RNA and protein. The **genes** for all of the cell's proteins, including the enzymes that make the other cell components, are encoded in the structure of DNA. A prokaryotic chromosome may contain about 2,500 genes and there are many thousands of genes in the nucleus of a eukaryotic cell. The structure of DNA is usually constant from generation to generation; any change is a **mutation,** and most such changes in DNA result in altered or deranged cell function. It seems to be highly adaptive for an organism to keep most of its genes identical from generation to generation. The structure of DNA, which inherently provides a mechanism for its exact replication, allows almost perfect conservation of our genes.

The building blocks of DNA are **deoxyribonucleotides,** each of which contains one **deoxyribose** 5 carbon sugar, to which is attached a **phosphate** group and a nitrogenous **base.** The phosphate group joins to the sugar of the adjacent nucleotide in a **condensation reaction;** hundreds of nucleotides are joined end-to-end in this way to make up the backbone of the DNA molecule, in which sugar and phosphate groups alternate. A base extends from each sugar. Two such backbones coil around each other in a **double helix,** with the backbones on the outside of the helix and the bases on the inside. (See text Figure 13-4.) Each base pairs with its opposite number and is held precisely in position by **hydrogen bonds** between appropriate functional group, as shown in Figure 13-1.

The key to DNA's structure, function, and replication is the arrangement of the bases. This is the secret of life. The bases used are the double-ringed **purines, adenine** and **guanine,** and the single-ringed **pyrimidines, thymine** and **cytosine.** The distance between the backbones is just wide enough to accommodate a purine and a pyrimidine, but not two purines. There cannot be two pyrimidines either, because they would be too short to bridge the gap. A second constraint is that their respective functional groups permit adenine and thymine to hydrogen bond and likewise guanine and cytosine. The other combinations cannot form the requisite hydrogen bonds and are not normally found. The permitted combinations are called **complementary base pairs: AT, TA, GC** and **CG.**

The next constraint on the structure of DNA is the order of the base pairs along the length of the molecule. This **sequence** is the code that is interpreted during protein synthesis to make the specific proteins characteristic of an organism. The fixed sequence of the bases allows millions of amino acids to be specified in exactly the right order to make the thousands of proteins needed by every cell.

Finally, the pairing of the bases provides a mechanism for the **self-replication** of DNA. The information in one backbone of the helix is sufficient to specify the

— covalent bond
····· hydrogen bond
S deoxypentose
P phosphate

Figure 13-1. A dinucleotide section of DNA. There are two base pairs in which the bases are held together by hydrogen bonds. Each base is part of a nucleotide composed of one deoxyribose sugar, one phosphate, and one base. The two strands of DNA run in opposite directions and so are antiparallel.

structure of the entire double helix.

Certain cells of fly larvae are very large and necessarily have many times the amount of nuclear DNA normal for the organism. In the salivary glands of *Drosophila* larvae, for example, each chromosome contains over one thousand times as much DNA as other cells, and it is highly organized into giant chromosomes. All of the DNA strands are bundled together lengthwise and show the same pattern of coiling: Parts of the chromosome are more condensed and other parts are more fluffy and expanded. The dense regions are all in register and likewise the less dense regions. When the cells are treated with a stain that binds most strongly to DNA, the most dense regions of each chromosome will stain darker and other regions will stain less well. The result is a pattern of dark and light bands that is characteristic for a particular chromosome.

Most genes are under some form of **regulation,** so that they can be switched on or off according to the prevailing conditions. Visible evidence of this can be seen in giant chromosomes when they form **puffs** or **Balbiani rings** at different locations along the chromosomes during larval development (see text p. 289). It can be shown that the active RNA synthesis goes on in the puffs, so

they represent genes that are turned on.

In bacteria there is genetic and biochemical evidence of regulation as well. If the colon bacterium *Escherichia coli* is given two sugars to metabolize for energy, it does an interesting thing: It uses up one completely before starting to use the second. This phenomenon is called **diauxie** (= double eating) and led to the idea that the second sugar was not used right away *because the enzymes needed for its metabolism were not present.*

If the sugars are glucose and lactose, for example, glucose will be metabolized first, appropriately enough since the enzymes for glycolysis are always present in all cells. Lactose, on the other hand, is a disaccharide and must be split to glucose and galactose before it can enter the glycolytic pathway. The presence of lactose will usually cause the **induction** of the synthesis of the required enzymes within a few minutes. In this process, genes that have previously been inactive in transcription are switched on. They begin making mRNA which is then translated into proteins needed for lactose metabolism.

The system of lactose induction is quite sophisticated in that if glucose is present along with lactose, it acts to block induction of lactose-digesting enzymes while glucose itself is being used up. When the glucose is finally finished, induction proceeds and the bacteria continue to grow on their new carbon source.

There is an obvious selective advantage in having a mechanism to regulate or switch genes on or off: If there is no immediate need for certain genes, a lot of energy can be saved and used for other purposes if these unnecessary enzymes are not made. There must be a quick, specific mechanism for their synthesis, however, as soon as a need arises. In *E. coli*, the enzymes for lactose metabolism can be immediately switched on whenever its host mammal drinks milk. At other times the enzymes are not needed and are not made.

The **lactose operon** consists of a **repressor** gene, the **structural** genes under its control and the **operator** switch by which the repressor turns them on or off. The **inducer** that switches the operon on is lactose.

■ Identify the genes of the lactose operon in Figure 13-2:

I codes for the repressor protein.
O, the operator, is the 27-base segment of DNA to which the repressor protein binds.
P, the promoter, is the DNA sequence where RNA polymerase binds and begins transcription.
Z, a structural gene coding for β-galactosidase, the enzyme that hydrolyzes lactose into glucose and galactose.
Y, a structural gene coding for permease, which transports lactose into the cell.
A, a structural gene coding for transacetylase.

Only genes I, Z, Y, and A are transcribed and code for proteins. O and P are gene sequences important in regulation but they do not code for proteins. Gene I is always transcribed and translated into repressor protein. There are only about 10 molecules of repressor per cell.

■ Study the following situations shown in Figure 13-2:

A. REPRESSION. When *E. coli* is in the typical situation where there is no lactose present, repressor binds to the operator (shown in Figure 15-3 in your text). This binding is extremely specific for the lactose operator and extremely tight. The RNA polymerase cannot bind to the promoter while the repressor is bound to the operator, because the P and O sequences partly overlap. There is no transcription or translation of structural protein. The operon is OFF.

B. INDUCTION. When lactose arrives, it binds to the repressor and converts it to an alternate, inactive form. It cannot bind to DNA, and so transcription and translation of structural genes proceed. The operon is ON and lactose is metabolized.

C. CONSTITUTIVE SYNTHESIS. One of the many interesting mutations that changes regulation is an operator constitutive (O^c) mutation. It alters the operator sequence so that repressor fails to recognize it and cannot bind. The result is the same as if the repressor had been inactivated: The operon is ON, structural genes are made, and lactose could be metabolized, if present. Induction is not possible because the genes are on all the time.

■ Turn to Table 13-1 at the end of this topic and be sure you understand how to complete it for each of these situations.

DNA IN GIANT CHROMOSOMES

■ Obtain two slides, two teasing needles, and physiological saline.
■ Place a large *Drosophila* larva on a slide and add a drop of saline.
■ Locate the anterior end of the larva and estimate the position of the salivary glands; they extend back about one third of the body length (see Figure 13-3).
■ Hold the body about midway back, with one teasing needle laid flat across the body; lay the other needle flat across the head and slowly pull off the head. The salivary glands may be attached to the exposed gut or be attached to the head.
■ Identify the transparent, glassy salivary glands, distinct from the grainy gut and body tissue.
■ Separate the salivary glands from other tissue and transfer them to a clean slide.
■ Put a drop of acetocarmine stain (for DNA) on the salivary glands and add a coverslip.
■ Take two or three paper towels and fold them over several times to make a thick pad.
■ Place the slide on a very flat, hard surface; cover the slide with the pad, then pound the slide once with your fist: **BANG!**
■ Remove the pad and inspect your slide. If you are lucky, it will have remained intact and you will now have a nice *squash* of salivary gland cells. If your slide broke, try it again or share with another student.
■ View the slide under low, then high power in the compound microscope. Use oil immersion if your microscope has an oil immersion lens.
■ Locate the cell nuclei, which look like clumps of tangled necklaces. Try to find one in which the chromosomes are extended so that you can see the banding pattern.

Each band in a giant chromosome corresponds to a single gene. The different intensities of staining reflect the physical state of the DNA (i.e., how tightly it is coiled). The coiling in turn is correlated with the activity of the genes: Genes that are active seem to be more expanded, and the most active genes are greatly expanded into large **puffs.** The pattern of puffs changes as development of the larva progresses and different gene products are required.

REGULATION OF THE LACTOSE OPERON

In the following experiment, you will study these situations:

wild type (normal) *E. coli* grown on maltose, which will be repressed
wild type *E. coli* grown on lactose, which will be induced and will synthesize β-galactosidase
O^c *E. coli* grown on either maltose or lactose, which will show constitutive synthesis of β-galactosidase

The activity of the enzyme β-galactosidase can be measured in cells first made permeable by adding toluene. An artificial substrate, ONPG (o-nitrophenyl galactoside) is added and is split by the enzyme into galactose and o-nitrophenyl, a bright yellow compound. The amount of yellow color will show the amount of β-galactosidase present in the cells. The color may be esti-

Figure 13-2. The lactose operon. Regulation of this operon involves gene I for repressor protein; gene P, the promoter (no protein); gene O, the operator (no protein); gene Z for the lactose splitting enzyme (β-galactosidase); gene Y for lactose permease; and gene A for transacetylase. (A) The operon is switched OFF and no enzymes are made in the absence of lactose. (B) Transcription is switched ON by lactose, enzymes are made and lactose is metabolized. (C) A mutation (∗) in the operator base sequence blocks repressor binding. Transcription is switched ON whether or not lactose is present.

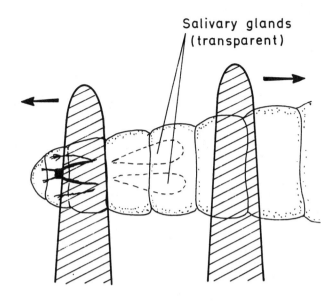

Figure 13-3. Salivary glands from a *Drosophila* larva. Press gently on the larva with two teasing needles. Then carefully separate the needles to pull the head region from the body. The salivary glands are transparent in contrast to the granular intestine.

mated qualitatively (+ +, +, or −) after incubating the toluene treated cells for 15 min at 30°C, if you do not have access to a spectrophotometer.

■ Working in pairs, obtain 5-ml samples of these *E. coli* K-12 cultures:

#1 wild type grown on lactose
#2 wild type grown on maltose
#3 O^c mutant grown on lactose
#4 O^c mutant grown on maltose
#5 unknown strain grown on lactose
#6 unknown strain grown on maltose

■ Add two drops of toluene to each tube, cover, and shake vigorously.
■ Allow ten minutes for the toluene to act, shaking the tubes frequently.
■ Set the wavelength of the spectrophotometer to 440 nm and adjust the absorbance to ∞.
■ Use a pipettor to add 0.2 mL of ONPG to 5 mL of distilled water, pour into a spectrophotometer cuvette, and adjust the absorbance to zero.
■ Likewise add 0.2 mL of ONPG to tube #1, pour into a cuvette and read the absorbance. Record the value in Table 13-2 at the end of this topic.
■ Read the absorbance at 1-min intervals for 6 min.
■ Repeat for tubes #2-#6. Record the results.
■ Plot your data in Figure 13-4 (at the end of this topic) and decide whether the unknown strain was wild type or constitutive.
■ Complete Table 13-2 and answer the questions.
■ When you are finished with this lab, return all materials and dispose of the bacterial cultures as directed. Follow the directions of your instructor for cleaning your glassware, and store your microscope properly.

EXPLORING FURTHER

Alberts, Bruce, D. Bray, J. Lewis, M. Raff, K. Roberts, J. D. Watson. *Molecular Biology of the Cell.* New York: Garland, 1983.
Watson, J. D. *Molecular Biology of the Gene.* 3rd ed. Menlo Park, Calif.: W. A. Benjamin, 1976.

Journal Articles

Beerman, Wolfgang, and Ulrich Clever. "Chromosome puffs." *Scientific American,* April 1964 (#180).
Cohen, S. N. "The manipulation of genes." *Scientific American,* July 1975 (#1324).
Crick, F. H. C. "The structure of the hereditary material." *Scientific American,* October 1954 (#5).
Diener, T. O. "Viroids." *Scientific American,* 66, January 1981.
Drake, John W., Barry W. Glickman, and Lynn R. Ripley. "Updating the theory of mutation." *American Scientist* 71 (6): 621, November-December 1983.
Federoff, Nina. "Transposable genetic elements in maize." *Scientific American,* 84, June 1984.
Gilbert, W., and B. Müller-Hill. "Isolation of the *lac* repressor." *Pro. Nat. Acad. Sci.* 56: 1891, 1966.
Grivell, Leslie A. "Mitochondrial DNA." *Scientific American,* 78, March 1983.
Harvey, Ronald G. "Polycyclic hydrocarbons and cancer." *American Scientist,* 70 (4): 386, July-August 1982.
Howard-Flanders, Paul. "Inducible repair of DNA." *Scientific American,* 72, November 1981.
Jacob, F., and J. Monod. "Genetic regulatory mechanisms in the synthesis of proteins." *J. Mol. Biol.* 3:318, 1961.
Ptashne, Mark, Alexander D. Johnson, and Carl O. Pabo. "A genetic switch in a bacterial virus." *Scientific American,* 128, November 1982.
Watson, J. D. and F. H. C. Crick. "Molecular structure of nucleic acids: A structure for deoxyribose nucleic acid. *Nature: 171,* 737, 1953.

Student Name _____ **Date** _____

TABLE 13-1. REGULATION OF THE LACTOSE OPERON.

Indicate for the following situations the condition of each of these components (yes or no).

	wild type no lactose	wild type lactose	Oᶜ no lactose	Oᶜ lactose
repressor synthesized				
repressor binds to lactose				
repressor binds to operator				
operator is on				
operator is off				
promotor binds RNA polymerase				
transcription of Z,Y,A occurs				
translation of Z,Y,A mRNA occurs				
lactose is split				

TABLE 13-2.   DATA FOR INDUCTION OF THE LACTOSE OPERON.

Record your absorbance data for each culture. Then plot your results in Figure 13-4.

	Tube #1	Tube #2	Tube #3	Tube #4	Tube #5	Tube #6
E. coli	*w.t.*	*w.t.*	*O^c*	*O^c*	*unknown*	*unknown*
Sugar	lactose	maltose	lactose	maltose	lactose	maltose
0 min						
1 min						
2 min						
3 min						
4 min						
5 min						
6 min						
ONPG split (yes/no)						
operon is ON/OFF						

Maltose is a dissaccharide of glucose subunits and is structurally very similar to lactose.
Explain why it does not switch on the lactose operon.

_____

_____

Name at least two ways in which an O^c mutant strain could mutate again so that it fails to produce β-galactosidase in the presence of lactose.

_____

_____

Student Name _____ **Date** _____

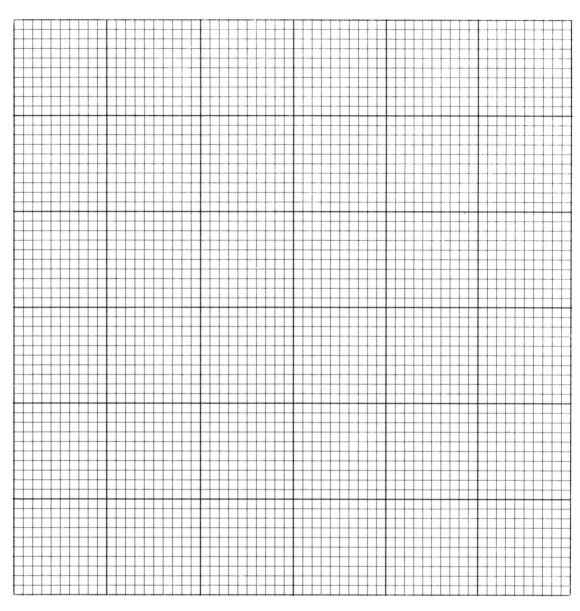

time in minutes

Figure 13-4.   Activity of β-galactosidase. Plot the absorbance at 440 nm versus time in minutes.

Introduction to the Diversity of Life (Topics 14-21)

KEY TOPICS

Five Kingdoms: Monera, Protista, Fungi, Plantae, Animalia; Domains: Prokaryota, Eukaryota; fossil record.

As more information about the evolutionary history and biochemistry of organisms has become available, the old division of organisms into plants, animals, and protists was no longer sufficient. Although the boundaries between the kingdoms listed below are somewhat unclear, the following scheme* is used in Topics 14-21:

Kingdom Monera: All prokaryotic organisms (bacteria, cyanobacteria).

Kingdom Protista: Eukaryotic unicellular heterotrophs and most unicellular autotrophs (protozoa, diatoms, dinoflagellates, euglenoids).

Kingdom Fungi: Eukaryotic hetereotrophs that absorb food, mostly multicellular (yeasts, molds, mushrooms).

Kingdom Animalia: Eukaryotic multicellular heterotrophs that ingest food (sponges to vertebrates).

Kingdom Plantae: Eukaryotic autotrophs, usually multicellular, with cell walls of cellulose (algae, mosses, ferns and fern allies, seed plants).

The characteristics of the kingdoms given here are to provide a general idea of the type of organism that you might find in each one, and are by no means definitive. (A yeast, for example, is a unicellular heterotroph, but it is placed in the kingdom Fungi because it is much more closely related to fungi than to the protozoans or unicellular algae.)

The differences between prokaryotes and eukaryotes are so significant that Kingdom Monera is set apart in its own **Domain Prokaryota.** The other four kingdoms belong to **Domain Eukaryota.** The relationships of the

*See R.H. Whittaker, "New concepts of kingdoms of organisms." *Science 163:* 150-160, 1969.

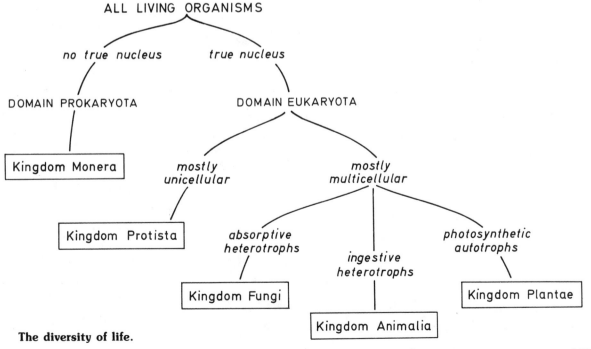

The diversity of life.

five kingdoms within these domains is shown in the following figure.

In the discussion of the five kingdoms in Topics 15-21 you will become familiar with the diversity of living organisms. The structures and life histories are given in considerably more detail than you may be required to learn. This will allow you some flexibility to concentrate more on those organisms that you find most interesting and that the instructor is able to provide. The point of these laboratories is not to have you learn a stupendous number of biological "facts," but rather to introduce you to the different ways that organisms cope with their common biological needs: protection, nutrition, excretion, reproduction and dispersal.

Classification of Living Things

TOPIC 14

OBJECTIVES

When you have completed this topic, you should be able to:
1. Define taxonomy and taxon.
2. List the major taxa in the correct hierarchy from most general to least general.
3. Correctly classify an unknown organism using a simple dichotomous key.
4. Define numerical taxonomy.
5. Arrange a set of imaginary organisms into a taxonomic array to show their possible evolution.

KEY TOPICS

Species, binomial nomenclature, taxonomy, Five Kingdoms, Domains.

INTRODUCTION

In order to understand some of the relationships between living organisms, biologists use the process of classification called **taxonomy.** Taxonomy is simply the naming and ordering of a set of organisms according to some system. Animals are classified within domains according to the following scheme.*

Kingdom
  Phylum
    Class
      Order
        Family
          Genus
            Species

Can you classify yourself (*Homo sapiens*) according to this scheme? (*See* text discussion on why you are *Homo sapiens*.)

Kingdom _____

  Phylum _____

    Class _____

      Order _____

        Family _____

          Genus _____

            Species _____

Plants are classified in the same way except that Division is used instead of Phylum.

The members of each taxonomic group, or **taxon,** all share certain characteristics. Within the taxon, the members may be divided into smaller groups whose members share certain characteristics that are not found in the members of the other groups.

The presence or absence of certain traits will allow you to determine whether an organism belongs to a certain taxon, which more specific taxon it belongs to within the first taxon, which taxon within the second taxon, and so on. These traits, however, are not always the ones that are obvious in an intact animal or plant. Assignment to a certain taxon may depend on the careful study of an organism's biochemistry, embryology, or parts of its life cycle that are difficult to observe.

The basic principle underlying present-day taxonomy is to attempt to reveal the "natural" taxonomy in which organisms are classified in perfect accordance with the actual history of their evolution. Each taxon would be **monophyletic** in that all of its members would be descendants of a common ancestor. In practice, the difficult part is deciding which characteristics should be considered and which are the most important and should therefore be given the greatest weight in defining a taxon.

---

*An easy way to remember this scheme is by a mnemonic device such as "Kindly Professors Cannot Often Fail Good Students."

In **cladistic taxonomy,** great importance is given to the evolutionary history of groups of organisms. The pattern of branching off from common ancestors takes precedence over the degree of similarity and difference between the descendants. In **phylogenetic taxonomy,** organisms are classified on the basis of the number and similarity of shared characteristics and descent from a common ancestor. In **numerical taxonomy,** described later, only the number of shared phenotypic characteristics counts. Each approach has its advantages and drawbacks in actual practice.

In order to identify the taxon to which a certain organism belongs *in the field or without extensive study* we use a shorthand guide to readily discernible features called a **dichotomous key** (dichotomous means "two forks"). Such a key divides a certain group of organisms into two groups on the basis of a certain trait, then divides each of those groups into two groups, and so on, until the desired level of identification is reached. These groups are for convenience in identifying organisms and are not the same as the taxa described above.

Because the purpose of a key is to identify something quickly, each key will be limited in scope. If it starts out with a broad group of organisms, say, invertebrates or algae, it will not be able to identify the species of each organism but perhaps only the family or order. If the key is more limited in content, limited, for example, to spring wildflowers of a certain geographical area, it will be able to include genus- and species-level identification. The person using a key can use prior knowledge or the constraints of geographical region or season to choose a key that will give as precise an identification as possible.

Dichotomous keys can be used in series to identify organisms of special interest when the first key is very general. A person studying seashore life might use a key to marine invertebrates in conjunction with a key to bivalves to identify a certain clamlike organism.

Consider the dichotomous scheme shown in Figure 14-1 for grouping all organisms. Each step in keying out an organism is simply a yes or no answer to successive questions in a key, part of which would look like this:

1a. Is the organism motile? (2a)
1b. Is the organism stationary? (3a)
2a. Is the organism aquatic? (4a)
2b. Is the organism terrestrial? (5a)
3a. Is the organism aquatic? (6a)
3b. Is the organism terrestrial? (7a)
4a. Does the organism have ray fins? (class Osteichthyes, or bony fish)

4b. Does the organism lack ray fins? (9a)
5a. Does the organism have four legs? (10a)
5b. Does the organism have zero, two, six, eight, or many legs? (11a)
6a. Is the organism green? (12a)
6b. Is the organism not green? (13a)
7a. Does the organism have a woody stem? (14a)
7b. Does the organism have a herbaceous stem? (15a)

To use the key, you would begin with question 1a. If the answer to this question were yes, you would proceed to question 2a; if the answer were no, you would go to question 1b. You would then continue from 1b to 3a to 6a, and so on. Three consecutive yes answers would identify an organism as a fish in the class Osteichthyes, but the identification of most organisms, including other fish, would require several more questions. A more detailed key would be necessary to identify the fish more specifically.

In today's laboratory exercise you will use simple dichotomous keys to identify members of a class that are similar in their general features but easily distinguished when you know what to look for.

CONIFER KEY (SUBDIVISION SPERMOPSIDA, CLASS CONIFERAE)

Conifers are plants that usually have evergreen leaves and produce gametes in male and female cones.

■ Select one of the specimens of a conifer on demonstration in the lab, and key it out using the key in Table 14-1. This key includes some of the conifers that will be found in your region of the country. Your instructor may give you additional information about species that may be especially common in your area. To use the key, begin with question 1a. If this item applies, go to question 2a; if not, go to 1b. continue from 1b to 14a, from 14a to 15a, and so forth.

Specimen number: _____

Identification: _____

■ If living conifers are available in the field for class study, select a specimen and key it out in your spare time.

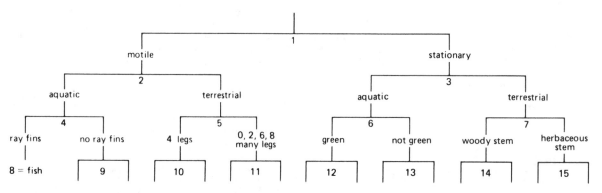

Figure 14-1. A simple dichotomous key.

TABLE 14-1. A KEY TO THE CONIFERS

After you have identified a given conifer, refer to a field guide and check that the description matches the characteristics of your specimen.

1a.	Leaves are in clusters	2a
1b.	Leaves are borne singly along the stem.	14a
2a.	More than 5 leaves in a cluster.	3a
2b.	Leaves occur in clusters of 2-5; persistent for several seasons.	4a
3a.	Leaves are deciduous (fall off in winter), soft, flattened.	LARCH or TAMARACK
3b.	Leaves are persistent, stiff, 4-sided (ornamental in warmer areas).	TRUE CEDAR
4a.	Leaves mostly 5 in a cluster.	WHITE PINE
4b.	Leaves 2-3 in a cluster.	5a
5a.	Leaves mostly 3 in a cluster.	6a
5b.	Leaves mostly 2 in a cluster.	8a
6a.	Twisted leaves, less than 5 in. long.	PITCH PINE
6b.	Straight leaves, more than 5 in. long.	7a
7a.	Leaves 5-10 in., cones very thorny (South).	LOBLOLLY PINE
7b.	Leaves mostly over 11 in. long, cones not thorny (South).	LONGLEAF PINE
8a.	Leaves longer than 3 in.	9a
8b.	Leaves shorter than 3 in.	11a
9a.	Leaves rigid, bark grayish.	AUSTRIAN PINE
9b.	Leaves narrower than $1/16$ in., bark reddish brown or brown.	10a
10a.	Twigs brown, cones thornless (North).	RED PINE
10b.	Twigs whitish, cones strongly thorny (South).	SHORTLEAF PINE
11a.	Leaves wider than $1/16$ in.	12a
11b.	Leaves narrower than $1/16$ in.	13a
12a.	Leaves longer than $1 1/2$ in.	MOUNTAIN PINE
12b.	Leaves shorter than $1 1/2$ in.	JACK PINE
13a.	Twigs whitened.	SCRUB PINE
13b.	Twigs not whitened.	SCOTCH PINE
14a.	Leaves are scalelike or triangular and opposite or whorled.	15a
14b.	Leaves needlelike or flattened.	18a
15a.	Branchlets flattened; all leaves scalelike, opposite.	WHITE CEDAR or ARBOR VITAE
15b.	Branchlets not flattened.	16a
16a.	Leaves needlelike to triangular in tight spirals (frost-free areas).	MONKEY PUZZLE TREE
16b.	Leaves needlelike in whorls or pairs.	17a
17a.	Leaves 3-sided in whorls of 3 on 3-sided twigs.	DWARF JUNIPER
17b.	Leaves 3-sided in pairs in 4 rows on 4-sided twigs.	RED CEDAR
18a.	Leaves soft, on green branchlets (like compound leaves): (South or West).	19a
18b.	Leaves rigid on brownish branchlets (solitary).	21a
19a.	Leaves dark green, persistent.	REDWOOD
19b.	Leaves light yellow-green, deciduous.	20a
20a.	Leaves to 1 in., subopposite.	DAWN REDWOOD
20b.	Leaves less than 1 in., alternate (South).	BALD CYPRESS

21a. Leaves 4-sided with persistent woody, petiole.	22a
21b. Leaves flattened in cross section.	26a
22a. Leaves dark green or yellow green.	23a
22b. Leaves blue-green.	24a
23a. Branchlets droop.	NORWAY SPRUCE
23b. Branchlets do not droop.	RED SPRUCE
24a. Leaves are at right angles to the stem.	BLUE SPRUCE
24b. Leaves point forward.	25a
25a. Leaves have whitish powder; twigs hairy.	BLACK SPRUCE
25b. Leaves lack whitish powder; twigs not hairy.	WHITE SPRUCE
26a. Leaves lack stomata underneath; seed in red berry; shrub.	27a
26b. Leaves have 2 lines of stomata underneath; tree.	28a
27a. Leaves ¾ in. long or less with inconspicuous midrib.	AMERICAN YEW
27b. Leaves 1 in. or longer with prominent midrib.	JAPANESE YEW
28a. Leaves round-tipped, whitened beneath.	29a
28b. Leaves pointed, green beneath.	30a
29a. Leaves shorter than ¾ in., attached by slender stalks; twigs rough.	EASTERN HEMLOCK
29b. Leaves longer than ¾ in., unstalked, alternate; twigs smooth.	BALSAM FIR
30a. Leaves are dark green and straight; bracts with prongs on cones.	DOUGLAS FIR
30b. Leaves are light bluish-green and strongly curved.	FIR

Characteristics of field specimen:

_____

_____

_____

_____

_____

_____

_____

_____

Identification: _____

Your instructor may ask you to key out other preserved or live specimens.

NUMERICAL TAXONOMY

It is very difficult to decide which characteristics should be considered in setting up a given category, or taxonomic group. All the organisms within the category will have some characteristics in common, but none of the organisms would be expected to have every one of the characteristics associated with the category.

The introduction of computers has made it possible to consider large numbers of characteristics in determining the degree of relatedness of different organisms and to sidestep the problem of deciding weights for various characteristics. Classification can then be based not on the relative importance of certain characteristics, but rather on the number of characteristics held in common. This type of classification is called **numerical taxon-**omy, or **phenetic taxonomy.** It has been widely used in the classification of organisms, diseases, plant communities, politicians, psychological types, socioeconomic neighborhoods, and so forth.

An experimental system to test the procedure of numerical taxonomy was devised by Joseph H. Camin. It involves a set of imaginary animals, christened "Caminalcules," which was generated "according to rules known so far only to him, but believed to be consistent with what is generally known of evolutionary principles."*

Study the set of 29 Caminalcules illustrated in Figure 14-2, and try to arrange the set into some meaningful pattern of groups with anatomical features in common. For example, individuals with eyes might be grouped separately from those without eyes. Then animals with two eyes might have given rise to animals with a single eye or vice versa.

Your instructor will either provide you with a set of cutouts corresponding to Figure 14-2 or will ask you to cut up Figure 14-2 yourself so that you can try out different arrangements.

Arrange all of the individuals into a branching tree to show how they might have arisen through evolution from a common ancestor. The goal is to construct the tree so that it requires the *fewest number of postulated evolutionary steps*. A change from organism #7 to #15 (or vice versa) requires a single step, whereas a change from #7 to #8 would require two steps.

When you are satisfied with the arrangement that you have worked out, record the results in Table 14-2 (at

---

*From "Numerical taxonomy" by Robert R. Sokal. Copyright © 1966 by Scientific American Inc. All rights reserved.

Figure 14-2. Caminalcules. Imaginary organisms ready to be classified. (From "Numerical taxonomy" by Robert R. Sokal. Copyright © 1966 by Scientific American, Inc. All rights reserved.)

the end of this topic) in the form of an evolutionary tree. Use numbers to identify the individual Caminalcules, and work with a pencil so that you can change your mind if necessary. Consult your instructor to see how your tree compares with others produced by the class. Your instructor also has a computer-generated result which you can check when you have finished your own scheme.

Return all materials when you are finished with your work for this laboratory.

EXPLORING FURTHER

Blackwelder, R. E. *Taxonomy: A Text and Reference Book*. New York: John Wiley and Sons, 1967.

Hosie, R. C. *Native Trees of Canada*. 8th ed. Don Mills, Ontario, Canada: Fitzhenry and Whiteside Ltd. in cooperation with the Canadian Forestry Service and the Canadian Government Publishing Center, Supply and Services, 1979.

Petrides, George A. *Field Guide to Trees and Shrubs*. New York: Houghton-Mifflin, 1973.

Savory, T. *Animal Taxonomy*. London: Herremann Educational, 1970.

Journal Articles

Cracraft, Joel. "Cladistic analysis and vicariance biogeography." *American Scientist* 71 (3), 273–281, May 1983.

Sokal, Robert R. "Numerical taxonomy." *Scientific American*, December 1966 (#1059).

Whittaker, R. H. "New concepts of kingdoms of organisms." *Science* 163: 150, 1969.

Whittaker, R. H., and L. Margulis. "Protist classification and the kingdoms of organisms." *Biosystems* 10: 3–18, 1978.

Student Name _____ **Date** _____

TABLE 14-2.   CLASSIFICATION OF CAMINALCULES

Use the identifying numbers to record your classification scheme in the form of a branching diagram.

Kingdom Monera and Kingdom Protista

OBJECTIVES

When you have completed this topic, you should be able to:
1. Describe the characteristics of prokaryotic organisms.
2. List the types of organisms that are prokaryotic.
3. Demonstrate the occurrence of bacteria in the environment by culturing samples from locations where they might be found.
4. Using bioluminescent bacteria as an oxygen indicator, explain the effect of bacteria on the level of oxygen in a closed system.
5. Describe the features of cyanobacteria that distinguish them from other bacteria and discuss their role in nature.
6. List the features of eukaryotic cells that distinguish them from prokaryotic cells.
7. Describe the most common eukaryotes inhabiting the termite gut in terms of their appearance and locomotion and the phylum to which each belongs.
8. Describe the animal-like and plantlike characteristics of *Euglena,* a photosynthetic protist that also has features of a flagellate.
9. Distinguish diatoms from dinoflagellates, and state the importance of these organisms in nature.

KEY TOPICS

Prokaryotes, cyanobacteria, eubacteria, pathogenic bacteria, eukaryotes, protozoa, mastigophora, sarcodina, ciliata, diatoms, dinoflagellates.

INTRODUCTION

In this exercise you will study the variety of single-celled organisms and learn something about their importance to larger organisms like ourselves. Some single-celled organisms are prokaryotes and belong to the Kingdom Monera within the Domain Prokaryota. These include the **eubacteria** (true bacteria), the **cyanobacteria** (blue-green bacteria) and several other groups. As a taxonomic group, the bacteria are set aside from eukaryotes by virtue of their **small size,** rapid rate of **reproduction,** and **mutation** and by their metabolic and physiological **diversity.**

All other organisms belong to the Domain Eukaryota. Most of those that are single cells are grouped together in Kingdom Protista, although a few are classified with closely related organisms in one of the other kingdoms. Those protists that are generally motile and ingest their food are called **protozoa.** A few protozoans do have chloroplasts and can carry out photosynthesis. Most of the photosynthetic autotrophs, however, are considered **algae** and are grouped separately in their own phyla depending on their type of cell wall and chlorophyll. These relationships are shown in Figure 15-1.

Eukaryotes arose from prokaryotes about 1.45 billion years ago and gave rise to the immense variety of higher organisms we have today. The prokaryotes, however, existed for some 3 billion years before that time and also underwent extensive evolution so that they are an equally diverse group at present. They continue to compete successfully with eukaryotes and are vital in maintaining the stability of our biosphere.

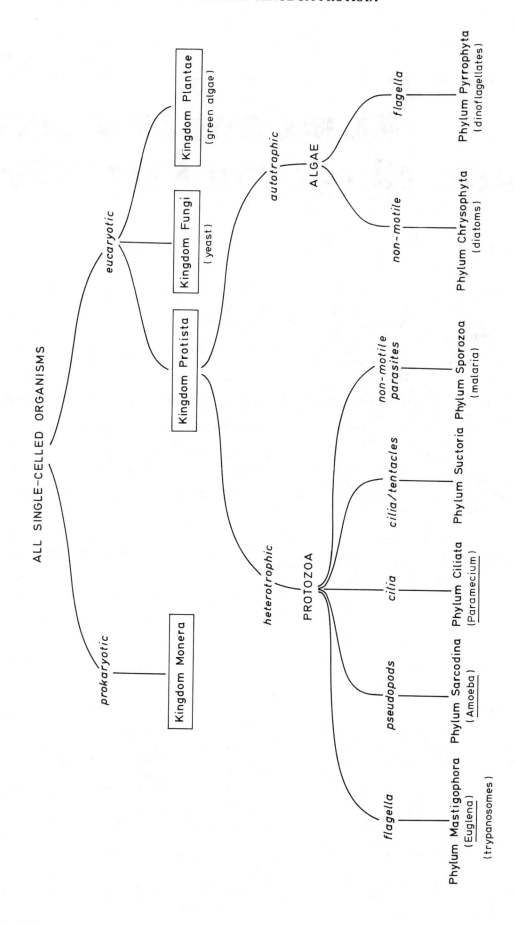

Figure 15-1.   Classification of single-celled organisms.

KINGDOM MONERA

Cyanobacteria (Blue-Green Bacteria)

Cyanobacteria are widespread in the environment and can exist under extremely harsh conditions in which organic nutrients are entirely lacking. They are a problem in the laboratory because they are able to contaminate distilled water supplies that are exposed to light by using the light for energy and obtaining minerals from the traces that remain in the distilled water. Most cyanobacteria carry out **photosynthesis** with the production of **oxygen** and thus help recycle CO_2 into organic compounds. Many also carry out **nitrogen fixation** by converting atmospheric N_2 into ammonia (NH_3), which can be used to synthesize amino acids. The ability of these forms to obtain energy, carbon, and nitrogen from the air makes them the most nutritionally independent organisms on earth. In addition, their prokaryotic features make them very hardy and allow them to compete successfully with eukaryotes. When conditions favor their rapid multiplication, they tend to form a mat on the surface of a body of water and cause the suffocation of the aerobic organisms. Their gelatinous capsules and toxins make them poor food for predators. When the oxygen is depleted, anaerobic bacteria flourish and produce foul-smelling gases, such as hydrogen sulfide, that make the water unfit for drinking or recreation.

■ Examine a drop of *Anabaena* culture under high power in your microscope.

Is this organism in the form of single cells, colonies, or filaments? _____

Are all the cells alike? _____

The larger cells are called **heterocysts** and are specialized for nitrogen fixation. (They may not be present in your sample.)

What color are the majority of the cells?

_____

What color are the heterocysts? _____

Do you see chloroplasts? _____

Cyanobacteria are not always blue green in color, but they always contain chlorophyll *a*, as do green plants. The accessory pigments may give them a red, purple, or brown color. The pigments are located on membranes, but there are no membrane-bound chloroplasts. In contrast to other photosynthetic bacteria, cyanobacteria generate oxygen as a product of photosynthesis.

Bacteria in the Environment

Bacteria are so small (often only about 1 μ in size) that their internal structure is not visible in the light microscope. For this reason, their identification depends on their shape, their arrangement in groups, the appearance of their colonies on culture plates, and the metabolic reactions that they can carry out.

SHAPE

The form of a bacterium may be a sphere (**coccus**), a rod (**bacillus**), or a spiral (**spirillum**). Any of these forms may have one or more **flagella** and thus be motile.

■ Review the basic bacterial forms by examining a prepared stained slide under oil immersion.

COLONIES: AIRBORNE BACTERIA

Any organism of sufficient size is covered with a collection of bacteria called its "natural flora." Most of these bacteria are harmless (**commensal**) or even helpful (**mutualistic**), but some of them are **pathogens,** which have the potential of causing disease. Even otherwise harmless bacteria can cause infection and disease if they gain access to parts of our body that are normally protected. The harmless bacteria of our natural flora help protect our bodies by maintaining conditions that are unfavorable for the growth of pathogens.

Many bacteria on our bodies, in the air, and in our immediate environment can be grown in the laboratory or **cultured** by providing them with a suitable medium that simulates the conditions to which they are accustomed. The medium can be either a liquid broth or a solid gel that is made by adding agar to a liquid medium and pouring the sterilized liquid into a flat Petri plate where it hardens and can be kept sterile. When sterile medium is **inoculated** by adding a sample of bacteria, the bacteria will multiply rapidly due to the lack of competition and will soon exhaust the nutrients. A liquid broth will become cloudy due to the presence of billions of cells, and an agar Petri plate will become covered with dots of **colonies,** or clones, consisting of 10^9 or so cells all descended from a single cell. The size, shape, color, and appearance of the colony help identify the type of bacterium producing it. **Indicators** may be added to the agar to show whether a certain reaction has been carried out. Any bacterium can be identified if you can find conditions under which the bacterium will grow in the laboratory and have the patience to carry out a sufficient number of tests.

IN THE FOLLOWING EXPERIMENT, FOLLOW THE DIRECTIONS GIVEN BY YOUR INSTRUCTOR FOR SEALING THE CULTURE PLATES AND FOR DISPOSING OF THEM PROPERLY. NEVER OPEN PLATES THAT HAVE BEEN INCUBATED BECAUSE THEY MAY CONTAIN PATHOGENIC BACTERIA.

Using nutrient agar plates, test for the presence of airborne bacteria.

■ Label the plate AIR, and add your initials and the date.
■ Place the plate near a source of moving air such as an open window, a hallway with traffic, or an air conditioner, and open it fully for 5 min.
■ Close the plate and place it upside down in the incubator at 37°C for 24-48 hr.
■ Label a second plate COUGH, and add your initials and the date.
■ Open the plate and cough over it with your mouth open three times.

■ Close the plate and place it upside down in the incubator at 37°C for 24-48 hr.
■ Label a third plate SUPPRESSED COUGH, and add your initials and the date.
■ Cough over the plate three times but either keep your mouth closed or use a handkerchief. Close the plate.
■ At the end of the experiment record the number of colonies on each plate, and enter the results in Table 15-1 at the end of this topic. If there are too many colonies on a plate, count only a sector such as one quarter or one tenth; multiply by the appropriate factor to determine the number of colonies estimated for the total plate.
■ Dispose of the plates properly.

Are you or the air in general a better (or worse!) source of bacteria? _____

_____

Did suppressing your cough cut down on the number of bacteria that you spread? _____

_____

METABOLISM: ORAL BACTERIA

BRING A TOOTHBRUSH TO THE LABORATORY FOR THIS EXERCISE.

The natural flora of your mouth is important in determining the susceptibility of your teeth to decay. *Lactobacillus* is a type of bacterium that contributes to conditions favoring decay by producing acid, which lowers the pH at the tooth surface. Even though this bacterium does not actually cause the decay, there is a strong statistical correlation between the activity of *Lactobacillus* and susceptibility to decay. It is possible to test for the presence of this bacterium by using Snyder's medium, which contains an indicator (bromcresol green) that turns yellow when acid is produced.

■ If you have not already looked at some of your own bacteria in the microscope, turn to Topic 3 and do so now, following the directions for obtaining and staining a sample.
■ Obtain 2 sterile test tubes, 2 sterile pipets, 3 tubes of Snyder's medium, and some sugarless gum.
■ Place the tube in a boiling water bath for 10 min to melt the agar and then keep it warm (45°C) until it is inoculated.
■ Chew the sugarless gum without swallowing, and drool into the test tube until you have at least 1 mL of saliva liquid, not counting the bubbles.
■ Use a sterile pipet to transfer 0.2 mL of saliva to the tube of agar.
■ Cover it and mix the saliva with the medium by tapping the tube while holding it firmly with the other hand.
■ Allow the tube to cool at room temperature until the agar has gelled.
■ If you have brought your toothbrush, brush your teeth thoroughly, repeat the saliva collection in a second tube, and inoculate a second tube of melted medium using a fresh sterile pipet.
■ Incubate the tubes at 37°C and also incubate a third uninoculated tube as a control.

■ After 24 hr, 48 hr, and again after 72 hr, record the color of each tube in Table 15-2.
■ Use the interpretation chart to determine your susceptibility to tooth decay.

Bioluminescent Bacteria

Some marine bacteria can produce light under favorable conditions in the presence of oxygen. These bacteria are quite plentiful in sea water and are also **mutualistic symbionts** in the light organs of certain fish. The fish provide the bacteria with nutrients and oxygenation and then utilize the light produced by the bacteria for their own purposes—for example, communicating, attracting prey, and defending against predators.

The reaction requires free **oxygen,** the enzyme **luciferase,** and reduced **flavin mononucleotide** (FMN_{red}):

$$aldehyde + FMN_{red} + O_2$$
$$\downarrow luciferase$$
$$acid + FMN_{ox} + light$$

The bacteria must be actively growing to produce enough enzyme and reduced FMN to carry out the reaction in which aldehyde and FMN are oxidized by oxygen.

■ Fill a test tube two-thirds full with an active culture of luminescent bacteria such as *Photobacterium fischeri*.
■ Cork the tube, and take it into a dark closet or darkroom.
■ Shake the tube gently to mix it well.

What color of light is produced? _____

■ Hold the tube very still and watch the light fade away.

What part of the tube becomes dark most quickly?

_____

_____

Which component of the reaction is being used up so that the cells become dark? _____

_____

■ Test your answer by gently swirling the tube again.

Why does mixing the tube allow the cells to light up?

_____

_____

_____

Do the cells at the air interface ever become dark?

_____

    These bacteria are indicators of the amount of oxygen in the environment. There is very little oxygen in the part of the tube that is dark, and this is not enough to support bioluminescence.

How is oxygenation of bodies of water such as ponds and streams maintained so that fish and other aerobic organisms can survive?

_____

_____

_____

_____

KINGDOM PROTISTA

Phylum Mastigophora: *Euglena*

The members of this phylum have a long whiplike **flagellum** for locomotion. They are a diverse group and have other adaptations for locomotion as well, such as amoeboid motion. Some are autotrophic completely or in part.

You may have already examined an example of a unicellular green alga, *Chlamydomonas*, in Topic 2. Such cells may form colonies, and resemble plants with which they are classified. Photosynthetic protists, such as *Euglena*, are not as closely related to green plants; *Euglena* may be related to the simple ancestral flagellates that gave rise to both modern plants and animals. A diagram of *Euglena* is shown in Figure 15-5 at the end of this topic.

Euglena has structures in which starch is stored, a characteristic of green algae. Like *Chlamydomonas*, it has a photosensitive eyespot which allows it to perceive and respond to light. Also like *Chlamydomonas*, *Euglena* has chlorophylls *a* and *b* contained in chloroplasts, and a flagellum, but it does not have a thick cell wall composed of cellulose. Instead it has a tough elastic pellicle which incorporates the cell membrane. This allows *Euglena* to move by changing its shape and wriggling along the substrate in a unique form of locomotion called **euglenoid movement.** Furthermore, this organism is capable of absorptive nutrition just like a heterotroph. If it is deprived of light, but given a rich medium, it will survive. Its photosynthetic pigments will be lost, and it will not be able to resume autotrophy if the nutrients are removed. This conversion of an autotroph to its sister heterotroph can also be caused artificially by treatment with certain drugs.

Would you expect *Euglena* to show a positive or negative

response to light? _____

■ Cover a culture dish of *Euglena* with black paper or plastic, and make a small hole on one side.
■ Place the dish so that the hole is near a source of strong light such as a lamp or sunlit window.
■ Examine the dish at the end of the period, and observe whether the *Euglena* have migrated toward or away from the source of light.

What kind of response does *Euglena* show?

_____

■ Make a wet mount of a *Euglena* culture, add a drop of Protoslo, and observe under high power.
■ Try to locate the **eyespot** near the attachment of the flagellum.

What color is the eyespot? _____

■ Locate the **reservoir** (gullet) in which the base of the flagellum is attached.
■ Locate the **contractile vacuole** near the reservoir.
■ Identify the green **chloroplasts** which take up much of the space within the cell.
■ Locate the large **nucleus.**
■ Locate the **pellicle** which gives the cell support at the outer boundary of the cell. Note the location of the **cell membrane** within it.
■ Scan the slide for cells that may have become attached to the substrate. Observe their method of locomotion.

Does *Euglena* have a rigid cell wall? _____

■ Stain the slide with Lugol's solution, and allow a few minutes for the stain to penetrate.
■ Locate the **paramylum bodies,** which stain dark. Paramylum bodies contain paramylum, a storage form of glucose.
■ Study the **flagellum,** which should now be clearly visible. It has the typical "9 + 2" internal structure of eukaryotic flagella (not visible in a light microscope).

How is the base of the flagellum attached?

_____

■ Label these structures in Figure 15-5.

Protozoa in the Termite

There are five groups of protozoa:

1. **Phylum Mastigophora:** Movement by one or more whiplike flagella, like *Euglena.*
2. **Phylum Sarcodina:** Movement and feeding by pseudopods, like *Amoeba.*
3. **Phylum Ciliata:** Movement by many coordinated cilia, like *Paramecium.*
4. **Phylum Suctoria:** Movement by cilia in the young and feeding by tentacles in the adult, like *Paracineta* (see Figure 20-18 of your text).
5. **Phylum Sporozoa:** Nonmotile parasites, like *Plasmodium*, which cause malaria.

Examples of the first three types can be seen in any environment that favors the growth of protozoans, such as the internal organs or intestine of a higher animal. Sporozoans are generally parasites of mammals.

Termites need a healthy population of protists in their hindgut in order to survive on their normal diet of wood, which is very rich in cellulose. Certain flagellates produce the enzyme **cellulase**, which hydrolyzes the wood fragments ingested by the termite. The flagellates in turn release some of their nutrients into the gut of the termite. The termite absorbs and lives on these nutrients. The termite and the flagellate are mutualistic symbionts, because each derives benefit from the presence of the other. Young termites must become infected with the flagellates at an early age or they will starve to death. Because termites shed their hindgut and foregut lining and content at each molt, termites that are isolated after molting will not become reinfected and will also starve.

■ Place a termite in a drop of physiological saline (0.85%) on a slide, and press on the abdomen with the forceps to hold it in place.
■ Pull off the head with another forceps; most of the intestine will come out with the head. Separate the free part of the intestine from the head and abdomen.

■ Discard the rest of the termite, and tease apart the intestine with needles or insect pins.
■ Add a coverslip and observe the intestinal flora under low power in your microscope.

Which are the most prevalent: amoebalike organisms, flagellates, or ciliates?

_____

■ Add a drop of Protoslo and/or a drop of methylene blue stain and observe under high power.

Some of the common symbionts of termites are shown in Figure 15-2. Try to identify one or more of them in your slide.

Phylum Chrysophyta: Diatoms

Most members of this phylum are **diatoms,** which make up the bulk of the phytoplankton in the sea and in fresh water. Some diatoms occur in soil as well. These tiny autotrophs contain chlorophylls _a_ and _c_, and their accessory photosynthetic pigment, fucoxanthin, gives them a greenish-brown or golden brown color. Some forms have a gliding motion, but most are nonmotile. Other related organisms may have flagella. Diatoms store food as the polysaccharide leucosin or as oil.

The intricate skeletons of these organisms are impregnated with silica and manganese and often take the form of two overlapping **valves** that fit together like a round, flat box and its cover. Because the skeletons are highly resistant to decomposition, they accumulate in huge quantities and produce beds of **diatomaceous earth.** This material is an excellent abrasive and is widely used in industrial products such as fine polishes and toothpaste. A few of these delicate microorganisms are shown in Figure 15-3.

■ Examine a wet mount or prepared slide of diatoms.
■ If you are observing living cells, identify a cell that is pointed at either end.

Does the cell show any movement? _____

■ Make a wet mount of diatomaceous earth and examine it for round, pillbox-shaped diatoms. Such diatoms are marine and therefore found only in the ocean.

Was your sample of diatomaceous earth of marine origin? _____

Phylum Pyrrophyta: Dinoflagellates

This phylum contains the **dinoflagellates,** which are primitive autotrophs and most of which contain chlorophylls _a_ and _c_ for photosynthesis. Their accessory photosynthetic pigments often give dinoflagellates a red color. When conditions favor their reproduction, dinoflagellates "bloom" in huge numbers causing a **red tide.** The chromosomes contain DNA but not protein, and the division of the nucleus during reproduction of the cell is a bizarre intermediate between prokaryotic and eukaryotic nuclear division. Most have two flagella, and some have distinctively formed cellulose armor covering the cell membrane. Figure 15-4 illustrates some dinoflagellates.

One species of _Gonyaulax_ produces a toxin that kills fish and mussels that ingest it during a red tide. Other species are bioluminescent and cause the "sparks" in sea water at night during the hot summer months. _Noctiluca,_ as its name (= night light) implies, also causes flashes of bioluminescence at night. Each cell produces repeated bursts of light in response to the agitation of wave action or the movements of a nighttime swimmer.

■ Examine a prepared slide of some dinoflagellates in your microscope.

How big are the organisms?

_____ micrometers

When you are finished with your work, return the prepared slides, clean up your work place, and store your microscope properly.

Figure 15-2.   Termite gut flagellates. These symbionts must digest the cellulose that the termite ingests or it will starve. A few typical types are shown, including several species of _Trichonympha_. The large pear-shaped individual is _T. collaris_, the diamond-shaped species is _T. agilis_, and the round type is _T. sphaerica_.

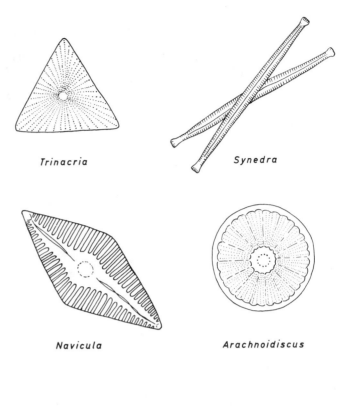

Figure 15-3. Diatoms. These members of Phylum Chrysophyta are photosynthetic and are the most important group of marine phytoplankton.

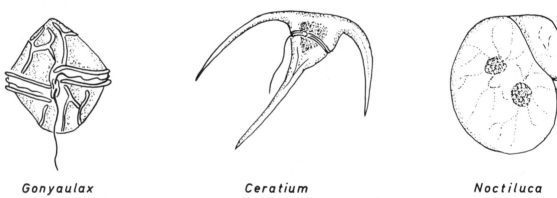

Figure 15-4. Dinoflagellates. These motile autotrophs belong to Phylum Pyrrophyta and may be toxic to fish and shellfish.

EXPLORING FURTHER

Barnes, R. D. *Invertebrate Zoology,* 4th ed. Philadelphia: W. B. Saunders, 1980.

Buchsbaum, R. *Animals without Backbones.* 2nd rev ed. Chicago: University of Chicago Press, 1975.

Jahn, T., and F. Jahn. *How to Know the Protozoa.* 2nd ed. Dubuque, Iowa.: W. C. Brown, 1979.

Kudo, R. *Protozoology,* 5th ed. Springfield, Ill.: Charles C. Thomas, 1977.

Nester, E. W. *et al. Microbiology.* 3rd ed. Philadelphia: W. B. Saunders, 1983.

Stanier, R. Y., E. A. Adelberg, and J. L. Ingraham. *The Microbial World.* 4th ed. Englewood Cliffs, N.J.: Prentice-Hall, 1976.

Journal Articles

The September 1981 issue of *Scientific American* is devoted to the topic of Microbiology.

Abraham, E. P. "The beta-lactam antibiotics." *Scientific American,* 76, June 1981.

Adler, J. "The sensing of chemicals by bacteria." *Scientific American,* April 1976 (#1337).

Barghoon, Elso S. "The oldest fossils." *Scientific American,* May 1971 (#895).

Berg, H. "How bacteria swim." *Scientific American,* August 1975 (no offprint).

Braude, A. I. "Bacterial endotoxins." *Scientific American,* March 1964 (no offprint).

Brill, Winston J. "Biological nitrogen fixation." *Scientific American,* March 1977 (#922).

Costerton, J. W., G. G. Geesey, and K.-J. Cheng. "How bacteria stick." *Scientific American,* January 1978 (#1379).

Fraser, David W. and Joseph E. McDade. "Legionellosis." *Scientific American,* October 1979 (#1447).

Jannasch, Holger W. and Carl O. Wirsen. "Microbial life in the deep sea." *Scientific American,* June 1977 (#926).

Mandel, I. D. "Dental caries." *American Scientist* 67:680, 1979.

McCosker, John E. "Flashlight fishes." *Scientific American,* March 1977 (#693).

Prestwich, Glenn D. "The chemical defenses of termites." *Scientific American,* 78, August 1983.

Schopf, J. William. "The evolution of the earliest cells." *Scientific American,* September 1978 (#1402).

Vidal, Gonzalo. "The oldest eukaryotic cells." *Scientific American,* 48-57, February 1984.

Walsby, A. E. "The gas vacuoles of blue-green algae." *Scientific American,* August 1977 (#1367).

Woese, Carl R. "Archaebacteria." *Scientific American,* 98, June 1981.

Student Name _____ **Date** _____

TABLE 15-1. CULTURES OF BACTERIAL SAMPLES

Nutrient Agar	Source of Inoculum	Amount of Growth or Number of Colonies
Plate 1	AIR	
Plate 2	COUGH	
Plate 3	SUPPRESSED COUGH	

TABLE 15-2. CULTURES OF ORAL BACTERIA

A. DATA

Tube	Source of Inoculum	Color after 24 hr*	Color after 48 hr*	Color after 72 hr*
1	Before brushing			
2	After brushing			
3	Sterile control			

*The color is considered "green" if there is no change or only slight change and green is dominant. The color is considered "yellow" if green is no longer dominant.

B. INTERPRETATION

Color after 24 hr	48 hr	72 hr	Susceptibility to Caries
Yellow			Marked
Green	Yellow		Moderate
Green	Green	Yellow	Slight
Green	Green	Green	Very low

How likely is it that your oral flora will make your teeth susceptible to decay? _____

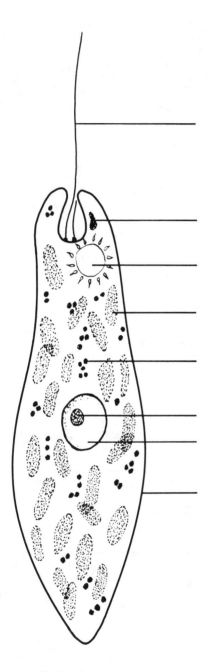

Figure 15-5. *Euglena.* Label the indicated structures.

Kingdom Fungi and the Simpler Plants

OBJECTIVES

When you have completed this topic, you should be able to:
1. List the plantlike characteristics of fungi.
2. List the characteristics that set fungi apart from the members of the plant kingdom.
3. Name three classes of true fungi (Eumycophyta) and an example from each class.
4. Describe the two main types of nutrition found in the fungi.
5. List the three divisions of algae, and give the characteristics of each division.
6. Define alternation of generations in plants, and give an example in which the sporophyte is dominant, another in which the gametophyte is dominant, and one in which neither the sporophyte nor the gametophyte is dominant.
7. Name the processes giving rise to plant spores, plant gametes, and plant zygotes.
8. Define: dikaryon, mycelium, coenocyte, hyphae, fruiting body, gill, basidium, ascus, zygospore, conidia, sporangium.
9. Define: holdfast, stipe, blade, air bladder, zoospore, embryophyte, antheridium, archegonium.
10. Describe the adaptations of a moss that allow it to live on land.
11. List the problems of terrestrial life that bryophytes have not solved.
12. State some commercially important uses of fungi, algae, and mosses.

KEY TOPICS

Alternation of generations, zygomycetes, ascomycetes, basidiomycetes, slime molds, lichens, red algae, brown algae, green algae, mosses.

INTRODUCTION

Algae and fungi each have a relatively simple body known as a **thallus.** Their cells show little differentiation, and the egg cells are not protected by a layer of sterile jacket cells. The algae are all photosynthetic and the fungi are heterotrophs.

Bryophytes, the group to which mosses belong, are non-vascular terrestrial plants that are not much different from the more complex algae. Their important distinguishing feature is that the egg cells are enclosed in a layer of sterile jacket cells. Unlike more complex plants, they lack true vascular tissue.

Most of these organisms are multicellular, but unicellular stages are involved in their life histories. A generalized life history for plants includes both stages (Figure 16-1). The multicellular stage may be haploid or diploid (N or 2N). Sometimes a multicellular haploid stage is followed by a multilcellular diploid stage, and then by multicellular haploid, and so on. In this case, the plant is said to show **alternation of generations:** The haploid and diploid stages alternate with each other.

In plants and fungi, unlike in animals, the cells produced by meiosis are **spores.** If the haploid organism that grows from the germinating spore produces gametes, the gametes arise by differentiation, not by meiosis. (The cells are *already* haploid.) Fusion of haploid cells or nuclei produces the diploid stage of the next generation. In

Figure 16-1. Generalized life history. Plant life histories may include one or both multicellular stages.

algae and higher plants, the diploid plant that produces spores is called the **sporophyte** ("spore plant"), and the haploid plant that produces gametes is called the **gametophyte** ("gamete plant").

THE FUNGI (KINGDOM FUNGI)

Fungi are heterotrophic organisms that have many plantlike features. They are nonmotile and have rigid cell walls that may contain cellulose. Because they can neither carry out photosynthesis nor ingest food, they must obtain nutrients by **absorption** through their cell membranes. If they feed on living cytoplasm, they are **parasites,** and if they feed on dead organisms or detritus, they are **saprobes.** Such fungi, the decomposers, are vital in recycling the dead bodies of organisms so that the nutrients in them can be used by living plants and animals.

Fungi prefer a dark, moist habitat. Because billions of hardy fungal spores permeate the environment, fungi will begin to grow wherever and whenever suitable organic material becomes available.

The true fungi are classified as the **Division Eumycophyta.** You will study examples of true fungi from three of the five classes: the zygomycetes, ascomycetes, and basidiomycetes.

Rhizopus (Class Zygomycetes)

The black bread mold *Rhizopus nigricans* forms a mat, or **mycelium,** of threadlike **hyphae.** The nuclei are haploid, and the fungus lives in a terrestrial environment.

■ Obtain a Petri dish containing an asexually reproducing mycelium of *Rhizopus.*
■ Examine the mold under the dissecting microscope without opening the dish.
■ Note the tiny black spheres of the **sporangia** that grow at the ends of some erect hyphae. The sporangia release spores.

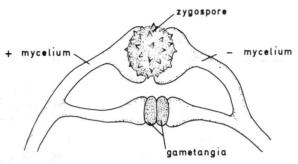

Figure 16-2. Sexual reproduction in *Rhizopus.* The diploid zygospore will undergo meiosis to produce a new haploid mycelium.

■ Make a wet mount of mycelium with sporangia, and examine it in the compound microscope.
■ Note the cluster of rootlike hyphae at the base of the hypha bearing the sporangium. These hyphae anchor the hypha and are called **rhizoids.**
■ Note the horizontally growing hyphae called **stolons.**

A fungus without cross walls is said to form a **coenocyte,** in which all of the nuclei are in a common cytoplasm. If there are cross walls, the fungus is **septate.**

Is the mycelium of *Rhizopus* coenocytic or septate?

The haploid spores released by the sporangia are formed by mitosis, and their dispersal is a form of asexual reproduction. The spores will give rise to new haploid mycelia.

■ Obtain another culture of *Rhizopus* in which two mating types (+ and −) of mycelia have fused and undergone sexual reproduction.
■ Note the dark line in the mycelium where the + and − mating types fused. The dark color is due to the formation of **zygospores.**
■ Make a wet mount of a bit of mycelium from the black region, or view a prepared slide, and look for cross bridges between the hyphae.
■ Examine such a cross bridge for the presence of a dark sphere, the **zygospore.**

When the two types of mycelia come into contact, the bridge is formed and the cell wall breaks down so that the cytoplasms of the two sides are in contact. A nucleus from each side moves into the bridge, and the haploid nuclei fuse to form a diploid nucleus. The zygote nucleus divides several times, and then undergoes meiosis to form a sporangium containing haploid spores. These zygospores, unlike the spores produced asexually, will be genetically different from either parent. Sexual reproduction in *Rhizopus* is shown in Figure 16-2.

Yeast (Class Ascomycetes)

A yeast such as brewer's yeast (*Saccharomyces cerevisiae*) is a unicellular ascomycete. It has an unusual method of reproducing asexually by budding off. It also reproduces sexually by forming a saclike **ascus** containing spores produced by meiosis. The life history of a yeast is shown in Figure 9-1.

Dimorphic fungi can grow in a yeastlike form under favorable environmental conditions, such as in sugary solutions. At other times they grow as a mycelium.

■ Make a wet mount of a drop of actively growing yeast culture, and observe the cells in the microscope under high power.
■ Note the cells that are producing smaller buds or short chains of buds.

Yeasts are important in the baking and brewing industries and are used to produce important industrial chemicals.

What by-product of yeast fermentation is important in baking? _____

What by-product is important in brewing?

_____

Which of these by-products is produced in both aerobic and anaerobic respiration? _____

Cup Fungi (Class Ascomycetes)

Cup fungi such as *Peziza* (and also the mushrooms and their relatives) are the fungi with which we are the most familiar because they are the most conspicuous. The large part of the fungus that we see is formed of masses of hyphae fused together in the **fruiting body** or **ascocarp.** Each fruiting body is supported by an underground mycelium that is much larger than itself. Part of the fruiting body is called a **dikaryon** (dikaryon means "two nuclei") because each of its cells has two haploid nuclei. The cells in this part are different from diploid cells and are designated N + N rather than 2N. During sexual reproduction, some of the cells of the fruiting body undergo nuclear fusion to produce true diploid (2N) nuclei. Meiosis, which follows, produces haploid (N) **ascospores.** The large size of the fruiting body helps disperse the spores. The spores germinate to produce mycelia, and different mating types (+ and −) of mycelia interact to form a new dikaryon and fruiting body.

■ Obtain and examine a preserved specimen of a cup fungus such as *Peziza.* The cup shape of the fruiting body allows rain to collect and splash around inside where the ascospores are produced and aids in splashing out the ascospores.
■ Examine a cross section of a cup fungus under high power.
■ Locate an **ascus.**

How many spores does an individual ascus contain?

_____

Cup fungi can also reproduce asexually by forming chains of spores called **conidia** at the tips of the hyphae. These tiny, airborne spores are the result of mitosis rather than meiosis. They pervade the entire biosphere, and germinate at every opportunity.

Ascomycetes are biologically interesting because some of them have become obligate symbionts with algae to form **lichens.** (Lichens will be considered later in this exercise.) Ascomycetes such as morels and truffles are gourmet delicacies, and the mold *Penicillium* is the source of the antibiotic penicillin. Other ascomycetes such as smuts and rusts are serious agricultural pests.

Mushroom (Class Basidiomycetes)

The common edible mushroom (*Agaricus campestris*) is the fruiting body or **basidiocarp** of a basidiomycete. As in the cup fungus, it is formed by the fusion of masses of hyphae. In sexual reproduction, underground mycelia of two mating types fuse and form a mycelium with two nuclei per cell. This mycelium is an N + N dikaryon. As in the ascomycetes, the mycelia are septate.

■ Obtain a common mushroom, and make a cross section of it with a razor blade.
■ Note the **stalk** and the **cap** that bears the **gills** on its undersurface.
■ Examine the gills with the dissecting microscope.

The reproductive cells, the **basidia,** are located on the surface of the gills. Each basidium undergoes nuclear fusion to form a fused nucleus which immediately enters meiosis. The haploid nuclei form **basidiospores,** which are released from the surface of the gills. Each spore will germinate to form a new mycelium. Sexual reproduction in basidiomycetes is described in Figure 16-3.

■ Make a wet mount of a small piece of gill, or examine a prepared slide through the cap of a mature mushroom such as *Coprinus.*
■ Note the small, dark basidiospores on the edges of the gills. Each basidium produces four basidiospores.

Which cells in the life history of a basidiomycete can undergo meiosis? _____

What is the difference between a diploid organism and a dikaryon?

_____

_____

Slime Molds (Division Myxomycophyta)

Slime molds are grouped separately as the myxomycetes because they have more animal-like features than the other fungi. The **cellular slime molds (Class Acrasiomycetes)** have amoeboid cells that can aggregate to form fruiting bodies. Each fruiting body produces spores that disperse and germinate into more amoebae. Reproduction in *Dictyostelium* is shown in Figure 21-18 in your text.

■ Examine the demonstration culture of a cellular slime mold such as *Dictyostelium* in the dissecting microscope.
■ Locate a sluglike **pseudoplasmodium** (grex), an aggregate of many amoebae that creeps over the agar leaving a slimy trail.
■ Locate a **fruiting body** (sorocarp), which is supported by a thin stalk. When mature, it will burst to release the spores.

Acellular slime molds (Class Myxomycetes) have the form of a gigantic coenocyte called a **plasmodium** in which hundreds of nuclei share a common cytoplasm.

■ Obtain a Petri dish containing a culture of an acellular slime mold such as *Physarum,* and place it on the stage of your compound microscope.
■ Examine the plasmodium under low power (100×).
■ Note the "veins" of streaming cytoplasm with many nuclei.

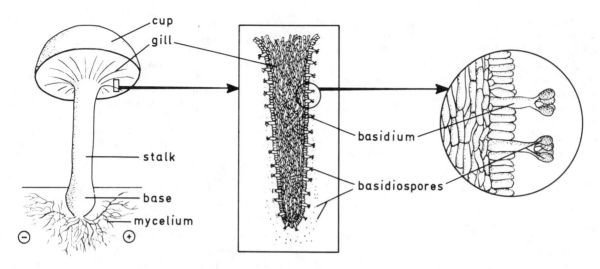

Figure 16-3. Basidiomycete reproduction. The mushroom is the fruiting body formed when + and − mycelia meet and fuse.

If conditions become unfavorable, the plasmodium will dry up and turn into a resting stage known as a **sclerotium.** Pieces of dried sclerotium can be used to start new cultures of a plasmodium. *Physarum* can also reproduce by sporangia that form on its surface and contain haploid spores. Two types of haploid cells (amoebae and swarm cells) emerge from the spores and fuse to produce new plasmodia.

Lichens (Division Mycophycophyta)

These symbiotic organisms are usually classified by the type of fungus that they contain. The photosynthetic algal component may be a cyanobacterium or a green alga. The hyphae of the fungus protect and support the alga, and the photosynthetic ability of the alga provides nourishment, so the lichen can flourish where neither the fungus nor the alga could live by itself. This relationship would be an example of **mutualism.** In some cases the fungus benefits more, so that the relationship is **commensalism** or even controlled **parasitism** by the fungus. Lichens are pioneers and can colonize harsh and unfavorable environments. They contribute to the breakdown of rocks in the early stages of soil formation.

There are three basic types of lichens. **Foliose** lichens have a leaflike cell body and are the type most commonly seen. **Crustose** lichens live as a very thin coating that is tightly bound to its substrate. **Fruticose** lichens have a fruiting body produced by the ascomycete fungus that is one of the symbiotic partners. The internal structure of lichens is shown in Figure 16-4.

■ Examine the specimens of crustose, foliose, and fruticose lichens on demonstration.
■ Note that the color of lichens is highly variable.
■ Examine a prepared slide showing a lichen in cross section. Alternatively, with your instructor's permission, tease apart a small bit of lichen, make a wet mount, and examine it in the compound microscope.
■ Note the hyphae and the algal cells.

Lichens often reproduce by **fragmentation,** in which a piece of the organism simply breaks off and is passively moved to a new location, where it grows into another lichen. Lichens are important in colonizing harsh environments in which other organisms cannot survive, and they are widespread in the tundra region where they are an important source of food for herbivores. One such example is reindeer "moss."

THE SIMPLER PLANTS (KINGDOM PLANTAE)

The photosynthetic autotrophs in Kingdom Plantae usually contain chlorophylls *a* and *b*, and the carotenoids carotene and xanthophyll organized within chloroplasts. They have cellulose cell walls and usually store food as starch. They are typically multicellular or closely related to multicellular forms.

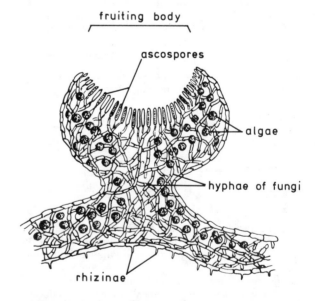

Figure 16-4. Lichen in cross section. This lichen shows the fruiting body of its ascomycete fungus. Fungi from the germinated spores may pick up algal symbionts by chance. The lichen may also reproduce by fragmentation.

Green Algae (Division Chlorophyta)

Green algae contain unicellular and multicellular organisms and are thought to be more closely related to higher plants than the other algae. They are good candidates for possible ancestors of the more complex plants because of the similarity of their cells and the nature of their life cycles. They contain chlorophylls *a* and *b*, carotene, and xanthophyll in their chloroplasts. Many green algae are motile and the more complex forms show body differentiation and plantlike patterns of growth.

Among the **motile colonial** green algae, some of the unicellular and multicellular forms are very closely related. For example, the individual cells of *Gonium* or *Pandorina* are almost identical to those of the unicellular alga *Chlamydomonas*. These organisms may have arisen from unicellular ancestors whose cells failed to separate after mitosis. *Gonium* in turn may have given rise to more elaborate colonies such as that of *Volvox*, in which there are hundreds of cells and some division of labor.

■ Make a wet mount of *Chlamydomonas*, and view it under high power in your compound microscope.

■ Note the two **flagella,** the **chloroplast,** and the spot of red pigment (eye spot). The chloroplast contains a **pyrenoid,** where it stores starch.

How is *Chlamydomonas* different from *Euglena*? (*Euglena* is described in Topic 15 and illustrated in Figure 15-5.)

_____

_____

In asexual reproduction, *Chlamydomonas* produces four or more progeny per parent by mitotic division. During sexual reproduction (isogamy) each parent cell produces many small gametes, again by mitosis. Gametes of equal size from two mating types fuse to form a diploid zygote. The zygote may form a dormant **zygospore,** which can survive the harsh conditions that brought about sexual reproduction. Eventually the zygospore will undergo meiosis to produce spores without going through a multicellular diploid stage. These **meiospores** are motile and become independent cells of the next vegetative generation. The zygote is thus the only diploid stage in this life history.

■ Make a wet mount of *Pandorina* and examine it under low power.

How many cells are there, on the average, in a colony?

_____

Do the cells of *Pandorina* appear any different from

those of *Chlamydomonas?* _____

The gametes produced by *Pandorina* in sexual reproduction are flagellated but are different in size (heterogamy).

Volvox is a colony of hundreds of haploid algal cells.

■ Place a drop of *Volvox* culture on a slide without adding a coverslip, and view it under your dissecting microscope.

What structures propel the colony about?

_____

■ Add a coverslip and view the immobilized colony under high power in your compound microscope.

■ Note the spacing of the cells. They are connected by thin threads of cytoplasm that allow the swimming movements of the colony to be coordinated.

Refer to the life history of *Volvox*, which is illustrated in Figure 16-5.

Volvox produces egg and sperm cells, and the flagellated sperm must swim to the nonmotile egg (oogamy). The diploid zygote undergoes meiosis to form a new haploid colony. In asexual reproduction, vegetative cells are released inside the parent colony where they develop into new colonies. The progeny are released when the old colony breaks open.

■ Locate a colony of *Volvox* that contains small colonies produced by vegetative reproduction.

The **filamentous** algae also have unicellular and multicellular forms but they are usually nonmotile. An example is *Ulothrix*, which has a life history similar to

Figure 16-5. The life history of *Volvox*. The zygote is the only diploid stage of this colonial green alga.

that of *Chlamydomonas* except that it has a multicellular haploid stage.

■ Make a wet mount of living *Ulothrix*, or examine a prepared slide of this organism with your compound microscope.

What is the shape of the individual cells?

_____

Are all of the cells alike? _____

■ Look for the **holdfast** at one end of the filament. (It may be broken off.)

What is the shape of the single chloroplast?

_____

Do you see storage organs (pyrenoids)?

_____

   Ulothrix can reproduce asexually by forming flagellated **zoospores.** It can also form tiny gametes that are smaller than the zoospores and fuse to form zygospores. The zygospores undergo meiosis to form meiospores, each of which will grow into a new filament.
   Another green alga, *Ulva*, has a multicellular diploid stage that is identical in appearance to its multicellular haploid stage. It is the simplest of the higher algae. Its history follows the pattern shown in Figure 16-1.

■ Examine a specimen of *Ulva*, or sea lettuce.

What is the form of the body?

_____

Is there a stalk? _____

Into which stage do the motile spores grow?

_____

Which stage develops from the zygote?

_____

Brown Algae
(Division Phaeophyta)

These algae contain chlorophylls *a* and *c* and the carotenoid **fucoxanthin,** and they may be related to the unicellular diatoms. All of the forms are multicellular, and they are the largest and most complex of the algae.

■ Examine the specimen of a brown alga such as *Fucus* on demonstration.
■ Locate the **holdfast,** the **stipe** (stalk), and the **blade** ("leaf").

Does your specimen contain **air bladders** filled with gas? _____

■ Make a cut across one of the blades to see its internal structure.

Are all parts of the blade photosynthetic?

_____

   In algae of substantial size, the air bladders float the photosynthetic blade near the surface where it can obtain more light. The outer surface of the blade is covered by a gelatinous coating to prevent it from drying out when it becomes exposed to air.

■ Examine the tips of the blades for swollen sacs called **receptacles;** eggs and sperm are produced within the receptacles.

   The life history of *Fucus* is similar to the life cycle of animals. The plant itself is diploid, and cells within the receptacles undergo meiosis to produce eggs and flagellated sperm, thereby skipping the multicellular haploid stage. The gametes fuse to form zygotes, and then each zygote grows into a new diploid alga.
   The giant brown algae, the kelps, are the source of alginate, a thickening agent important in making ice cream, toothpaste, and many other products. Brown algae have also been used for fertilizer and livestock feed.

Red Algae
(Division Rhodophyta)

These photosynthetic plants may be more closely related to the cyanobacteria than are the other plant divisions. The plant body is usually filamentous or leaflike, and it is attached to the surface by a holdfast. Red algae contain only chlorophyll *a* and the accessory pigments **phycocyanin** and **phycoerythrin** (a red pigment unique to red algae and cyanobacteria). There is no flagellated form in the life history, and these algae are usually found in deep marine locations.

■ Examine the specimen of red alga, such as *Chondrus*, on demonstration.

What is the body form of the demonstration alga?

_____

The life history of a red alga includes a dominant haploid stage; sometimes a diploid zygote develops into a multicellular diploid stage as well.
   Commercially important substances such as carrageenan and agar are obtained from species of red algae, and these algae may be important in building up and maintaining the integrity of coral reefs. Red algae can live at greater depths than any other algae.

MOSSES (SUBKINGDOM EMBRYONTA, DIVISION BRYOPHYTA, CLASS MUSCI)

Bryophytes (mosses and liverworts) are different from the other land plants in that they lack vascular tissue. Because true roots, stems, and leaves must have vascular tissue, the organs of a moss are described as "rootlilke," "stemlike," and "leaflike." As a result, mosses are limited in several important ways. They cannot grow large in size because they have no strong supporting tissue to keep their bodies erect. They must live in damp places because their rootlike rhizoids cannot penetrate deep into the soil to extract the moisture they need. Finally, their photosynthetic parts above ground and the nonphotosynthetic parts below ground must be close together because there is no vascular tissue for the transport of nutrients and minerals.
   The life cycle shows alternation of generations with the **gametophyte** stage dominant. Fertilization can occur only in a moist environment because the sperm must swim to the egg. The feature that bryophytes share with other land plants is an important adaptation for life on

land: The zygote is held within the female reproductive organ where it is surrounded by a layer of sterile jacket cells. These cells protect the embryo while it starts to develop into a new sporophyte within the female reproductive organ. All of the land plants that reproduce in this way are included in **Subkingdom Embryonta.**

■ Obtain a single moss plant (gametophyte), and examine it under the dissecting microscope.
■ Note the filamentous **protonema** from which the skin grows. It is similar to a filamentous green algae.
■ Note the "**stem**," "**leaves**," and **rhizoids.**

Is any part of the moss plant nonphotosynthetic? If so, which part?

_____

_____

What are the functions of the rhizoids?

_____

_____

_____

■ Make a wet mount of a "leaf."

Are there guard cells or stomata? _____

■ Use a razor blade to make a very thin section of the "leaf" or obtain a prepared slide and view it in the compound microscope.

Do you see xylem, phloem, or large air spaces in the "leaf"? If so, which ones?

_____

Is there a cuticle? _____

During reproduction the flagellated sperm produced in the **antheridium** of the male moss plant (gametophyte) swims to the female gametophyte and fertilizes the egg held within the **archegonium.** The zygote grows into a sporophyte and remains attached at the tip of the female plant. (See Figure 16-6 at the end of this topic.) Usually the sporophyte is nonphotosynthetic and obtains its nutrition from the female gametophyte. The spores are formed in a capsule on the end of a long stalk and are released from as high up as the plant can possibly reach (3-4 cm).

Why should the spores be released as high as possible?

_____

_____

_____

■ Obtain a moss plant that has a sporophyte growing on it, if living material is available. If not, obtain a prepared slide of a moss sporophyte.
■ Note the long **stalk** and the **capsule.**

Is either part of the sporophyte photosynthetic?

_____

■ Mount the capsule in a drop of water on a slide, and remove the tip of it (calyptra) with teasing needles. Observe in the dissecting microscope.
■ Try to look into the capsule. You will see a circle of toothlike projections that help disperse the spores.
■ Tease apart the capsule to locate the spores.

Are the spores haploid or diploid? _____

Is the sporophyte haploid or diploid?

_____

What process gave rise to the spores?

_____

■ Label the location of meiosis in the female moss plant shown in Figure 16-6. Circle the names of all haploid parts shown in the figure.

The spore germinates into a threadlike **protonema,** which eventually forms the buds of the new gametophyte.

Mosses cope with the dryness of land by living in a damp environment and retaining as much water as possible. The mat of many moss plants crowded close together acts like a sponge to hold water and cut down evaporation. Some mosses even have special cells that are adapted to absorb water when it is available. Sphagnum moss, for example, has large, reinforced cells with pores in their cell walls for taking up water.

■ Obtain a 100-mL beaker and a weighed 1- to 5-g sample of dry sphagnum moss (note exact weight). Your instructor may ask you to weigh your own sample.

WEIGHT: _____

■ Fill the beaker about two-thirds full with water, and make a mark at the surface of the water with a wax pencil.
■ Immerse the moss in the beaker, and allow it to soak up as much water as possible.
■ Remove the moss with a forceps.
■ Fill a 100-mL graduated cylinder with water to exactly the 100-mL mark, and add water from it to your beaker until the water level again reaches the pencil mark.
■ Note how much water was needed to refill the beaker. This amount is equivalent to the amount removed by the moss.

VOLUME: _____

■ Calculate how many times its weight of water the moss can absorb:

$$\text{ABSORPTION} = \frac{\text{mL (g) of water removed}}{\text{dry weight of moss(g)}} = _____$$

Sphagnum moss is widely used by commercial greenhouses and home gardeners to hold moisture around the roots of plants, especially during shipping.

Although plant life histories may at first seem very confusing, they must all conform to the general pattern given in Figure 16-1. Meiosis always takes place in a diploid cell (or dipoloid nucleus, as in fungi) and must produce haploid cells, which are almost always spores. It may be helpful to learn an example of each type of life cycle:

1. Neither multicellular haploid nor multicellular diploid stage present:

_____

2. Multicellular haploid stage present:

_____

3. Both multicellular haploid and multicellular diploid stages present:

_____

4. Multicellular diploid stage present:

_____

Which type of life cycle corresponds to that of humans
and other animals? _____

Which stage is present in *Ulva* or a moss but is absent in
a brown alga such as *Fucus*?

_____

    Return all demonstration materials and store your
microscopes properly before leaving the laboratory.

EXPLORING FURTHER

Alexander, M. *Microbial Ecology.* New York: John Wiley
and Sons, 1971.

Alexopoulos, C. J., and H. C. Bold. *Algae and Fungi.*
New York: Macmillan, 1967.

Bold, H. C., C. J. Alexopoulos, and T. Delevorya. *Morphology of Plants and Fungi.* 4th ed. New York:
Harper and Row, 1980.

Bold, H. C., and M. J. Wynne. *Introduction to the Algae: Structure and Reproduction.* Englewood Cliffs,
N.J.: Prentice-Hall, 1978.

Dawson, E. Y. *Marine Botany: An Introduction.* New
York: Holt, Rinehart and Winston, 1966.

Prescott, G. W. *How to Know the Freshwater Algae.* 3rd
ed. Dubuque, Iowa: W. C. Brown, 1978.

Smith, Alexander H., and Nancy Weber. *The Mushroom
Hunter's Field Guide.* Ann Arbor: University of
Michigan Press, 1980.

Journal Articles

Abraham, E. P. "The beta-lactam antibiotics," *Scientific
American*, 76, June 1981.

Bonner, J. T. "How slime molds communicate." *Scientific
American*, August 1963 (#164).

Gibor, A. "Acetabularia: A useful giant cell." *Scientific
American*, November 1966 (#1057).

Lamb, I. M. "Lichens." *Scientific American*, October
1959 (#111).

Litten, W. "The most poisonous mushrooms." *Scientific
American*, March 1975.

Matossian, Mary K. "Ergot and the Salem Witchcraft Af-
fair." *American Scientist* 70(4), 358-365, July 1982.

Niederhauser, J. S., and W. C. Cobb. "The late blight of
potatoes." *Scientific American*, May 1959 (#109).

Preston, R. D. "Plants without cellulose." *Scientific
American*, June 1968 (#1110).

Strobel, Gary A., and Gerald N. Lanier. "Dutch elm disease." *Scientific American*, 56, August 1981.

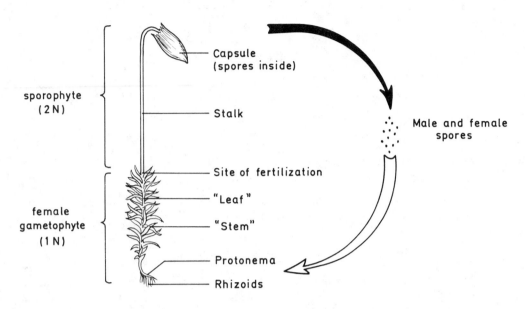

Figure 16-6. Sexual reproduction in a moss. The diploid sporophyte is parasitic on the haploid female gametophyte.

Vascular Plants: Division Tracheophyta

OBJECTIVES

When you have completed this topic, you should be able to:
1. Define tracheophyte and list the characteristics of these plants that link them to the green algae.
2. Describe the problems faced by plants that moved onto the land.
3. Describe adaptations of land plants to each problem listed in Objective 2.
4. Describe the life history of club mosses, horsetails, and ferns.
5. Compare a club moss and a bryophyte with respect to structure and life history.
6. Compare horsetails and ferns with respect to the following features: size of presently living species, stem, leaves, roots, vegetative propagation, type of gametophyte, and type of sporangium.
7. Given a plant specimen or description, place it correctly in one of these groups: Lycopsida, Equisetophyta, Filicophyta, Gymnospermopsida or Angiospermopsida.
8. Describe the gametophyte of a fern and of a conifer.
9. Give some reasons why gymnosperms persisted, even though angiosperms became dominant.

KEY TOPICS

Club mosses, horsetails, ferns, gymnosperms, angiosperms.

INTRODUCTION

Although some of the simpler plants can eke out a living on land, their relatively undifferentiated bodies never allowed them to develop adaptations for a truly terrestrial life. Most members of the plant groups that you will be studying in this exercise are well adapted to living exclusively on land. They have been able to cope in some fashion with the resulting problems and have taken advantage of the benefits.

Land plants are thought to have arisen from the green algae. Both groups contain chlorophylls *a* and *b*, carotenoids, and they usually store their food reserves in the form of starch. An alga that developed some kind of waterproofing and rootlike structures to draw water up from the soil would have been able to live out of water on the shore. Such a plant may have given rise eventually to the more highly adapted land plants. All such plants have evolved with an important feature in common: The zygote is held within the female reproductive organ where it is surrounded by a protective layer of ster-

ile jacket cells. Mosses and all of the higher plants have this feature during reproduction and are grouped in the **Subkingdom Embryonta.**

All of these plants show alternation of generations. Sometimes there is a large, photosynthetic gametophyte and a tiny sporophyte. In other cases the sporophyte is a large, photosynthetic plant that also propagates the species through dispersal of spores or seeds. In many cases reproduction still involves a flagellated sperm that must swim to the egg through a film of water. Such plants are restricted to a moist environment for fertilization to occur.

Vascular plants belong to the **Division Tracheophyta** and have true **vascular tissue.** This system of **xylem** and **phloem** conducts water, minerals and the products of photosynthesis from one part of the plant to another. The organs of the plant are considered **true roots** and **true leaves** because they contain vascular tissue. The presence of vascular tissue had tremendous implications for the evolution of this group: The plant could grow tall and the root system could become extensive. Plants lacking vascular tissue, such as bryophytes, are small in size, because there is no way for water to move from deep in the soil to the leaves or for the leaves to nourish distant roots. The photosynthetic and nonphotosynthetic parts of a nonvascular plant must be quite close together.

CLUB MOSSES
(CLASS LYCOPSIDA)

Club mosses and horsetails are fern allies because all these plants have a similar life cycle. They have a large sporophyte with true vascular tissue, and the spores grow into tiny gametophytes that are independent of the parent sporophyte. There is a flagellated sperm, and the zygote grows into a new sporophyte. Although present-day ferns and their allies do not have woody tissue, in former times they did and reached the proportion of trees. Some species of tree ferns have survived to the present.

■ Examine a living or preserved club moss such as *Lycopodium,* and note the leaves, stems, and roots.

What is the form of the leaf?

_____

What is the value of this adaptation?

_____

■ Cut through the tip of one of the branchlets.

Is the interior hollow or solid? _____

The leaf remains green through the winter, so it is **evergreen,** as are some ferns, most gymnosperms, and some angiosperms. Possession of evergreen leaves is therefore not a good characteristic for classifying plants.

The club moss reproduces vegetatively by its underground stem, its **rhizome,** which sends up shoots to form new photosynthetic stems.

■ Examine the rhizome of your specimen.

Does it have leaves? _____

During sexual reproduction cones called **strobili** form at the tips of the branches, and the spores are produced within them in **sporangia.** The sporangium always forms on the surface of a leaf called a **sporophyll.** (See Figure 17-4, at the end of this topic.)

■ Examine the strobilus, if your specimen has one. It consists of a cluster of sporophylls.

After the spore germinates, growth of the gametophytes and fertilization go on underground. Sexual reproduction in club mosses is so slow that most propagation is by the spreading out of the rhizomes. Label the parts of the club moss shown in Figure 17-4.

Although ancient club mosses included very large trees, the present species are all small. It is illegal to collect them in most areas because they are so few in number.

HORSETAILS
(CLASS FILICOPSIDA, ORDER
EQUISETOPHYTA)

Fossil horsetails grew as large as trees, but there is only a single genus of small plants that survives today.

■ Examine a living or preserved specimen of a horsetail such as *Equisetum hyemale* or *Equisetum arvense.* (In *E. arvense* the green shoots that look like pine needles are the branches. Look for the tiny leaves on these branches.)

Describe the **leaves:**

_____

_____

Where do they occur?

_____

Is the **stem** photosynthetic? _____

■ Note the ribs along the sides of the hollow stem, and the joints or **nodes.**

The stem continues underground as a rhizome. The stalks die in the fall, but the **rhizome** survives the winter and send new shoots up in the spring. The horsetail spreads vegetatively as the rhizome grows and sends up more shoots. True roots grow from the rhizome.

If your specimen is *E. arvense,* sexual reproduction involves separate nonphotosynthetic **fertile shoots,** which bear conelike **strobili** at the tips and are different in structure from the green **sterile shoots.** (See Figure 17-4.) The spores are formed within the sporangia, which are within the strobili. If your specimen is *E. hyemale,* the strobili are found at the ends of the photosynthetic shoots. Winglike **elaters** on the spores aid in their dispersal by the wind after they are shed from the sporangium.

■ Examine a strobilus. The sporangia contained within it form the spores.

The spores germinate into nonphotosynthetic gametophytes, which grow underground. After fertilization, the zygote grows into another sporophyte. Label the parts of the horsetail shown in Figure 17-4. If you studied *E. hyemale,* label the parts described above on the left-hand shoot only.

Although this group is not very important today, during the time of the first settlers and the pioneers, horsetails were called scouring rushes and were used as an abrasive for cleaning pots and for polishing. The stems of the horsetails contain grains of silica (the material of which sand is made), which are good for scouring.

FERNS
(CLASS FILICOPSIDA, ORDER
FILICOPHYTA)

Although you would never name a child "Horsetail" or "Liverwort," you might choose the name "Fern" in honor of these beautiful woodland plants. The life history of a fern is shown in Figure 17-1. It is similar to those of the fern allies (club mosses and horsetails). The fern gametophyte, however, is an independent, photosynthetic plant that produces both eggs and sperm.

■ Obtain a fern plant (sporophyte) and study its structure.
■ Note the deeply lobed leaves, called **fronds.**

Do the fronds have many veins? _____

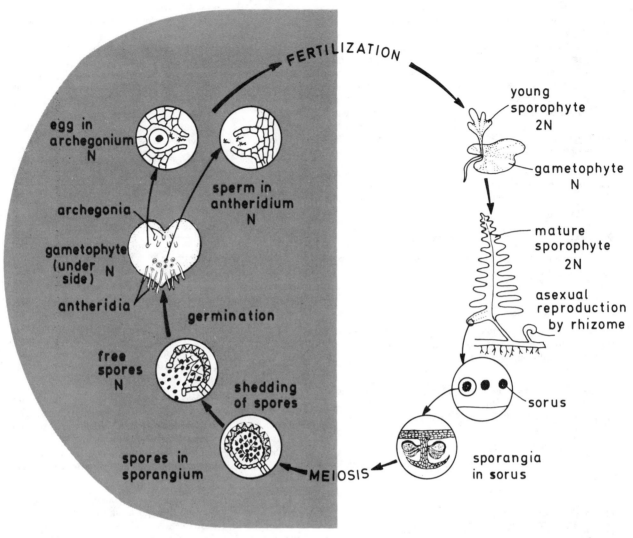

Figure 17-1. Life history of a fern. The sporophyte is dominant and the small gametophyte (valentine plant) is independent and photosynthetic.

Ferns, gymnosperms, and angiosperms are grouped as **Subdivision Pteropsida** because of their large, many-veined leaves.

■ Note the **petiole** (stalk) of the frond. It attaches the frond to the underground stem.
■ Follow the petiole underground to where it joins the horizontally growing stem, the **rhizome.**

Fronds of most ferns do not survive the winter, but the rhizome does. It sends up new fronds in the spring in the curled-up form known as **fiddleheads.** Each season the rhizome grows longer and sends up new fronds to spread the fern by vegetative propagation.

■ Examine a prepared cross section of a fern stem and note the arrangement of the vascular tissue.

Certain leaves called sporophylls bear the sporangia in which the spores are produced. Sometimes there are separate, fertile fronds, but more often the ordinary fronds take on the reproductive function.

■ Examine the undersides of your fronds for the presence of **sori,** which are little brown or colored dots. A sorus is a cluster of sporangia.

■ Examine a prepared slide showing the sorus of a fern in cross section.
■ Locate a **sporangium,** which is a sphere-shaped capsule suspended from a stalk.
■ Note the heavy, segmented ring around most of the sphere. This is the **annulus,** which is sensitive to moisture and helps release the spores by snapping the capsule shut suddenly.
■ Note the **spores** within the capsule of the sporangium.
■ If your frond has sori, scrape the surface of one into a drop of water, make a wet mount, and examine the sporangia in the microscope.
■ Locate the spores that are visible through the transparent walls, and find the annulus, which has thick cell walls.
■ Find the place in the annulus that is not thick-walled. This is where the capsule will break open to release the spores.

After the sporangium is mature, the cells of the annulus dry out, and the annulus straightens out to form a rod, thereby breaking open the capsule. At a certain point the annulus becomes so strained that is snaps back and flings the spores out of the capsule. The spores are thus actively spread out away from competition with the parent plant.

Each spore grows into a small plant called a **prothallus,** which is heart-shaped. (It is sometimes called a "valentine plant.") It bears both an **archegonium** (female) and **antheridium** (male) and produces both eggs and sperm. The prothallus is anchored onto the substrate by **rhizoids.** The sex organs and rhizoids are all located on the undersurface. The sperm must swim over to the eggs, which are fertilized and retained within the archegonium.

■ Examine the living prothallus of a fern if living material is available; otherwise look at a prepared slide.
■ Locate the **archegonia,** which are vase-shaped. They may not be present if you are looking at a living prothallus.
■ Locate the globe-shaped **antheridia.**

Why is it advantageous to have sex organs located beneath the plant?

_____

_____

The young sporophyte grows right out of the archegonium. The leaves grow upward from the apical notch of the prothallus and the rhizome, and the roots grow downward.

■ Examine living or preserved young fern sporophytes.
■ Note that the prothallus persists even after the sporophyte is well established.

Ferns have survived in spite of competition with the seed plants, and they are plentiful and widespread today. Most ferns are small, but there are some tree ferns still in existence.

GYMNOSPERMS (SUBDIVISION SPERMOPSIDA, CLASS CONIFERAE)

Angiosperms and many gymnosperms have mastered the problems posed by living on land by doing away with the flagellated sperm. Instead the male gametophyte produces large numbers of **pollen grains** which are not susceptible to drying out and which can be spread about by the wind. In addition, the young sporophyte embryo does not have to develop into a mature sporophyte at once but can remain **dormant** in a seed until the conditions become favorable because it is enclosed with its food supply inside a tough seed coat. The production of pollen and seeds allowed these plants to reproduce in the absence of free water and was an important factor in their evolutionary success.

Gymnosperms and angiosperms have **woody tissue,** which supports the stem of the plant so that it can reach great size. A large, taller plant has an advantage in obtaining sunlight for photosynthesis and in dispersing its seeds. These plants also have **hormones** that control the growth and development of the plant organs. They were able to become highly adapted to the environment and to change in response to the seasons by producing seeds and becoming dormant at the right time because of the control of these processes by hormones.

Gymnosperms include the cycads, which look like palm trees but bear cones; the ginkgo tree, *Ephedra;* and the familiar conifers.

■ Obtain a branch of a conifer, or observe one in a field demonstration.
■ Note the needlelike **leaves** and the **bark** on the branches and trunk.
■ Note that the leaves are **evergreen** and do not drop off in the fall as do the leaves of **deciduous** trees. (A few conifers are deciduous, the larch (tamarack), for example.)
■ Examine a prepared slide of a cross section of a leaf (needle). Compare what you see with Figure 17-2.

What is the advantage of evergreen leaves?

_____

Why are evergreen leaves usually needlelike or covered with a thick protective cuticle?

_____

_____

Seed bearing in conifers is restricted to the **sporophylls** that make up the **cone.** Gymnosperm seeds are located on the surface of the sporophyll rather than within a fruit as are angiosperm seeds. Male and female cones are separate and produce small, nonphotosynthetic gametophytes that are nourished by the sporophyte. Thus the gametophyte can live wherever the sporophyte lives. Fertilization and early development occur within the female gametophyte.

■ Locate some developing cones, which are green and soft. The larger ones are the female **seed cones.** The brownish male **pollen cones** are smaller and usually occur in clusters; they are present for only a short time.
■ Examine a male pollen cone. Each sporophyll or scale bears a pollen sac, also called the **microsporangium** because meiosis takes place there.

Pollen is formed within the pollen sac, and each grain can develop into a tiny, parasitic male gametophyte. During the formation of a pollen grain, a cell undergoes meiosis to form four microspores. Each microspore grows into a pollen grain containing several cells by means of mitosis. One cell nucleus becomes the reproductive nu-

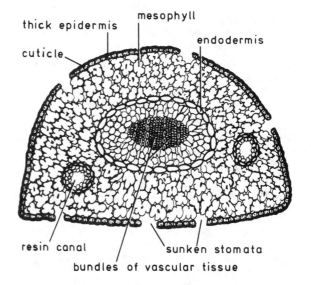

Figure 17-2. Pine leaf in cross section. This evergreen leaf has a reduced surface area and a thick cuticle to conserve moisture.

cleus (sperm nucleus), and one gives rise to the pollen tube (tube nucleus), which allows the sperm nucleus to reach the egg. When the mature pollen grain is released from the pollen cone, a few of the grains will reach the scales of a female cone and land on a mature ovule (immature seed). This is the process of **pollination.** After pollination, the pollen tube germinates, grows through the tissue of the female gametophyte, and allows the sperm nucleus to fertilize the egg.

■ Examine a prepared slide of pollen from a conifer.
■ Note the winglike projections of the mature grains that help them to travel further in the wind.

What are the advantages of a pollen grain over a flagellated sperm cell?

_____

_____

■ Examine an older **seed cone;** remove one scale.
■ Look for two **ovules** containing **megasporangia** on its upper surface. If the ovules have already matured into seeds, they may have been shed, leaving two hollow impressions where they once grew.

Within each megasporangium, meiosis followed by mitosis gives rise to the cells that make up the parasitic female gametophyte, including several egg cells. When pollen lands on the sticky surface of the ovule, the pollen tube grows through an opening in the ovule called the **micropyle** and on through the tissues of the female gametophyte until it reaches an egg cell. The sperm nucleus enters the egg in the process of **fertilization,** and the new embryo starts to develop within the megasporangium. A diagram of fertilization is shown in Figure 17-3. The seed of the pine can be understood as an extended pine family in which the young sporophyte is contained within the tissue of its parental female gametophyte, and the gametophyte in turn is contained within the reproductive organs of the grandparental sporophyte. Although several eggs may be fertilized within the female gametophyte, one embryo will win out and be released in the mature seed. The seed contains stored food as well as the embryo, has a tough seed coat, and is carried by the wind.

The structure of angiosperms will be studied in more detail in a later exercise (Topic 23). Reproduction in angiosperms is similar to that in gymnosperms. **Pollen** from the stamen lands on the pistil, and a **pollen tube** grows down to the ovule at its base. The **female gametophyte** within the ovule consists of only a few cells, including a haploid **egg cell** and a special diploid cell. This cell is also fertilized and forms the **endosperm,** a source of nutrients that is incorporated into the seed. **Double fertilization** of both the egg cell and the endosperm cell is unique to angiosperms. (See Figure 17-7.) The outer layer of the ovule forms the **seed coat** to protect the embryo and endosperm. Finally, the base of the pistil containing the ovules—namely, the ovary—develops into a fruit. The fruit may be fleshy, as in a peach, or hard, as in a bean pod. The fruit serves to protect or disperse the seeds.

For your own review, complete Table 17-1 at the end of this topic by checking each feature that applies to the groups you have studied. List the characteristics of all tracheophytes in the space below the table.

Before leaving the laboratory, be sure to return all demonstration materials and store your microscopes properly.

EXPLORING FURTHER

Banks, H. *Evolution and Plants of the Past.* Belmont, Calif.: Wadsworth, 1970.
Bold, H. C., C. J. Alexopoulos, and T. Delevorya. *Morphology of Plants and Fungi.* 4th ed. New York: Harper and Row, 1980.
Gray, A. *Gray's Manual of Botany.* 8th ed. New York: Van Nostrand Reinhold, 1950.
Jensen, W. A., and F. B. Salisbury. *Botany: An Ecological Approach.* 2nd ed. Belmont, Calif.: Wadsworth, 1984.
Thomas, Barry. *The Evolution of Plants and Flowers.* New York: St. Martin's Press, 1981.
Weier, T. E., C. R. Stocking, and M. G. Barbour. *Botany: An Introduction to Plant Biology.* 6th ed. New York: John Wiley and Sons, 1982.

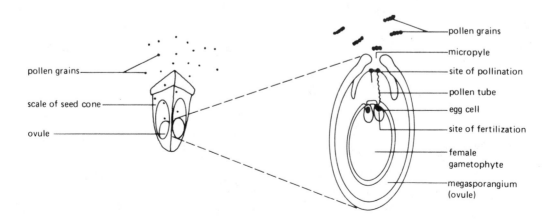

Figure 17-3. Fertilization in a pine cone. Pollination occurs when the pollen grains reach the surface of the ovule and the pollen tube begins to grow. Fertilization occurs when the sperm nucleus from the pollen tube unites with the egg nucleus within the female gametophyte. These two events may be separated by a long period of time.

Journal Articles

Altschul, Siri von Reis. "Exploring the herbarium." *Scientific American,* May 1977 (#1359).

Echlin, Patrick. "Pollen." *Scientific American,* April 1968 (#1105).

Shigo, Alex L. "Compartmentalization of Decay in Trees." *Scientific American,* 96, April 1985.

Student Name _____ **Date** _____

TABLE 17-1. CHARACTERISTICS OF THE TRACHEOPHYTES

Characteristics	Lycopsida (Club Moss)	Sphenopsida (Horsetail)	Filicineae (Fern)	Gymnospermae (Conifer)
Cuticle				
True roots, stems, leaves				
Flagellated sperm				
Rhizoids in gametophyte				
Vascular tissue				
Rhizomes				
Separate male and female gametophyte				
Parasitic or nonphotosynthetic sporophyte				
Photosynthetic gametophyte and sporophyte				
Parasitic or nonphotosynthetic gametophyte				
Airborne spores				
Pollen				
Embryo protected by seed coat				
Seed enclosed within fruit				
Woody vascular tissue				

Characteristics common to all tracheophytes:

_____
_____
_____
_____
_____
_____

CLUB MOSS

_____ phyte

CLUB MOSS

_____ phyte

sperm from
antheridium

egg in
archegonium

rhizoids

HORSETAIL

_____ phyte

HORSETAIL

_____ phyte

flagellated sperm
from antheridium

egg in
archegonium

rhizoids

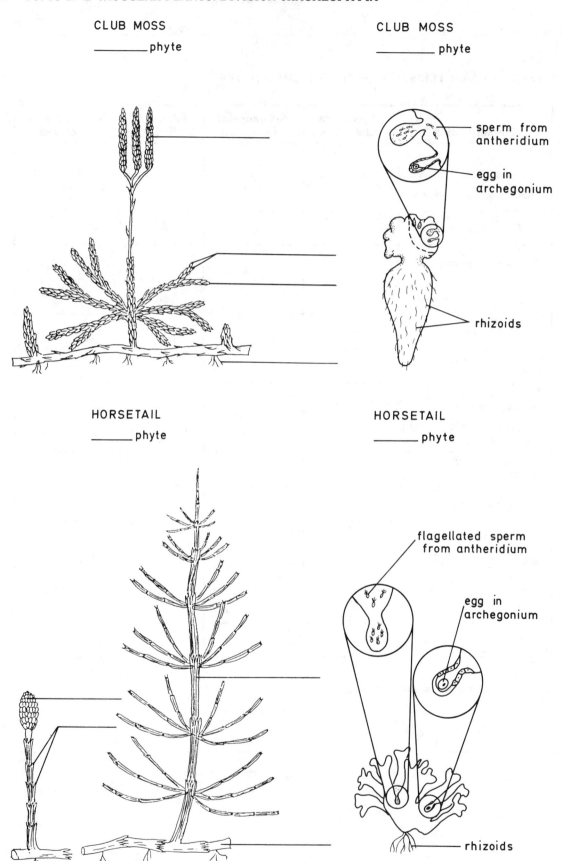

Figure 17-4.   Stages in the life history of a club moss and a horsetail. Label each stage as a sporophyte or gametophyte and label the parts of each plant marked with label lines.

Kingdom Animalia: Animals Without a Coelom

OBJECTIVES _____

When you have completed this topic, you should be able to:
1. Describe the advantages of multicellularity, larger size, bilateral symmetry, the mobile stage of life history, the sessile stage of life history, the sense organs, a complete digestive tract, cephalization, and the nervous system.
2. Define coelom, coelomate, and acoelomate, and state the advantage that a coelom gives to an organism possessing it.
3. Give the distinguishing features of members of the phyla Cnidaria, Platyhelminthes, Nematoda, and Rotifera.
4. Describe the following structures and give the phylum or phyla in which each of them is found: tentacles, nematocysts, choanocytes, gastrovascular cavity, flame cells, pseudocoelom, polyp, medusa, and gonads.

KEY TOPICS _____

Body symmetry, coelom, alternation of generations, cnidarians, flatworms, nematodes, rotifers.

INTRODUCTION

As competition between unicellular organisms became intense, larger and more complex organisms had a selective advantage, and multicellular organisms came into existence. **Multicellularity** allowed differentiation of cells that performed different specific functions. Different types of cells became organized into **tissues** and the tissues into **organs,** specialized structures adapted to carry out a certain function or process. For example, a complete digestive tract, in which there is a one-way passage of food from mouth to anus, can have specialized parts and is much more effective than a simple bag.

In organisms with more sophisticated organs and organ systems, the body plan changed to accommodate the new complexity. In nematodes, rotifers, and more complex organisms, there is a space between the gut and body wall called the **coelom.** This space allows the gut and body to move independently and provides a protective space in which the internal organs can be contained.

When the coelom is not fully lined by mesoderm, as in nematodes and rotifers, it is a **pseudocoelom.** In annelids, mollusks, and the other organisms that we will be studying in subsequent exercises, the coelom is a true coelom, because it is fully lined by mesodermal tissue.

Compare the body plans shown in Figure 18-1 and be sure you can relate each type to the phyla in which it is found.

In the descriptions of organisms to follow, we will be using certain terms that you need to understand:

symmetry: the body can be split at least once to form halves that are mirror images.
radial symmetry: many planes of symmetry around a central axis, as in a starfish.
bilateral symmetry: one plane of symmetry, as in a fish.
sagittal or **longitudinal section:** the body is cut from head to tail, dividing the fish into right and left halves.

163

ACOELOMATE   ACOELOMATE   PSEUDOCOELOMATE   COELOMATE

⊞ ectoderm

▦ mesoderm

▥ endoderm

Figure 18-1.   Body plans. Cnidarians are acoelomates with two cell layers and a mesoglea. Flatworms are acoelomates with three cell layers including a true mesoderm. Pseudocoelomates such as the nematodes and rotifers have a body cavity, but it is between the inner and middle layers of cells. In true coelomates, the body cavity is formed within the middle cell layer and the organs are protected and supported by this layer.

frontal section: body is cut in half from head to tail, separating the fish's back from its belly.

cross section: body is cut in half from top to bottom to separate the head end of the fish from the tail end.

PHYLUM PORIFERA

The household sponges with which everyone is familiar, are the synthetic imitations of real sponges with internal skeletons made of **spongin.** Other types of sponges have skeletons of **calcium carbonate** or **silica.** The basic structure of a sponge is a mass of cells organized around a central cavity called the **spongocoel.** Water enters through small pores (porifera means "pore bearer") and exits through the **osculum,** which is usually raised above the surface of the body. Lining the interior of the sponge or of the canals leading into the spongocoel are specialized flagellated cells called **choanocytes** or **collar cells.** These are very similar to flagellated protozoans that exist as single cells or as simple colonies. These protozoans and sponges may have had a shared ancestor. Sponges are **hermaphroditic,** so an individual can form both eggs and sperm during sexual reproduction. Since adult sponges are sessile, hermaphroditic sexual reproduction is possible even for isolated individuals. The **flagellated larva** leaves the spongocoel of the parent, swims to a new location, and attaches to grow into a new sessile adult. Such a mobile part of the life history allows the species to spread to new locations.

■ Study a specimen of a sponge such as *Scypha,* which has been cut in longitudinal section after placing it in a culture dish partly filled with water. Use your dissecting microscope when appropriate.

■ Locate the **osculum,** the **base,** and the calcium carbonate **spicules.** The composition of the spicules places this particular sponge in the Class **Calcispongiae.** Sponges may reproduce asexually by budding off new individuals near the base.

■ Note the hollow **spongocoel** from which water exits through the osculum. When sponges reproduce sexu-

ally, eggs and sperm are produced and fertilization occurs within the spongocoel.

■ Find the **ostia** (singular ostium) or pores on the surface of the sponge through which water enters the **incurrent canals** within the body wall.

■ Label these structures in Figure 18-6 at the end of this topic.

■ Obtain a prepared slide that shows the structure of the body wall of *Scypha* and view it in the compound microscope.

■ Note that the incurrent canals lead into the **radial canals,** which in turn lead to the spongocoel. The choanocytes line these canals but not the interior of the spongocoel.

The sponge is organized to maintain a steady flow of water through its body for food collection, gas exchange, and excretion. The animal feeds on tiny food particles that the choanocytes ingest by phagocytosis. Since the choanocyte is of such central importance to the life of the sponge, it is reasonable that there may be an evolutionary relationship between sponges and certain protozoans that strongly resemble choanocytes. Sponges apparently elaborated on the capabilities of this one-cell type but did not develop other types of specialized cells. They seem to be unrelated to the other phyla of multicellular animals and represent an offshoot of evolution that ended without reaching the tissue level of organization.

PHYLUM CNIDARIA: *HYDRA*

Cnidarians have a saclike body consisting of two cell layers, epidermis and gastrodermis, surrounding a cavity with a single opening called the **gastrovascular cavity.** In the **polyp** form the organism is more or less sessile, and the opening to the cavity is directed upwards. In the motile **medusa** form the opening is underneath. Both forms usually have fingerlike extensions of the body called tentacles, and specialized cells called nematocysts are present. There is much cellular specialization in the form of reproductive, sensory, secretory, and true nerve cells. Movement is accomplished by the contraction of muscle fibers coordinated by a network of nerve cells.

Hydra is an example of a polyp that never produces a medusa stage. During sexual reproduction, its reproductive cells form gametes. The fertilized zygote will eventually develop into a small version of the adult. *Hydra* can also reproduce by budding off a small individual complete with tentacles, from the side of the body. The internal structure of *Hydra* is shown in Figure 18-2.

■ Examine a living *Hydra* using the dissecting microscope. Locate the basal disc by which it is attached, the cylindrical body, and the crown of tentacles.

What kind of symmetry does Hydra show?

_____

■ If brine shrimp are available, add a drop of *washed* brine shrimp to your *Hydra* and observe its eating behavior. (Salt water will quickly kill the *Hydra* by upsetting its water balance.)

Is the shape of the *Hydra* different after ingestion?

_____

Is digestion of the food intracellular or extracellular?

_____

What happens to the wastes after the edible parts of the brine shrimp have been absorbed?

_____

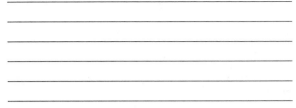

The tentacles are studded with specialized cells called **cnidocytes.** Each such cell produces a **nematocyst,** which stings and entangles prey so that it can be brought to the mouth and ingested. The touch of brine shrimp on the tentacles will trigger the nematocysts.

■ Examine a prepared slide of nematocysts in the microscope.

The nematocyst consists of a tiny thread coiled up inside a capsule. Firing of the nematocyst is under nervous control. When it is triggered by the touch of prey, the thread turns inside out and then entangles or paralyzes the prey organism. Toxins in the nematocysts of cnidarians such as fire coral and the Portuguese man-of-war can be harmful or even fatal to humans.

Other cnidarians, such as hydroid *Obelia* and the jellyfish *Gonionemus*, have both a medusa stage and a polyp stage in their life histories. Organisms that have both a polyp and medusa stage show **alternation of generations:** The medusa gives rise to the polyp, the polyp then gives rise to the medusa, and so forth.

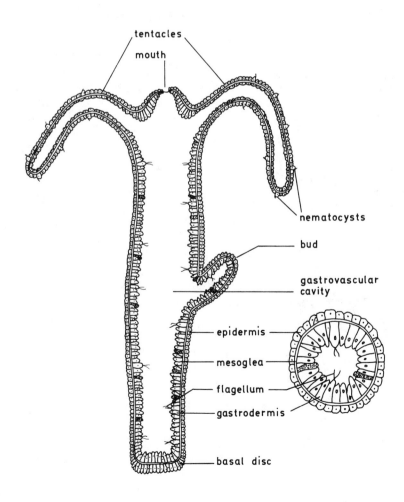

Figure 18-2. *Hydra.* Prey is captured by the stinging or entangling nematocysts and stuffed into the mouth by the tentacles. Movement occurs by contraction of muscle fibers in the mesoglea.

PHYLUM PLATYHELMINTHES

Flatworms have three body layers, **ectoderm, mesoderm,** and **endoderm,** but there is no body cavity, so they are **acoelomate.** As in the cnidarians, the gastrovascular cavity has a single opening. Flatworms have true organs and organ systems. Motile flatworms show **cephalization** and **bilateral symmetry.**

Class Turbellaria

Look at Figure 18-7 (at the end of this topic), which is the outline of a planarian, and note the shape of the anterior (front) and posterior (rear) ends of this animal.

What type of symmetry does a planarian have?

_____

■ Examine a living planarian, such as *Dugesia,* or look at a prepared slide in the microscope.
■ Locate the anterior end and note the earlike **auricles** with which the worm smells and pigmented **eyespots** for light perception. This concentration of sense organs at the front of a motile organism is a form of **cephalization.**

  Cilia on the underside of the worm are used in its locomotion. The **pharynx,** mouth, and genital pore are also located on the underside.

■ Turn the worm upside down to look for these structures.
■ Feed your planarian with a bit of meat or liver. Try to observe the extension of its pharynx as it feeds.

If you are looking at a prepared slide, how many branches does the gastrovascular cavity have?

_____

  The **excretory system** consists of highly branched interconnecting tubes lined with ciliated **flame cells** that move the contents along to the excretory pores. Its major function is probably water balance.

The nervous system consists of nerve cells grouped in nerve cords along each side of the worm and concentrated in the **ganglia** (two masses near the eyespots), sometimes called the "brain." This "ladder" type of nervous system reflects the cephalization and bilateral symmetry obvious from the outside.

An individual worm is **hermaphroditic,** producing both eggs and sperm but does not fertilize itself. Two individuals mate by transferring sperm to each other during copulation. Fertilization is internal, and eggs are laid in cocoons or jelly. The most common method of reproduction is asexual reproduction by transverse fission in which the animal splits in half behind the pharynx, and each half regenerates the missing parts.

Class Cestoda

The members of this class are highly specialized parasitic tapeworms. The adult tapeworm lives in the intestine of a vertebrate and is firmly attached by its **scolex,** which contains suckers and hooks. The rest of the ribbonlike body is a series of segments called **proglottids.** Each proglottid contains male and female reproductive organs, nerves, and excretory canals. Nutrition and gas exchange are carried on by diffusion across the very flat body. There is no digestive system.

How does the tapeworm obtain food?

_____

_____

_____

■ Examine a preserved whole tapeworm such as the dog tapeworm, *Dipylidium caninum,* and locate the scolex.

  Immature proglottids are found at this end, and the ripe proglottids stuffed with eggs are broken off from the opposite end and leave the body in the feces. The structure of a mature proglottid is shown in Figure 18-3.

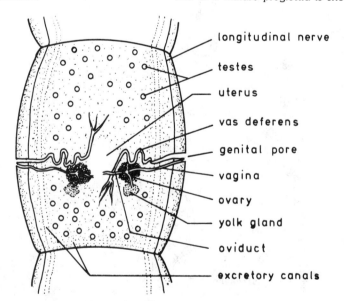

longitudinal nerve

testes

uterus

vas deferens

genital pore

vagina

ovary

yolk gland

oviduct

excretory canals

Figure 18-3. Mature proglottid of the dog tapeworm, *Dipylidium caninum*. Copulation between two proglottids results in internal fertilization of eggs. Fertilized eggs completely fill the ripe proglottid, which breaks off from the tapeworm and eventually bursts to release the eggs.

■ View a mature proglottid in the microscope, and identify the **ovaries,** which are centrally located; the **uterus** between the ovaries; and the **vaginas,** which lead out through the genital pores at the sides of the proglottid.

■ The **testes** fill most of the proglottid. Sperm pass out through the vas deferens to the genital pore.

■ Find the **excretory canals,** which run along the sides and posterior of the proglottid.

■ Find the **longitudinal nerves,** which pass down the sides of the proglottid.

The proglottids of a tapeworm fertilize themselves or an adjacent proglottid. In an infected animal, competition will lead to the success of one individual tapeworm and the rest will be eliminated.

PHYLUM NEMATODA: *ASCARIS*

Roundworms may be the most abundant animals on earth. They occur by the millions in soil, where they damage plants and crops and may reach a large size, as in the giant roundworm that parasitizes humans. The **complete digestive tract** of the roundworm is a tube from mouth to anus within the tube of the body wall. The space between the inner and outer tubes is called a **pseudocoelom** because it is not completely lined by mesoderm. There is a protective **cuticle** covering the outside of the worm's epidermis. The mesoderm contains longitudinal muscles, so the worms can move by a whip-like thrashing of the body, but they cannot creep like an earthworm. There are dorsal and ventral nerve cords but no respiratory or circulatory system.

External Anatomy

■ Examine preserved specimens of male and female roundworms such as *Ascaris.*

■ Identify the male, which has a distinctly curved posterior end with copulatory spicules.

■ The opposite anterior end has a **mouth** surrounded by three **lips.**

■ Locate the **anus,** which is a slit across the posterior end of the worm on its ventral side.

■ Find the female **genital pore** on the ventral side of the worm about one-third of the way from the head.

Internal Anatomy

The internal organs of *Ascaris* are shown in Figure 18-4.

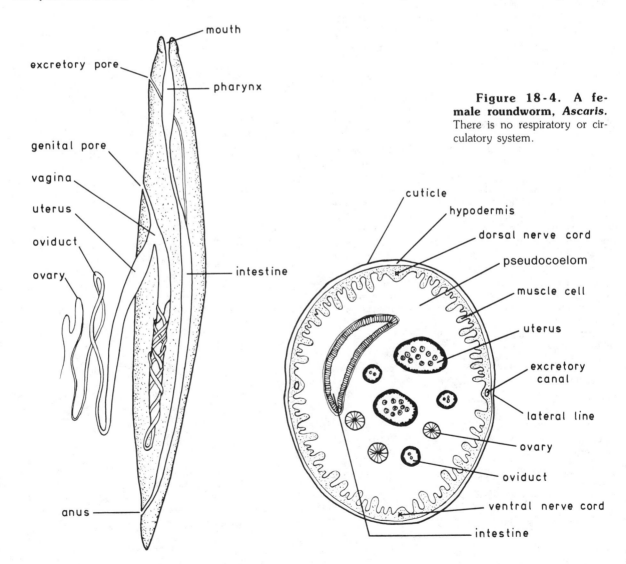

Figure 18-4. A female roundworm, *Ascaris.* There is no respiratory or circulatory system.

mouth

excretory pore

pharynx

genital pore

vagina

uterus

oviduct

ovary

intestine

anus

cuticle

hypodermis

dorsal nerve cord

pseudocoelom

muscle cell

uterus

excretory canal

lateral line

ovary

oviduct

ventral nerve cord

intestine

■ Make a longitudinal slit along the dorsal side of the female worm, and pin back the sides.

■ Cover the worm with some water to minimize drying.

■ Find the **intestine,** which runs through the body from mouth to anus.

■ In the middle of the intestine, locate the coils of the female reproductive system. The **ovaries** are threadlike and connect to the **oviducts,** which in turn lead into the larger **uteri.** The uteri join just before exiting through the genital pore.

These structures can be seen more easily in cross section. (See Figure 18-4.)

■ Examine a cross section of *Ascaris* in the microscope and find the large, flattened **intestine.**

■ Identify the small, round structures, which are sections through the tubes of the **oviduct,** and the larger **uterus,** which is filled with eggs; the **ovary** is solid.

■ Locate the dorsal and ventral **nerve cords.**

■ Identify the **cuticle** surrounding the worm and the longitudinal **muscle cells,** which are the large cells surrounding the body cavity.

■ The space just under the cuticle on either side of the worm is the **lateral line** in which the **excretory canals** are located.

In the male *Ascaris*, a threadlike testis leads into ducts that empty into the cloaca at the posterior of the digestive tract. As you already learned in Topic 9, fertilization is internal, and the eggs have passed through the early stages of development before they leave the body of the female.

Anatomy of a Nematode Cyst

A parasite has a great advantage if its eggs or larvae are well protected and can survive adverse conditions until they can reach a new host. In *Trichinella spiralis*, the parasitic roundworm that causes the disease trichinosis, fertilized eggs develop into larvae within the reproductive tract of the female worm and are then deposited within the host's lymphatic system. The larvae are carried throughout the body, and those that invade skeletal muscle will form cysts and survive. The cysts have a low metabolic rate and a protective wall. If the host is a pig, its meat might be ingested by a person without being properly cooked, and the cyst walls would be broken down in the digestive tract of the new human host. The young worms quickly mature and produce hundreds of offspring. These larvae enter the lymphatic system, burrow into the host's skeletal muscle, and again encyst.

■ Examine a prepared slide that shows the cysts formed in skeletal muscle by young trichina worms.

Do the encysted worms harm their host?

_____

What are two ways in which the disease trichinosis could be controlled?

1. _____

_____

2. _____

_____

PHYLUM ROTIFERA

Rotifers are small, pseudocoelomate animals that move about actively and can ingest small particles of food. The structure of a typical rotifer is shown in Figure 18-5. The beating of circles of cilia in the **corona** gives the phylum its name (rotifer means "wheel bearer"). These cilia draw food into the mouth. Food is then ground up in the **mastax** and passes on through the stomach, intestine, cloaca, and anus. The corona is also used in locomotion.

Rotifers have an excretory system with flame cells and a bladder. The body is covered by a protective cuticle. Muscle bands can contract to change the shape of the body.

■ Examine a living rotifer or a prepared slide.

■ Locate the **corona** and **sensory antenna** at the anterior end.

■ Find the **toes** and **spurs** at the posterior end.

■ Locate the **mastax.**

How could you decide that a rotifer is not a giant protozoan?

_____

_____

_____

corona
antenna
mouth
pharynx
mastax
salivary gland
stomach
ovary (vitellarium)
intestine
anus
pedal gland
foot
toes
spurs

Figure 18-5. A rotifer, *Philodina*. This type of rotifer is always female and reproduces by parthenogenesis.

In certain species of rotifers there are no males, and the unfertilized eggs develop into new female rotifers. The eggs may develop in a brood pouch that is located within the body of their mother. When males are present and involved in reproduction, they are usually small and degenerate and fertilize the female by the crude process of **hypodermic impregnation:** The male stabs the female in any part of her body with his penis and releases sperm which have to swim through the body to the eggs in order to fertilize them.

Rotifers can withstand drying and will lose most of their body water to enter a desiccated form that can survive for years. When water again becomes available, the animal will rehydrate and become active shortly.

When you are finished with this exercise, return your materials and store your microscope properly.

EXPLORING FURTHER

Barnes, R. D. *Invertebrate Zoology.* 4th ed. Philadelphia, W. B. Saunders, 1980.

Buchsbaum, R. *Animals Without Backbones.* 2nd rev. ed. Chicago: University of Chicago Press, 1975.

Buchsbaum, R., and L. J. Milne. *The Lower Animals: Living Invertebrates of the World.* Garden City, N.Y: Doubleday, 1962.

Russell-Hunter, W. D. *A Life of Invertebrates.* New York: Macmillan, 1979.

Villee, Claude A., W. F. Walker, and R. D. Barnes. *General Zoology.* 6th ed. Philadelphia, W. B. Saunders, 1984.

Journal Articles

Gierer, A. "Hydra as a model for the development of biological form." *Scientific American,* December 1974 (#1309).

Goreau, T. F., N. I. Goreau, and T. J. Goreau. "Corals and coral reefs." *Scientific American,* August 1979 (#1434).

Mansour, T. E. "Chemotherapy of parasitic worms: New biochemical strategies." *Science* 205, (4405):462, 1979.

Savory, T. H. "Hidden lives." *Scientific American,* July 1968 (#1112).

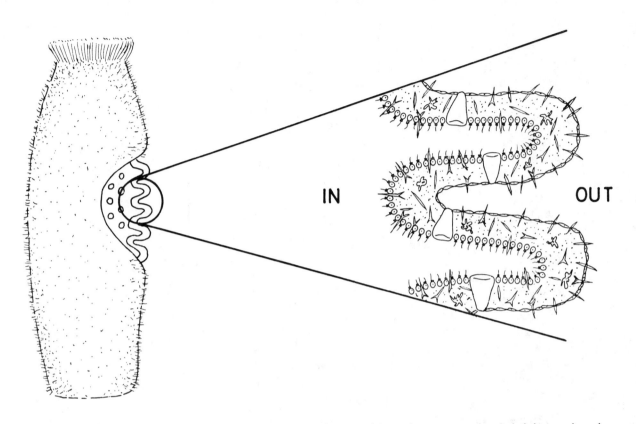

Figure 18-6. *Scypha.* This sponge is of the syconoid type and has calcareous spicules. Label the osculum, base, spongocoel, spicules, and the location of the choanocytes. Indicate with arrows how water enters and exits from the sponge.

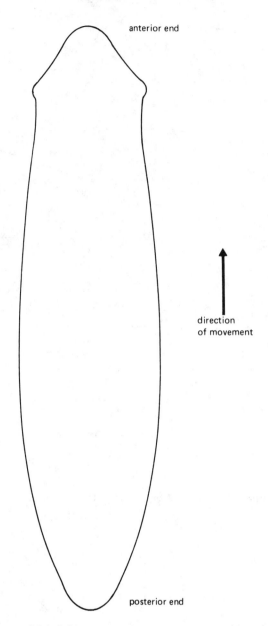

anterior end

direction
of movement

posterior end

Figure 18-7. A planarian. Draw in and label the parts of the digestive system, nervous system, and sense organs of the flatworm.

Kingdom Animalia:
Mollusks and Annelids

When you have completed this topic, you should be able to:
1. Define coelom and enumerate the advantages to an organism of having one over not having one.
2. List the features of protostomes that distinguish them from deuterostomes.
3. List the major features of a mollusk and of an annelid.
4. Describe the advantages and disadvantages of the exoskeleton in a mollusk.
5. Describe the adaptations of the earthworm that allow it to live on land.
6. Explain the evidence that mollusks and annelids share a common ancestor.

KEY TOPICS _____

Coelom, protostome, deuterostome, mollusk, annelid.

INTRODUCTION

Annelids and mollusks, as well as the animals that we will study in later exercises, have a true **coelom** that arises by the splitting of the middle layer of cells in the body, the mesoderm. (See Figure 18-1). The mesoderm surrounds all of the organs that develop within the coelom, protecting and supporting them, and it can give rise to layers of muscle so that the gut and other organs can move and function independently from the body wall. The space within the coelom makes room for an independently active circulatory system, internal organs, and large gonads. In some organisms such as the earthworm the fluid in the coelom acts as a **hydrostatic skeleton** on which the muscles of the body wall can exert pressure during locomotion. In many coelomates, the coelomic fluid helps in circulating nutrients and gas exchange.

Mollusks, annelids, and arthropods share some important features of embryological development and so are grouped together as **protostomes.** For example, there is a primitive opening in the embryo, the blastopore, which develops into the mouth in these animals (proto = "first", stoma = "mouth"). A second group of organisms, the **deuterostomes,** shares different features. The blastopore in these animals becomes the anus and the mouth is formed in a quite different way. Deuterostomes include the echinoderms (sea stars, sea urchins)

and the chordates (tunicates, vertebrates, ourselves).

PROTOSTOMES

1. blastopore becomes mouth
2. spiral cleavage of embryo
3. determinate cleavage (fixed fate)
4. coelom formed by mesoderm splitting

DEUTEROSTOMES

1. blastopore becomes anus
2. radial cleavage of embryo
3. indeterminate cleavage (fate can be altered)
4. coelom formed by mesoderm pouches

A common theme during the evolution of the mollusks and annelids was the appearance of **metamerism** or serial repetition of body parts. Annelids such as the earthworm are obviously segmented. Mollusks are thought to have arisen from an annelid ancestor, but the present-day forms have tended to lose the segmentation that was the outstanding feature of the ancestral mollusk. A recently discovered primitive mollusk, *Neopilina*, does show metamerism and supports the notion of a common ancestor with the annelids. Another important connection is the **trochophore larva** produced by both annelids and mollusks during reproduction.

PHYLUM MOLLUSCA

Mollusks have the following major body parts: a muscular **foot**, a **visceral mass,** and a hard protective **shell** secreted by the mantle, which lies over the **soft body.** Except for the bivalves, mollusks have a rasplike feeding organ, the **radula.** There is a complete digestive system and commonly an open circulatory system. The respiratory system usually has gills and the excretory organ has nephridia. Mollusks are true coelomates, with a body cavity surrounded by mesoderm.

Class Bivalvia: Clam or Mussel

As in many sessile animals, the bivalves (clams, mussels, oysters, and scallops) have developed protection in the form of hard shells, which can be very tightly clamped together to enclose the soft body and protect it from predators. In those forms that are subjected to periodic drying when the tide falls, the shells clamp together tightly to prevent the loss of moisture. The shells are secreted by the **mantle** and are hinged together. Some bivalves, such as the scallop, can swim after a fashion by closing and opening the valves. The muscle involved in swimming is the part of the scallop used for human consumption.

These animals show bilateral symmetry and, if you orient one with the hinge at the top and the "points" at the top left, as shown in Figure 19-1, you will be viewing the left side. Water passes in and out of the gill chamber through siphons, which are modified parts of the mantle. The gill chamber is sealed off from the rest of the viscera in which the organs are bathed in an open circulatory system that is sufficient for the needs of this slowly moving animal. Pigmented blood is pumped by a two-chambered **heart.**

Would you expect an active, predatory mollusk such as a squid to have an open or a closed circulatory system?

There is a complete digestive tract, a true **nephridium,** and a **foot** for digging or locomotion. Bivalves are filter feeders and there is no radula. They extract edible particles from the water circulating through the gill chamber. Labial palps aid in moving the food trapped in mucus into the mouth.

■ Orient a clam or mussel as shown in Figure 19-1. Focus on the large adductor muscles that close the shell. These are shown in Figure 19-3 and must be cut to open the shell.
■ Insert a tool into the space between the lower edges of the shells, and pry the shells apart enough to insert something to act as a wedge.
■ Use a scalpel to cut through the muscles without damaging the internal organs, especially in the region near the hinge. Separate the shells to expose the mantle.

Refer to Figures 19-2 and 19-3 to identify the internal organs.

■ Identify the **adductor muscles** and the muscular **foot.** Remove the **mantle,** which covers the **gills.**
■ Carefully remove the left gills. Slit the bottom of the foot in order to see the organs within it.
■ Trace the digestive tube from the mouth through the **gonad** (yellowish) and **heart** to the anus.
■ Locate the digestive gland and the **nephridium** (brown or green).
■ Pass a probe into the **siphons** at the animal's posterior to see where water circulates. Water enters the mantle cavity through the incurrent siphon, circulates through the filaments of the gills, and leaves through the excurrent siphon. The siphons are necessary to take in water free from sediment. The water moves by the action of cilia on the gills and particles in the water are the only food of the bivalve.

Because bivalves are filter feeders, any poisonous substances in their food particles will become concentrated in their bodies. During the season that toxic algae are prevalent, it is unwise to risk eating shellfish and the gathering of shellfish for food is usually prohibited by law.

Figure 19-1. A bivalve mollusk. If a clam or mussel is held in this orientation, with the hinge on top and the "points" aiming to the left, the anterior will be to the left and the dorsal part of the animal on top. The approximate location of the digestive tract is shown in black, and the position of the gills is marked by the dashed line.

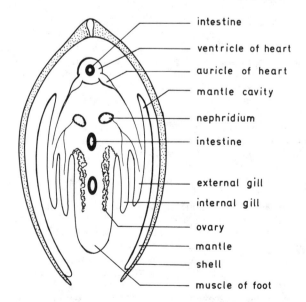

Figure 19-2. Cross section of a bivalve. Water circulates within the mantle cavity, bathing the gills for gas exchange.

Figure 19-3.   Internal structure of a bivalve. The left gill and mantle have been removed to show the internal organs.

Bivalves are usually either male or female, and they carry out reproduction by shedding a large number of gametes into the water, where fertilization takes place. Sometimes the young are brooded in a specialized part of the gill. The embryos develop into motile trochophore larvae. These in turn develop into veliger larvae, which become the sessile adults.

PHYLUM ANNELIDA

Annelids have **metamerically segmented** wormlike bodies, and most are divided into segments internally by partitions called **septa.** In polychaetes and oligochaetes the body wall contains ciruclar and longitudinal muscles that squeeze the fluid within each segment to lengthen or shorten the worm during its creeping movements. Thus the coelomic fluid acts as a **hydrostatic skeleton** and there is no hard exoskeleton as in mollusks. The **closed circulatory system** contains pigmented blood for efficient gas exchange. The **complete digestive tract** processes food in one direction from mouth to anus and has specialized parts. The nervous system shows **cephalization** with sense organs and masses of nerve cells called ganglia at the anterior end. The **nephridia** are true excretory organs (metanephridia) that can actively absorb and excrete substances to regulate the composition of the coelomic fluid.

Class Oligochaetae: Earthworm

Oligochaetes (oligochaete = "few bristles") have only four pairs of setae on each segment and lack parapodia. Gas exchange takes place over the entire body surface and is aided by an efficient circulatory system in which the blood is moved by little pumps ("hearts").

Many oligochaetes such as the earthworm have taken up a terrestrial life but have not really adapted to land; they secrete a thick mucus to keep their skin moist and must remain within their damp burrows in the ground unless the surface is soaking wet. They lack specialized respiratory organs and a support system for the body.

Earthworms feed on dead vegetation and have a well-developed digestive system to process their diet of decaying vegetation. The head is much reduced to adapt to its burrowing way of life.

The individual earthworm is **hermaphroditic,** producing both eggs and sperm, but does not fertilize itself. Rather, eggs and sperm are shed into a protective cocoon of mucus where external fertilization takes place. Earthworms, in contrast to polychaetes, do not have a trochophore larva. Instead, a young worm hatches directly from the cocoon.

EXTERNAL ANATOMY AND BEHAVIOR

■ Examine a live or preserved earthworm and find the **clitellum,** an enlarged section near the anterior end that secretes mucus during copulation.
■ Locate the **mouth** under the protruding **prostomium.**
■ Counting back from the prostomium, find the ninth segment, and look for openings of the **seminal receptacles** between the ninth and tenth and the eleventh and twelfth segments on the worm's ventral surface. Sperm are stored here when worms copulate.
■ The **oviducts** open on the fourteenth segment to release the eggs.
■ **Seminal vesicles** open on the fifteenth segment to release sperm.
■ Look at one segment closely, and locate the **setae** on the lower part of the side of the worm.

■ Find the **excretory pores** that occur on the sides of most of the segments. Each pore is the opening of one **nephridium,** or excretory organ.

Earthworms do have a very important adaptation to terrestrial life: a special type of external fertilization. When two worms mate, they overlap ventral surfaces so that the anterior tip of one worm is a little past the clitellum of the other and vice versa. Sperm are released by both worms but have to migrate over many segments in mucus-covered grooves, so the worms must remain joined for quite a long time. After mating, the mucus secreted by the clitellum passes over the head of the worm and picks up eggs from the oviduct openings and sperm from the sperm receptacles as it moves. The cocoon is deposited in the soil and a young worm hatches from it eventually.

If live earthworms are available, investigate locomotion and other behavioral responses.

■ Place the worm on a moist paper towel in a dissecting pan. Study its locomotion under the dissecting microscope.

Referring to Figure 19-5, which muscles contract to cause elongation of a segment? _____

Which muscles contract to cause shortening of a segment? _____

How does the worm respond to the bright light of your microscope?_____

_____

■ Touch the front end of the earthworm gently with a probe. What is the response? _____

■ Hold the probe still in the path of the moving earthworm. How does the worm respond to this foreign object?

_____

_____

■ Dip your probe in 5% acetic acid. (This is similar to vinegar and not acidic enough to injure the worm.) Move the probe toward the front end of the worm until you get a response. Describe the response.

_____

_____

How do you think the response is important to the earthworm?

_____

_____

INTERNAL ANATOMY

Use Figures 19-4 and 19-5 as guides to the internal structure of the earthworm.

■ Open the worm from the darker **dorsal side,** and keep it covered with water while you work.
■ Notice the internal segmentation that corresponds to the external segmentation. Identify the internal **septum** between adjacent segments.
■ Locate the **dorsal blood vessel,** which carries blood from the anterior to posterior. The circulatory system has hemoglobin and the vessels have one-way valves.

■ Locate the five pairs of pumping blood vessels ("**hearts**") that connect the dorsal and ventral blood vessels.
■ Find the **ventral blood vessel,** the **ventral nerve cords,** and the subneural blood vessel. Blood in these vessels flows from posterior to anterior.
■ Indicate with arrows in Figure 19-4 how blood flows to and from the hearts.
■ Follow the large digestive tube back from the mouth as far as the clitellum, identifying the muscular **pharynx,** the **crop** (about segment 16), the **gizzard** (about segment 19), and the **intestine** (all the rest).
■ Within each segment find the paired **nephridia.** Each of these excretory organs is a coiled tube beginning with a nephrostome and leading to an **excretory pore.** The beginning of the tube is in the anteriorly adjacent segment. Fluid enters by ciliary action, and the tube excretes waste into the fluid and reabsorbs needed substances as it passes out of the body.
■ Locate the saclike **seminal receptacles** in segments 9 and 10.
■ Sperm made in the tiny testes are stored in the multilobed **seminal vesicles** until copulation. Then they pass out through the **vas deferens.**
■ **Ovaries** are located in segment 13, and the eggs are stored in the adjacent **egg receptacles** before being released through the **oviducts.**

The earthworm does not have eyes or ears, but the epidermis contains light-sensitive cells and sensory bristles that are sensitive to vibration. The paired ventral nerve cords have fast-conducting neurons that allow the worm to retreat rapidly if it senses danger. In the head region, the nerve cords connect to swellings of nerve cells, called **ganglia,** by tracts of fibers that pass on either side of the digestive tract, just in front of the pharynx.

■ Locate the whitish paired ganglia at the anterior end of the central nerve cord that represent the earthworm's "brain." They are located dorsal to the digestive tract and just anterior to the pharynx.
■ Obtain and study a prepared slide of the cross section of an earthworm; compare your slide with Figure 19-2.
■ Locate the intestinal epithelium that forms the gut.
■ Locate the large space it surrounds, which is the **lumen** or interior of the intestine; the infolding at its top is the **typhlosole,** which increases the surface area available for absorption.
■ Notice the large coelom, which is the fluid-filled space between the muscular body wall and intestine, and which contains the body organs. In the earthworm the coelom acts as a hydrostatic skeleton.
■ Locate the blood vessels and the ventral nerve cord.
■ Surrounding the gut are **chloragen cells,** which aid in digestion and may represent primitive liverlike cells.
■ Find the coils of nephridium within the coelom. Depending on the section, you will see only parts of these paired organs, which are found in each segment.
■ Surrounding the coelom is a thick layer of longitudinal muscle. It functions to shorten the worm.
■ A thinner layer of circular muscle surrounds the longitudinal muscle. It contracts to lengthen the worm.
■ Locate the **cuticle** on the outside of the worm and the **hypodermis,** which secretes it.

When you are finished with your work, dispose of your specimens, return the demonstration materials, and store your microscope properly.

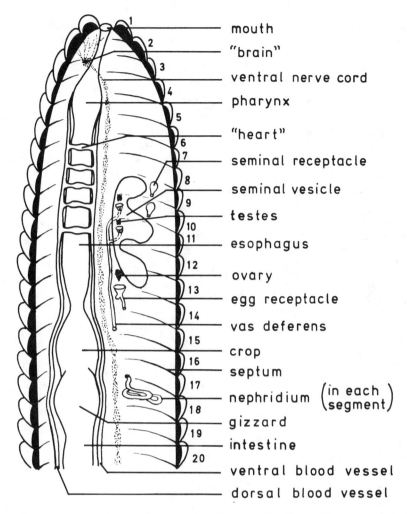

1 — mouth
2 — "brain"
3 — ventral nerve cord
4 — pharynx
5 — "heart"
6
7 — seminal receptacle
8 — seminal vesicle
9 — testes
10
11 — esophagus
12 — ovary
13 — egg receptacle
14 — vas deferens
15 — crop
16 — septum
17 — nephridium (in each segment)
18 — gizzard
19 — intestine
20 — ventral blood vessel
— dorsal blood vessel

Figure 19-4.   Internal structure of the earthworm, *Lumbricus*. The dorsal side is toward the left. Sense organs are lacking, but there is a well developed nervous system, closed circulatory system, complete digestive tract, and excretory organs.

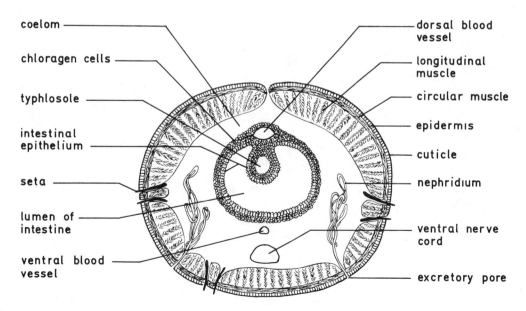

coelom
chloragen cells
typhlosole
intestinal epithelium
seta
lumen of intestine
ventral blood vessel

dorsal blood vessel
longitudinal muscle
circular muscle
epidermis
cuticle
nephridium
ventral nerve cord
excretory pore

Figure 19-5.   Cross section of the earthworm, *Lumbricus*. The surface area of the intestine is doubled by the typhlosole, and the spacious, fluid-filled coelom acts as a hydrostatic skeleton in locomotion.

EXPLORING FURTHER

See also Topic 18 references.

Barrington, E. J. *Invertebrate Structure and Function.* 2nd ed. Boston: Houghton Mifflin, 1979.
Lane, F. W. *Kingdom of the Octopus.* New York: Sheridan House, 1965.
Morton, J. E. *Molluscs.* 4th ed. London: Hutchinson, 1979.

Journal Articles

Boycott, Brian B. "Learning in the octopus." *Scientific American,* March 1965 (#1006).
Feder, Howard M. "Escape responses in marine invertebrates." *Scientific American,* July 1972 (#1254).
Gosline, J. M., and M. E. DeMont. "Jet-propelled swimming in squids." *Scientific American,* 96, January 1985.
Jones, Douglas S. "Sclerochronology: Reading the record of molluscan shells." *American Scientist* 71(4):384–391, 1983.
Nichols, John G., and David Van Essen. "The nervous system of the leech." *Scientific American,* January 1974 (#1287).
Reid, R. G. B., and R. R. Bernard. "Gutless bivalves." *Science* 208:609, May 1980.
Roper, Clyde F. E., and Kenneth J. Boss. "The giant squid." *Scientific American,* 96, April 1982.
Stanley, Steven M. "Mass extinctions in the ocean." *Scientific American,* 64. June 1984.
Ward, Peter, Lewis Greenwald, and Olive E. Greenwald. "The bouyancy of the chambered nautilus." *Scientific American,* October 1980.
Willows, A. O. D. "Giant brain cells in mollusks." *Scientific American,* February 1971 (#1212).

Kingdom Animalia: Arthropods

OBJECTIVES

When you have completed this topic, you should be able to:
1. List the features of the phylum Arthropoda.
2. Describe adaptations of terrestrial arthropods that allow them to live on land.
3. List three factors that contributed to the success of insects.
4. Define metamorphosis and explain the difference between ametabolous, paurometabolous, hemimetabolous, and holometabolous metamorphosis.
5. Define the following arthropod structures and give the group(s) in which they are found: trachea, gill, book lung, spiracle, hemocoel, green gland, swimmerets, spinnerets, Malpighian tubules, antennule, antenna, labium, mandible, simple eye, compound eye, cephalothorax, carapace, chelicerae.

KEY TOPICS

Coelom, arachnids, crustaceans, insects.

INTRODUCTION

The majority of animal species are arthropods, and the biomass of insects alone outweighs that of human beings. Arthropods and annelids share a common ancestry, but the arthropods have gone on to fill every possible habitat on land and in the sea. Their success is mainly due to the development of a hard **exoskeleton** of chitin, a type of polysaccharide. This skeleton is light compared with the heavy shell of mollusks, and it is **jointed,** allowing flexibility of the body and appendages (arthropod = "jointed foot"). This versatile exoskeleton protects the animal's body and prevents terrestrial arthropods from drying out. It also serves as an attachment point for muscles so that well-developed locomotion is possible.

The presence of the exoskeleton also creates certain problems, however. Because the skeleton can't grow with the animal, it has to be shed or molted periodically, and the temporarily unprotected animal is vulnerable to attack during and immediately after the molting process. The skin cannot be used for detecting stimuli, so antennae and sensory bristles are used instead.

Although arthropods are coelomate, the **coelom** is mostly lost during development. The body cavity that you will see has a different origin. The body usually shows some signs of **segmentation,** and there is pronounced cephalization, with the mouth, nervous system, and sense organs concentrated in the region of the head. The **paired, jointed appendages** may be modified for other purposes in addition to locomotion. The original ancestral appendage was probably branched, as shown in Figure 20-1. Usually one branch or the other was lost, but sometimes both were retained. Modified appendages are used for chewing, biting, stinging, transferring sperm, chemoreception, and touch perception.

The sexes are separate, and arthropods usually copulate and have internal fertilization. Most arthropods care for the eggs in some way, either by depositing them in or on a food source, or carrying them around on their bodies until the young hatch. The larvae are often very different from the adults and must undergo **metamorphosis,** in which they change into the adult form in a short period of time.

All arthropods have a **complete digestive tract,** a **ventral nerve cord,** a body cavity filled with blood that serves as an **open circulatory system,** a **dorsal heart,** and an excretory organ.

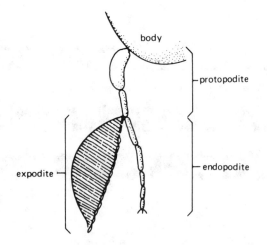

Figure 20-1. The basic arthropod append-age. In most arthropods, one branch or the other of the basic two-branched appendage is lost, but sometimes both branches are retained, especially in the crustaceans.

SUBPHYLUM CHELICERATA: CLASS ARACHNIDA

Spiders, ticks, mites, and scorpions are the major groups of arachnids. They all have **chelicerae,** appendages for piercing and sucking on their prey, and **pedipalps** that are sensory organs and help hold the prey during feed-ing. Pedipalps are modified for sperm transfer in males and they are the prominent pincers of scorpions. Arach-nids have four pairs of **walking legs.** Most arachnids are carnivorous predators or external parasites. The un-savory reputation of this group is well deserved, as far as humans are concerned: venomous spider bites, scorpion stings, Rocky Mountain spotted fever spread by ticks, scabies mites, and lice. There is even a mite that lives at the base of human eyelashes and sometimes causes se-vere irritation of the eyelids.

■ Examine the variety of preserved arachnids on dem-onstration. What obvious feature is shared by all arach-nids? _____

Do arachnids have antennae? _____

■ Note the division of the body into the **cephalo-thorax** and the large **abdomen.**

Are the legs attached to the cephalothorax or to the abdomen? _____

External Anatomy: The Spider

These predatory arachnids usually have **poison glands,** which open near the tips of the chelicerae. Once the prey is bitten, it will be quickly paralyzed by the poison. The spider will secrete digestive enzymes onto the prey tissue and then suck up the resulting broth. While spider bites are unpleasant, only a few species can inflict serious or fatal bites on humans.
    Spider anatomy is shown in Figure 20-2.

■ Examine a preserved spider in the dissecting micro-scope. Identify the **cephalothorax** with its **chelicerae** and **pedipalps.**
■ Examine the **eyes**: There are usually 4-8, and they are connected to the brain.

How many eyes does your specimen have?

_____

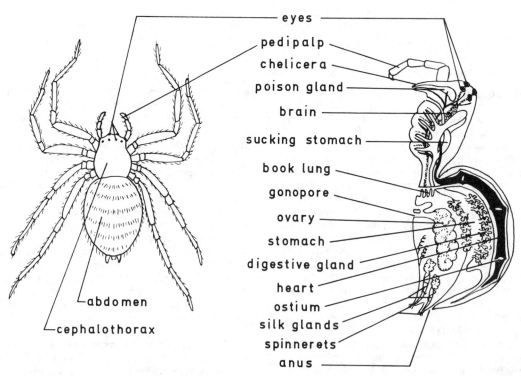

Figure 20-2.   Anatomy of a spider. The piercing mouth parts and sucking stomach obtain the liquid diet. Silk is spun from the silk glands and spinnerets in the abdomen.

The cephalothorax also contains the poison glands and a powerful **sucking stomach** with which the spider ingests its liquid diet.

Spiders spin their webs from a protein, produced by **silk glands,** that is extruded in liquid form from spinnerets at the tip of the abdomen and polymerizes into silk. The abdomen also contains gonads, digestive glands, and **book lungs** for gas exchange.

■ Look for the **spinnerets** on your spider specimen.

Manipulation of silk for a variety of purposes probably accounts for the great diversity and success of spiders.

SUBPHYLUM CRUSTACEA

Crustaceans are mostly marine and are predators or scavengers. They include a wide variety of animals: shrimp, lobsters, hermit crabs, brine shrimp, copepods, barnacles, beach fleas, and wood lice (sow bugs). Tiny crustaceans are an important link in the marine food chain and are the krill on which some whales feed. Along with centipedes, millipedes, and some insects, crustaceans have true jaws or **mandibles.** Crustaceans also have two pairs of feeding appendages, the **maxillae,** two pairs of **antennae,** and their appendages are often branched or biramous. In crustaceans such as the lobster, the shell is reinforced with calcium carbonate. Pigments in the shell give the animal protective coloration. The loss of one of these heat-sensitive pigments gives cooked lobsters their bright red color by revealing another pigment, which is heat stable.

External Anatomy: The Crayfish

■ Examine a preserved crayfish such as *Procambarus,* and use Figure 20-3 to locate the following structures: **antennae, antennules, rostrum, compound eyes, chelipeds** (pincers), the **carapace,** the covering of the **cephalothorax,** the segmented **abdomen** ("tail"), **walking legs, telson,** and **uropods.**

How many pairs of walking legs does the crayfish have in addition to the chelipeds? _____

■ On the ventral side locate the **swimmerets** on the abdomen, and examine the first pair. They are modified for the transfer of sperm in those mature males that are ready to mate.

Is your crayfish a mature male? _____

■ Also on the ventral side, locate the **mouth,** with the **mandibles** or true jaws, five pairs of specialized appendages between the mandibles and chelipeds, and the **anus.**

The mandibles tear the food, and the other appendages detect and hold the food during feeding. One pair is specialized to move water through the chamber around the gills.

■ Look for the excretory pore at the base of the antenna; it connects to the green gland that you will see later.

Internal Anatomy: The Crayfish

Use Figure 20-4 as your guide to the internal structure of the crayfish.

■ Carefully dissect away the dorsal half of the carapace to expose the internal organs of the cephalothorax.
■ Locate the diamond-shaped **heart** of the open circulatory system. The heart sends blood to the spaces around the organs through several arteries. After passing through the gills, the blood drains back into the heart through the openings (ostia) in it.
■ Remove the heart in order to see the **gonads** (ovaries or testes). Sperm exit at the base of the fifth walking legs, and eggs leave the oviducts at the base of the third walking legs.
■ Trace the digestive system from the mouth through the **esophagus** to the **cardiac stomach,** where food is ground up, then to the intestine leading to the anus.
■ Note the **extensor** (straightens) and **flexor** (curls up) muscles which fill the abdomen ("tail") of the crayfish.
■ Find the **green gland** or antennal gland located just behind each antenna; this excretory organ opens through the excretory pore that you identified previously.

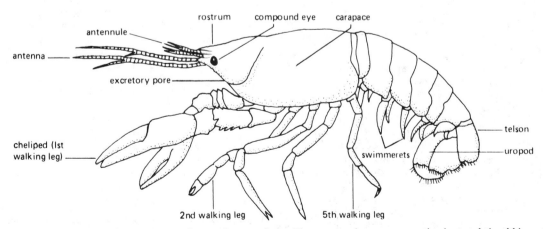

Figure 20-3. External structure of a male crayfish. The sperm ducts open at the base of the fifth pair of walking legs, and the first pair of swimmerets are modified for transferring sperm during copulation. In the female, the oviducts exit at the base of the third pair of walking legs.

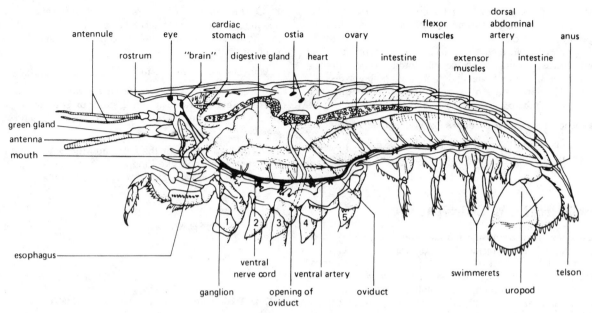

Figure 20-4. Internal anatomy of a female crayfish. In the male, the testes lead into paired sperm ducts, which open at the base of the fifth pair of legs. (From Wodsedalek, J. E., and Charles F. Lytle *General Zoology Laboratory Guide*. 8th ed. © 1971, 1977, 1981 by Wm. C. Brown Publishers, Dubuque Iowa. All rights reserved. Reprinted by permission.)

■ Note the large **liver,** or digestive gland, beneath the first part of the intestine.

■ Remove the internal organs to expose the **ventral nerve cord,** which lies along the bottom of the body cavity.

■ Locate a pair of nerves leading from the ventral nerve cord around the esophagus to the large ganglion, or **"brain"** in the head. Short nerves connect eyes, antennae, and antennules to the brain.

The nervous system is the main internal part of the crayfish that still shows segmentation: Each segment of the animal has a ganglion that controls most of the functions in that segment.

■ Find a **ganglion,** or swelling, along the ventral nerve cord. It controls the organs in its own segment but is also subject to influence by messages from adjacent ganglia and the brain.

The gills of the crayfish are located outside the body cavity in a space between the body wall and the carapace.

■ Remove a segment of the carapace on one side of the crayfish to expose the **gills.**

■ Detach one of the walking legs, and note the small gill that is attached to the leg.

The leg and gill are a modified form of the branched appendage shown in Figure 20-1. The leg represents the endopodite, the gill represents the exododite, and the base of the leg is the protopodite. Branched appendages are common in crustaceans.

Male and female crustaceans copulate, fertilization is internal, and the fertilized eggs are attached to the swimmerets of the female. She carries them around until they hatch into young that resemble the parents. In some marine crustaceans, the eggs hatch into a nauplius larva that bears three pairs of appendages.

SUBPHYLUM UNIRAMIA: CLASS INSECTA

Insects, centipedes, and millipedes are grouped together in subphylum Uniramia because their appendages have only one branch (see Figure 20-1). Insects are the most successful invertebrate group and the only group besides vertebrates to inhabit all terrestrial environments. They have come to occupy habitats in which they don't directly compete with vertebrates and have remained small in size. They survive on land by tolerating fluctuations in the salt and water content of the body, and they have developed a unique **tracheal system** for respiration. The insect body consists of three parts: head, thorax, and abdomen. The head has antennae, **compound eyes** (unique to insects), and modified mouth parts. The thorax always bears three pairs of walking legs and one or two pairs of wings, if wings are present. As in the other arthropods, the body cavity is filled with blood, which is pumped through the open circulatory system by the heart. Excretion is performed by **Malpighian tubules,** which empty into the gut. Most insects copulate and lay eggs. The young go through a series of molts before becoming sexually mature adults. Some insects have larval stages that are very different from the adult in structure, diet, and habitat.

External Anatomy: The Grasshopper

Grasshoppers are common herbivorous insects found in dry grasslands and open spaces. Use Figure 20-5 to identify the parts of its body.

■ Examine a preserved grasshopper, and note the large jumping legs and the huge compound eyes.

The compound eyes of insects consist of many units adjacent to each other (ommatidia). These individual

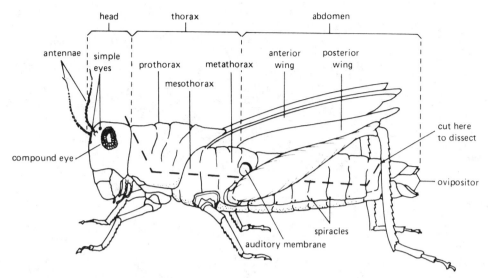

Figure 20-5. External structure of a female grasshopper. The male lacks the ovipositor and has a blunt abdomen. Open the exoskeleton by cutting along the dotted lines. (Redrawn from Peter Abramoff, and Robert G. Thomson, *Laboratory Outlines in Biology II.* San Francisco. W. H. Freeman and Company, © 1972.

units detect degrees of light and dark and combine to form a mosaic. The combination of the pattern of light and dark on the whole array of simple eyes can be interpreted by the grasshopper's brain as an image. The image on a TV screen is formed by light and dark spots in a similar way. The resolution of the image is not very good compared with that of the vertebrate eye, but detection of rapidly changing images is much better. Insects have color vision.

■ Find the three **simple eyes** (ocelli) on the top of the head. They detect quickly moving objects.

Are the **antennae** jointed? _____

■ Examine the mouth parts shown in Figures 20-6 and 20-7.
■ Find the **labrum** (upper lip), **labia** (lower lips, usu-

ally fused), **mandibles** (true jaws), which surround the mouth, and **maxillae** (second jaws).
■ Within the mouth parts is the **hypopharynx** ("tongue"). In other insects the hypopharynx may be modified for piercing or sucking.
■ The two pairs of appendages below the mouth (maxillary and labial palps) have sensory receptors.
■ The segmented **thorax** bears the three pairs of **legs** and two pairs of **wings.**
■ Stretch out the wings, and note the difference between the protective anterior wings and the posterior flight wings.
■ The abdomen is blunt in males and has a pointed **ovipositor** for laying eggs at the posterior end in females.

Is your grasshopper a male or female?

_____.

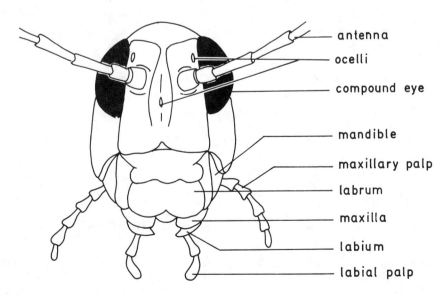

Figure 20-6. Head-on view of a grasshopper. The mouth is located below the labrum, and the tonguelike hypopharynx (not visible) is between the mandibles and labia.

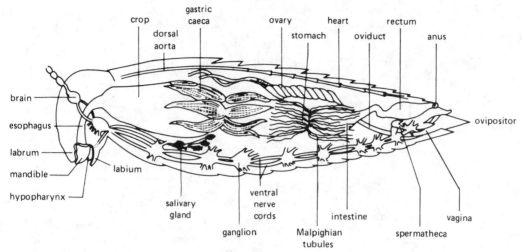

Figure 20-7.   The internal organs of a female grasshopper. In the male, the testes lead into seminal vesicles and then to the penis. There is no ovipositor. (Redrawn from Peter Abramoff and Robert G. Thomson, *Laboratory Outlines in Biology II.* San Francisco. W. H. Freeman and Company, © 1972.

■ Locate the **spiracles** along the sides of the thorax and abdomen. They connect to the **tracheal system** through which insects carry on gas exchange. The three anterior pairs of spiracles take in air, and the posterior ones let it pass out. The spiracles can be closed, if necessary, to prevent too much water loss under dry conditions.

■ Just above the jumping legs find the **auditory membranes.** These allow the grasshopper to detect sound and communicate with other grasshoppers, especially those of the opposite sex.

Internal Anatomy: The Grasshopper

■ Remove the wings of the grasshopper.
■ Cut along the dotted line as shown in Figure 20-5, and remove the dorsal part of the exoskeleton. Cover the internal organs with water to keep them from drying out.
■ Study the internal part of the exoskeleton that you have cut off, and find the muscles that attach to the wings; these are the **insect flight muscles,** which are rich in mitochondria and perform more efficiently than any vertebrate muscle.

The internal organs are shown in Figure 20-7.

■ Note the muscles along the body wall that move the legs. In an animal with an exoskeleton, muscles at the joints work in pairs to extend (straighten) or flex (bend) the joint.

■ Note the body cavity, or **hemocoel,** which in life is filled with blood. There is no respiratory pigment because respiration is carried out by the tracheal system.

What is the function of insect blood?

_____

_____

■ Look for the **dorsal aorta** and the **heart.** Blood entering the heart through small openings (ostia) is pumped forward and enters the hemocoel near the brain.
■ Locate the **esophagus** through which food passes from the **mouth** to the large **foregut.**

■ Find the outpocketings of the gut, called gastric caeca, at the posterior end of the crop.
■ The large **midgut** leads into the **hindgut.** The **Malpighian tubules** excrete nitrogenous wastes, mainly **uric acid,** into the gut at the point where these sections of the gut join.
■ Locate the **rectum,** which empties through the **anus**; it absorbs water.

The sex organs are located in the posterior part of the abdomen.

■ In the male, locate the **testes,** which produce sperm that are stored in the **seminal vesicles** and eventually deposited in the female by the **penis.**
■ In the female, the sperm are deposited in the **vagina** and stored in the **spermatheca.** Eggs produced in the large **ovaries** are fertilized by the sperm within the body of the female and are deposited with the ovipositor.
■ Remove the digestive organs to see the **ventral nerve cords.** At their anterior end, nerves pass around the esophagus to the **ganglion** of the brain.

Do the ventral nerve cords have ganglia in each segment, as in the crayfish? _____

Insect Metamorphosis

Metamorphosis differs in the various groups of insects: In some insects the young that hatches from the egg is similar to the adult, but in others it is completely different. There are four types of development.

1. **Ametabolous:** The young are tiny versions of the wingless adult.
2. **Paurometabolous:** The young nymphs are similar to the adults, but lack wings and are sexually immature.
3. **Hemimetabolous:** The young **naiads** are aquatic larvae with gills and are unlike the adults.
4. **Holometabolous:** The wormlike **larva** passes through the resting stage of the **pupa** before emerging as a mature adult.

Turn back to the LIFE HISTORY section of Topic 10, and review the developmental stages of *Drosophila,* a fly that belongs to the holometabolous order Diptera.

■ If you have not already done so, examine a culture bottle of *Drosophila* and identify the **egg, larva, pupa, and adult.**

■ Note the white, oval eggs. Each one has two tiny extensions.

■ Note the dark-colored pupae, which contain flies about to emerge as adults.

■ Try to find newly hatched adults whose wings are not yet fully extended. They need to dry in the air and stiffen before they can be used for flight.

■ The largest larvae are the ones that are about to pupate, and the smallest ones are newly hatched from the egg. Each stage of larval development is called an **instar,** and the stages are separated by **molting** (*Drosophila* has three instars).

When you are finished with this laboratory, dispose of your specimens as directed by your instructor, and clean your dissecting tools before putting them away.

■ Answer the review questions at the end of this topic.

EXPLORING FURTHER

Barnes, R. D. *Invertebrate Zoology,* 4th ed. Philadelphia: W. B. Saunders, 1980.

Borror, D. J., D. M. DeLong, C. A. Triplehorn. *An Introduction to the Study of Insects.* 4th ed. New York: Holt, Rinehart and Winston, 1976.

Buchsbaum, R. *Animals Without Backbones.* 2nd rev. ed. Chicago: University of Chicago Press, 1975.

Evans, H. E. *Life on a Little Known Planet.* Chicago: University of Chicago Press, 1984.

Russell-Hunter, W. D. *A Life of Invertebrates.* New York: Academic Press, 1979.

Wilson, E. O. *Insect Societies.* New York: Academic Press, 1971.

Journal Articles

Batra, Suzanne W. T. "Solitary Bees." *Scientific American,* 120, February 1984.

Burgess, J. W. "Social spiders." *Scientific American,* March, 1976.

Dyer, Fred C., and James L. Gould. "Honeybee Navigation." *American Scientist 71(6),* 587 (1983).

Heinrich, Bernd. "The regulation of temperature in the honeybee swarm." *Scientific American,* 146, June 1981.

Hinton, H. E. "Insect eggshells." *Scientific American,* August 1970 (#1187).

Hölldobler, Berthold D. K., and E. O. Wilson. "Weaver ants." *Scientific American,* December 1977 (#1373).

Horridge, G. Adrian. "The compound eye of insects." *Scientific American,* July 1977 (#1364).

Jones, Jack Colvard. "The feeding behavior of mosquitoes." *Scientific American,* June 1978 (#1392).

Merritt, R. W. and J. B. Wallace. "Filter-feeding insects." *Scientific American,* 132, April, 1981.

Rothschild, Miriam, Y. Schlein, K. Parker, C. Neville, and S. Sternberg. "The flying leap of the flea." *Scientific American,* November 1973 (#1284).

Seeley, Thomas D. "The ecology of temperate and tropical honeybee societies." *American Scientist 71(3),* 264 (1983).

Wicksten Mary K. "Decorator crabs." *Scientific American,* February 1980 (#1462).

Wilson, E. O. "Slavery in ants." *Scientific American,* June 1975 (#1323).

Student Name _____ **Date** _____

REVIEW

Figure 20-8. *Peripatus.* This rare, nocturnal animal lives in tropical rain forests and may be on the way to extinction. (Photo by Carolina Biological Supply Company)

Peripatus is a small, velvety animal that is particularly interesting because it combines several important features of arthropods and some features of annelids. (See Figure 20-8.)

State whether each of the following characteristics is also found among the annelids, arthropods, both, or neither. Then decide in which group you would place *Peripatus* and defend your answer.

wormlike body _____

thin, soft cuticle _____

unjointed legs _____

claws on legs _____

serially duplicated organs _____

jaws derived from appendages _____

open circulatory system _____

heart _____

coiled excretory tubes with external pores _____

carnivorous nutrition _____

2 ventral nerve cords _____

respiratory pores all over body _____

I suggest placing *Peripatus* in phylum _____. My rationale for this choice is

_____

_____

_____

_____

(Most biologists place *Peripatus* in its own phylum, Onychophora = claw bearer.)

Kingdom Animalia: Vertebrates

OBJECTIVES _____

When you have completed this topic, you should be able to:
1. Explain how cleavage, mesoderm formation, and coelom formation occur in protostomes and in deuterostomes.
2. List the three important characteristics of chordates.
3. List characteristics that would permit you to distinguish members of the following classes: Chondrichthyes, Osteichthyes, Amphibia, Aves, and Mammalia.
4. Name the class of any vertebrate presented to you.
5. Distinguish between analogous structures and homologous structures and give examples of each.
6. Describe the anatomy of one representative vertebrate in detail, and be able to describe the major features that are similar to and different from those of the other classes of vertebrates.
7. Identify any of the structures in the review list at the end of this topic in any vertebrate in which it occurs.
8. List and explain the problems encountered by water-dwelling vertebrates in adapting to life on land.
9. Explain the adaptations of a representative member of each of the terrestrial classes of vertebrates that allow it to live on land successfully.

KEY TOPICS _____

Deuterostome characteristics, chordate characteristics, vertebrate characteristics, analogy, homology, cartilaginous fish, bony fish, amphibians, reptiles, birds, mammals, transition to land.

INTRODUCTION

The remaining two phyla that we will consider, Echinodermata and Chordata, are the **deuterostomes.** In contrast to the protostomes, they are similar in having these important features of development:

1. The blastopore becomes the anus and the mouth develops in another way.
2. Cleavage of the egg is radial.
3. Cleavage is determinate.
4. Mesoderm is formed by pouches from the gut.
5. The coelom is formed from mesodermal pouches by enterocoely.

Evolutionary relationships among the deuterostomes are described in Figure 26-13 in your text. The development of a representative echinoderm, a sea urchin, will be considered in Topic 31.

Here we will study some vertebrates, members of Subphylum Vertebrata in Phylum Chordata. Along with the other chordates (urochordates and cephalochordates) vertebrates have at some point in their life history:

1. a dorsal notochord
2. a dorsal, hollow nerve cord
3. pharyngeal gill slits

A typical chordate is a coelomate with three germ layers. The body is a tube within a tube, segmented, and bilaterally symmetrical. There is an endoskeleton, a closed circulatory system with a ventral heart and a post anal tail. When these features are compared with those of an annelid or arthropod, the enormous divergence of the protostome and deuterostome branches of the animal kingdom becomes apparent.

In vertebrates: 1) A vertebral column replaces the embryonic notochord. It surrounds and protects the nerve chord and serves as the backbone in locomotion. 2) The dorsal hollow nerve cord develops a brain with three primary vesicles dividing it into forebrain, midbrain, and hindbrain and with many cranial nerves. 3) The pharyngeal gill slits that are present in the embryo develop into other structures (such as the Eustachian tubes). In addition, vertebrates have the following characteristics:

4. Along with the marked cephalization of the nervous system and sense organs, a cranium develops to surround and protect these structures in the head region.
5. There are red blood cells (erythrocytes), which contain hemoglobin.
6. The ventral heart has 2, 3, or 4 chambers.
7. There is a pair of nephric kidneys.
8. There is a solid liver.
9. There is a pancreas or pancreatic tissue.
10. There are specific endocrine organs.
11. The eye has a lens and a retina.
12. There are olfactory organs, which are usually paired.
13. There are one to three semicircular canals forming part of the inner ear.
14. Muscles attach to the endoskeleton for efficient locomotion, often by means of two pairs of appendages.

These are the classes of Vertebrata that we will be studying in this exercise:

Class Chondrichthyes (cartilaginous fishes: for example, sharks, skates, and rays)
Class Osteichthyes (bony fishes: for example, perch, mackerel)
Class Amphibia (amphibians: for example, frogs, toads, newts, and salamanders)
Class Aves (birds: for example, robin, osprey, penguin, duck, ostrich)
Class Mammalia (mammals: for example, cows, horses, whales, rabbits, humans)

Before beginning your examination of vertebrate diversity, take a few moments to focus on the vertebra, a small but important structure that has greatly contributed to the evolutionary success of this group.

■ Examine the **vertebra** on demonstration and identify the parts shown in Figure 21-1. The **dorsal process** is one of the sets of bumps you feel if you run your hand down a cat's back. The spinal cord runs through the large opening. Lateral displacement of adjacent vertebrae would put pressure on the spinal cord, resulting in severe pain and possibly permanent damage.

The centrum marks the position of the embryonic notochord, which has been surrounded and replaced by bone. A spongy **invertebrate disc** lies between the centra of adjacent vertebrae and allows some flexibility of the backbone. A "slipped" or ruptured disc will change the alignment of the vertebrae and put pressure on the spinal cord.

In this laboratory, you will learn something about the vertebrates by observing the demonstrations, dissecting a representative of one of the vertebrate classes, and studying the dissections made by other members of the class. At the end of this exercise there is a list of important structures that you should be able to identify in any vertebrate in which they occur.

When you study the structures of the various vertebrates, you will often notice structures that appear similar, such as the leg of a frog and that of a cat. If the structures develop from similar rudiments in the embryo and have a similar structure and development, they are considered **homologous** and point to an evolutionary relationship between the animals. Homologous structures may be modified for purposes as different as flight (the wing of a bird) and swimming (the fin of a whale).

Structures that appear externally similar and are used for similar purposes but have very different structures and development are **analogous.** The wings of butterflies and birds are analogous limbs used for flight, but their structure and development are distinct and their presence does not imply a close evolutionary relationship.

Your instructor will provide dissection guides to help you understand the structure of your specimen. If you are going to work with a preserved specimen, rinse off the preservative at the sink before examining the external features. Dissect from the ventral side, first removing the skin by separating it and peeling it back from the abdominal wall. Once the abdomen is open, use your fingers and blunt probe for most of the dissection. You can study much of the internal anatomy by moving organs aside so that you can look underneath. If it is necessary to remove a structure, do it carefully without damaging adjacent organs.

When working with preserved specimens, you should not wear contact lenses. Use eyeglasses or safety glasses, if you have them, and protect your hands with liberal amounts of hand cream before beginning work.

READ THE GENERAL PROCEDURES SECTION IN TOPIC 25 BEFORE BEGINNING WORK ON YOUR SPECIMEN.

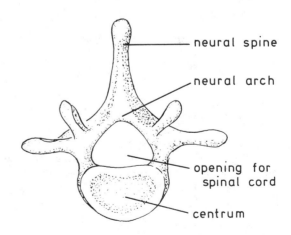

Figure 21-1. A vertebra. In the vertebral column the spinal cord would pass through the large opening and there would be soft discs between adjacent vertebrae to cushion the centra.

CLASS CHONDRICHTHYES

Classes Chondrichthyes and Osteichthyes are grouped together as the fish in Superclass Pisces. They are aquatic animals with highly vascularized gills.

■ Study the preserved dogfish shark on demonstration.

Sharks represent animals that are well adapted to a highly motile, carnivorous way of life. The skeletal elements in the region of the gills have been moved forward to form jaws used for predation. Fins are paired, and the shark's powerful musculature makes it an excellent swimmer and allows it to pursue and catch prey.

Where are the **jaws** located in relation to the head?

_____

■ Feel the skin of the shark. The roughness is caused by **placoid scales,** or dermal denticles, which arise from the dermis of the skin.

Modified denticles form the teeth, which can easily be replaced as they become worn or lost. The structure of a shark's jaw and denticles and the internal structure of a single denticle are shown in Figure 21-2.

■ Remove a section of skin on the side of the shark's body to see the segmented musculature underneath.

What other sign of segmentation do you see in the shark's external anatomy?

_____

How many pairs of fins does the shark have?

_____

If your specimen is a male, the posterior **pelvic fins** will be modified into claspers which transfer sperm during copulation.

Is your shark male or female?_____

■ Locate behind the eye the **spiracle** through which some water may enter the pharynx.

How does water leave the pharynx?

_____

_____

■ The **eye** has a lens and retina with rods and cones so the shark can apparently see color; its vision is not especially keen.

Does the eye have an eyelid? Explain why or why not.

_____

_____

_____

Along the side of the shark is a light stripe marking the position of the **lateral line organ,** which is sensitive to pressure changes in the water. Part of the system in the head region (ampullae of Lorenzini) is modified to sense electrical fields. This sense allows the shark to detect hidden prey. Because strong electrical fields repel sharks, this sense also allows humans to discourage sharks from visiting beaches by setting up artificial electric fields in the water.

■ Locate the **olfactory sacs** anterior to the mouth. If you pass a probe into one, you will see that it does not connect to the **oral cavity** and is a blind sac. It contains chemoreceptors that allow sharks to sense chemicals in the water.

Within the skull the shark has an inner ear with **semicircular canals.** There are three canals, in the three perpendicular planes. The inner ear detects movement of the head and allows the shark to keep track of its position. All vertebrates have a similar organ of equilibrium.

■ Open the shark's abdomen by cutting around the cloacal area and then toward the head. Cut through the pectoral girdle, and pin back the flaps of the body wall so that the dissection looks like the shark shown in Figure 21-3.

Figure 21-2. The jaw and tooth of a shark. As teeth become worn or are lost, they are replaced by new ones from the rows on the inner sides of the jaws. (Photo: C. Eberhard)

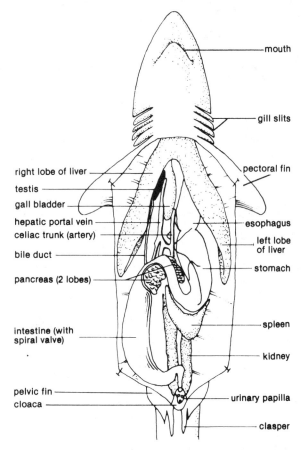

Figure 21-3. Internal anatomy of a male shark.

■ Locate the following internal organs (most of these appear in Figure 21-3):

Esophagus. Slit it open to see the papillae inside.
Stomach (J-shaped). Open the stomach to identify the last meal. Notice the rugae (folds) inside.
Small intestine. Open it to see the **spiral valve** inside.

What is the function of the shark's spiral valve?

_____

_____

Rectum. Empties into the cloaca.
Rectal gland. Excretes sodium chloride for osmoregulation.
Pancreas. Two lobes.
Liver. This organ is composed of three large oil-filled lobes and is critical in maintaining the buoyancy of open ocean sharks, which must swim or sink.
Gall bladder. A greenish organ located underneath the liver.
Spleen. Triangular shape, alongside stomach.
Kidneys. Long bandlike organs that extend along almost the entire length of the peritoneal cavity. They drain through the ducts into the cloaca. Most sharks are marine and must conserve water, but the kidneys are not efficient and remove a lot of water as they remove urea from the blood. Sharks osmoregulate by keeping the level of urea in the blood and tissue high, so that water actually tends to enter the body.

Testes or **ovaries.** Located near the anterior ends of the kidneys.

In the female, eggs enter the oviducts and pass down into the uterus, which will be enlarged if the shark is pregnant. In the male shark, sperm from the testes pass through common urogenital ducts along the ventral surface of the kidneys to the cloaca. The **claspers** are used to transfer sperm into the female's reproductive tract; therefore, fertilization is internal. In dogfish sharks, the young develop in the female's body and then hatch as small sharks, a system called **ovoviviparous** development. Development lasts up to two years, and many young are born at once.

Cloaca. Common opening of the digestive and urogenital systems. The **urinary papilla** within the cloaca has the opening of the urogenital system.
Heart. Four chambers. Note the **atrium** and **ventricle.** Blood from the body drains into the **sinus venosus** and then into the atrium. The atrium leads into the muscular ventricle, which then forces the blood out through the **conus arteriosus.** The conus arteriosus is also muscular and has internal valves. There is a single circulation because there is only one pathway through the single atrium and ventricle.

Blood from the heart travels to the gills in the **ventral aorta** and **afferent branchial arteries.** It is reoxygenated as it passes through the gill capillaries. It then leaves in the **efferent branchial arteries,** enters the **dorsal aorta,** and is distributed to the body.

Respiration in many sharks depends on continuous swimming through the water so that fresh water enters the pharynx from the mouth and spiracles, then passes over the gill capillaries and out through the **gill slits.** The muscular action of the floor of the mouth and in the branchial region helps suck in and expel the water.

The brain of the shark is protected by a cartilaginous braincase. Your instructor may ask you to open the braincase and study the anatomy of the shark's brain. The shark's existence is mainly concerned with sensations of smell, sight, and equilibrium with little provision for decision making. This animal is truly an "eating machine" and as such has been highly successful since its ancestors evolved over 300 million years ago during the Devonian period.

CLASS OSTEICHTHYES

Like sharks, many bony fish are fast-swimming carnivores, but they have also evolved into a great variety of other types. Study the preserved perch on demonstration. Handle the specimen carefully because the spines are sharp.

Is the body as flexible as that of the shark?

_____

■ Remove a few scales and examine them in the microscope. These are **ctenoid scales,** which provide the fish with a tough but flexible covering. All the scales are covered by a layer of very thin skin.
■ Locate the growth rings on the exposed surface of the scale. They can be used to determine the approximate age of the fish.
■ Note the spiny dorsal **fins.**

How many pairs of fins does the fish have?

_____

Most of the propelling force comes from the tail and caudal fin, with the other fins used for balance and direction control.

■ Find the **anus,** which serves only as the opening of the digestive tract, unlike the cloaca of the shark, which is also the urogenital opening. It is in front of the anal fin.
■ The **operculum** covers the gill slits, and water enters through the mouth. The pectoral fins are just behind the opercula.

Where is the **mouth** located in relation to the head?

_____

How is this an advantage?

_____
_____

■ Examine the inside of the mouth.

Do you find teeth or a tongue? _____

In bony fish that have teeth, the teeth are conical, all alike and set into the jaw bones.

Is there an eyelid to cover the **eye**?

_____

■ Find the pores of the **lateral line organ** along the side of the fish. This organ (as in the shark) senses pressure change in the water.
■ The **olfactory sacs** are located anterior to the eyes. They are blind sacs that do not connect with the oral cavity and that contain chemoreceptors used in olfaction.

Within the bony skull is the inner ear with three perpendicular **semicircular canals.** The inner ear is an organ of equilibrium used to detect the fish's position.

Some of the internal organs are shown in Figure 21-4.

■ Open the abdominal cavity of the fish by filleting away the muscles along one side, and locate as many organs as you can.

Liver. A reddish organ in the perch.
Esophagus. Leads to the stomach.
Stomach. Has three pouches called pyloric caeca; empties into the duodenum, the first part of the small intestine.
Intestine. There is no spiral valve, so the intestine is longer than in the shark; exits from the body via the anus.
Spleen. Located next to the stomach.
Swim bladder. This whitish, translucent organ fills the dorsal part of the body cavity. It is derived from the pharynx during development and makes the fish buoyant. As a result, the fish can remain stationary without moving its fins. Gases are secreted into the swim bladder by the red organ or rete mirabile.
Kidneys. Blackish organs that are diffuse and located dorsal to the swim bladder.
Urinary bladder. Located in the posterior of the body cavity; copious, dilute urine exits through the **urogenital pore** just posterior to the anus.
Testes or **ovaries.** The gonads fill much of the posterior part of the body cavity. Gametes (eggs and sperm) are shed to the exterior through the urogenital pore.

Most fish reproduce by external fertilization and a great many small eggs are shed. Some fish brood or care for the eggs and young. Many don't, however, and in this case there is often very high mortality among their offspring. This type of reproduction in which the eggs develop externally is **oviparous.**

Heart. This four-chambered organ has an **atrium** and a **ventricle.** Blood enters the heart from the body through the **sinus venosus** and leaves through the

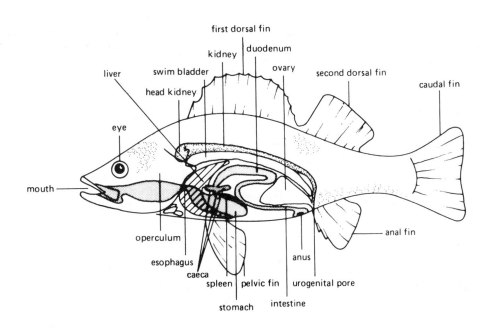

Figure 21-4. Internal anatomy of a female perch.

muscular **conus arteriosus.** The **ventral aorta** and **afferent branchial arteries** take blood from the heart to the gills where it is reoxygenated in the gill capillaries. It leaves in the **efferent branchial arteries,** enters the **dorsal aorta,** and is sent to the rest of the body. Fish have basically the same pattern of circulation as sharks.

■ Remove the bony **operculum** that covers the **gill slits.**

What is the function of the operculum?

_____

How many gill slits does the perch have?

_____

■ Notice the **gill rakers** that support and protect the delicate gill filaments.

Water enters the mouth, passes from the pharynx through the gills, aerating the capillaries in the gill filaments so that gas exchange can occur, and finally exits through the operculum. If the fish is not moving, it can pump water through the gills by opening and closing its mouth and using muscles of the pharynx to force water out through the gills.

The brain of the perch is small and deals mainly with smell, sight, and equilibrium. Olfactory nerves leading from the olfactory sacs to the olfactory bulbs are prominent.

■ Examine the teleost skeleton on demonstration.
■ Notice how the flexible fin rays interact with the fish's skeleton. They make the fish highly maneuverable.

How is the skull different from your own?

_____

_____

CLASS AMPHIBIA

Amphibia, Reptilia, Aves, and Mammalia are grouped together as the four classes of **tetrapods,** or **quadrupeds.** The amphibian ancestors of tetrapods evolved from fishlike ancestors that were aquatic, but present-day tetrapods have for the most part taken up a permanent existence on the land and become terrestrial. If you have ever watched a fish out of water suffocate and quickly die, you realize that the evolution from an aquatic to a terrestrial existence must have been gradual. Many adaptations arose during the transition.

Frogs and toads belong to a group of amphibians, the Aneurans, that have no tail and that have a skeleton adapted for jumping. The pectoral and pelvic girdles are fused to the backbone, which is very short.

■ Examine the frog skeleton on demonstration.

Are the vertebrae also fused? _____

If live frogs are available, study the behavior of the intact animal.

■ Observe its stance and its jumping and swimming motions.

Are the **limbs** attached to the sides or to the ventral side of the trunk? _____

How many **digits** ("fingers") are there on the forelimbs?

_____

On the hindlimbs? _____

Are the digits longer on the forelimbs or on the hindlimbs? _____

Do the digits have claws? _____

What adaptation for swimming do you see?

_____

If the frog is male, there may be an enlarged pad on the side of the inner digit of its forelimb. It helps the male grip the female during mating (amplexus).

Is the skin of the living frog dry or moist?

_____

■ Notice the **cloaca** at the posterior end of the abdomen into which the digestive and urogenital systems open.
■ Study the head region: The **eyes** are very large and adapted to spotting insects, which are the staple of the frog's diet.
■ Find the **nictitating membrane,** which is a transparent eyelid that can close over the eye to keep it clean without blocking the frog's vision.

Are upper and lower eyelids present? _____

■ Locate the external eardrum or **tympanic membrane.** The ear is derived from the lateral line organ, which is still present in aquatic and larval amphibians.

If you are studying a live frog, pith or anesthetize it according to the directions given by your instructor. Pithing instructions are given in Topic 27.

■ Open the mouth of the pithed, anesthetized or preserved frog, and find the sticky tongue with which it traps insects. It is a true tongue.

Is the frog's tongue attached like yours?

_____

■ Pass a hair or some soft probe into a **nostril** (external naris; pl.: nares) to see the connection with the oral cavity. The openings inside are the **internal nares.**
■ Locate the **vomerine teeth,** which are in the roof of the mouth. They hold the prey before it is swallowed by the frog.

Are there other teeth present on the upper jaw?

_____

On the lower jaw? _____

■ Cut the corners of the mouth so that you can open it all the way.
■ Find the large opening into the digestive tract and the small opening to the respiratory tract. The latter is called the **glottis,** and it is located on the floor of the pharynx (throat region).
■ Look for the openings at the posterior corners of the mouth that lead into the **vocal sacs** in a male frog.
■ Find the openings alongside the entrance to the esophagus that lead into the **Eustachian tubes** that connect with the middle ear.
■ Open the abdomen of the frog as follows: First cut the skin of the abdominal wall to **one side of the**

midline from the pelvic girdle to the throat region. Then cut the abdominal and chest muscles and the pectoral girdle. Continue the cuts to each side at the top and bottom of the incision. Then fold back the flaps so that your frog looks like the dissection shown in Figure 21-5. (This figure shows most of the organs in the frog's abdominal cavity.)

■ Find as many of these organs as you can.

Liver. Large with three lobes.

If your specimen is a female, the abdomen may be filled with masses of dark-colored eggs. Remove them carefully so that you can see the other organs.

Gall bladder. Bile from the liver is stored here and passes through the bile duct to the duodenum.

Esophagus. Leads to the stomach.

Stomach. Pyloric valve separates the stomach from the duodenum of the small intestine.

Small intestine.

Large intestine.

Rectum. Opens into the cloaca.

Fat bodies. Yellow structures with fingerlike projections.

Pancreas. Light-colored lobed organ located near the joining of the stomach and small intestine.

Spleen. Deep red round organ.

Kidney. The kidneys are flattened, reddish organs located in the dorsal part of the abdominal cavity, and extending about half its length. They can form concentrated urine.

Adrenal glands. Yellow bandlike organs on the ventral surface of the kidneys. They are endocrine glands.

Excretory ducts. Carry urine from the kidneys to the cloaca, where urine is stored in the bladder. Refer to a more detailed diagram before attempting to locate them.

Bladder. A thin, translucent sac in the ventral part of the posterior abdomen that opens into the cloaca. Water is actively reabsorbed from urine by the bladder.

Testes. Light yellow cylindrical organs located near the anterior ends of the kidneys. Sperm travel through **sperm ducts** into the kidneys, and then through the excretory ducts of the kidneys to the seminal vesicles from which they are released through the cloaca.

Ovaries. Located near the anterior end of the kidneys and attached to the body wall.

Oviducts. Long white coils. The enlarged **ovisac** at the posterior end holds the eggs prior to spawning.

During mating, the male mounts on the back of the female, a position called **amplexus,** and eggs and sperm are simultaneously released into the water. External fertilization follows amplexus, and the fertilized eggs develop into herbivorous larvae called tadpoles. The aquatic tadpoles undergo **metamorphosis** into the terrestrial, carnivorous adults.

■ If you have a live specimen, observe the beating heart. Locate the **right atrium, left atrium,** and **ventricle** of the three-chambered heart. The large branching vessel is the main artery, the **truncus arteriosus.**

■ Lift the ventricle to see the **posterior vena cava** and **anterior vena cava,** which lead into the thin-walled **sinus venosus.**

In frogs there are two circuits of the circulatory system, the **systemic circuit** to the body and the **pulmonary circuit** to the lungs, but they are only partially separated. Deoxygenated blood from the body returns to the right atrium, and oxygenated blood from the lungs

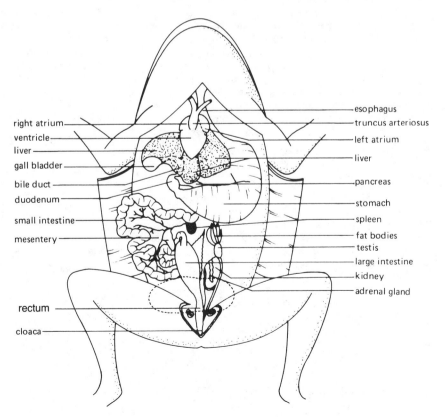

Figure 21-5. Internal anatomy of a male frog. The position of the bladder is shown by the dashed line. From *Laboratory Manual for Biology*, Fourth Edition. By W. H. Johnson, Louis B. Delaney, Thomas A. Cole, and Austin E. Brooks. ©1982 by Holt, Rinehart and Winston. Reprinted by permission of C. B. S. College Publishing.

right atrium
ventricle
liver
gall bladder
bile duct
duodenum
small intestine
mesentery
rectum
cloaca

esophagus
truncus arteriosus
left atrium
liver
pancreas
stomach
spleen
fat bodies
testis
large intestine
kidney
adrenal gland

returns to the left atrium. The blood enters the ventricle and is pumped out to the body and lungs. A spiral valve in the truncus arteriosus helps keep the oxygenated and deoxygenated blood separated. Some of the blood returning from the skin will be rich in oxygen, so there is mixing of oxygentated and deoxygenated blood in the ventricle to some extent. Thus the efficiency of the circulatory system is not as good as it would be if the circuits for oxygenated and deoxygenated blood were separated more completely. In reptiles, birds, and mammals, the skin is no longer used for respiration and the separation of the two circuits is more complete.

Be sure you understand how a frog heart differs from a fish heart and from your own mammalian heart.

■ Locate the small **lungs** by raising the liver. Both the lungs and the moist skin serve as respiratory organs to oxygenate the blood.

Does the frog have a diaphragm, a partition separating the heart and lungs from the other organs?

_____

The frog's brain has olfactory, visual, and equilibrium functions, but there are now cerebral hemispheres as well. The cerebral hemispheres help coordinate the activities of the other parts of the brain and allow the frog to take advantage of more complex behavior patterns.

CLASS AVES

Reptiles, birds and mammals are classed together as the **amniotes** because they produce an **amniotic egg** with a protective shell. They do not depend on water for respiration or reproduction and so are the only truly terrestrial vertebrates. In birds, the amniotic egg is fertilized internally and a shelled egg is laid. Development of the young bird is **oviparous.**

Birds and mammals are the only two classes of vertebrates that are **endothermic** and closely regulate body temperature. They use physiological and anatomical adaptations to maintain a high body temperature. As a result they can live where reptiles and amphibians cannot, and they can remain active during very cold weather. Their respiration and circulation efficiency must be high because they are such active animals and must continuously meet the demands of thermoregulation.

Birds are the only vertebrates that have **feathers.**

■ Look at the feathers on demonstration.
■ Study a contour feather in the dissecting microscope and identify its parts:

Quill. The hard, pointed end that attaches to the bird's skin.
Superior umbilicus. A small hole in the quill through which blood vessels pass.
Shaft. The hollow rod that supports the feather.
Barbs. The flexible filamentlike structures attached to the shaft. Notice how there is a system of tiny hooks called **barbules,** that lock the adjacent barbs into position. The **down** at the base of the contour feather lacks these barbules.

If there are down and pin feathers also on demonstration, describe how a down feather differs from a pin feather.

_____
_____

What are the two main functions of the feathers?

_____

■ Examine a preserved pigeon or other bird. There is only a tiny **tail,** and the forelimbs have become the **wings.** A special gland near the tail secretes oil for preening the feathers.

The jaws in birds move the horny bill or beak, in which are the external nares, and the brain is relatively large, filling much of the skull.

Does the bird have a **tongue?** _____

Is there a **nictitating membrane** over the eye?

_____

Are there **eyelids?** _____

The flexible neck allows great mobility of the head. Birds have very good color vision.

■ Examine the bird's feet, which retain **scales** like those of reptiles.

How many digits are present on each foot?

_____

Are there claws as in reptiles?

_____

One adaptation of birds for flight is that parts of the skeleton are fused for strength and many of the bones are hollow so that weight is reduced as much as possible.

■ Examine the internal structure of the bird skeleton on demonstration, and notice the internal struts that give the bones added strength. Some of the internal spaces in the bones are connected to the respiratory system.
■ Notice the enlarged breastbone, the **sternum.** The powerful pectoral muscles used in flight are attached to the sternum.
■ Locate the **cloaca,** which is the common exit for the urinary, genital, and digestive tracts. Birds have no bladder, so urine (mainly uric acid crystals) and feces are eliminated together in the bird's excrement, which in large deposits is called **guano** and makes excellent fertilizer.

The internal organs of the bird are shown in Figure 21-6.

■ Remove the skin and feathers over the region just below the neck, and expose the **crop,** which is an outgrowth of the esophagus.

What is the function of the crop?

_____

■ Cut open the crop to see what it contains.

In pigeons, the crop of both males and females produces "crop milk" during breeding season. It is regurgitated and used to feed the young birds.

■ Open the abdomen of the bird, first removing the skin and feathers, and locate the following structures, most of which are shown in Figure 21-6.

Liver. Empties into the small intestine directly through the bile ducts. There is no gall bladder.
Gizzard. Derived from the stomach and used to grind up the food, which is often hard kernels of grain.

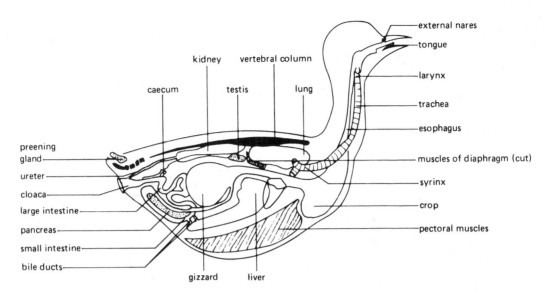

Figure 21-6. Internal anatomy of a male pigeon. There is no gall bladder or urinary bladder. The lungs connect to several air sacs within the abdominal and thoracic cavities and within the major bones (not shown).

Open the gizzard and see if any small pebbles are inside.

Small intestine.

Large intestine. Two small caeca (vestigial) are attached near the end of the large intestine.

Pancreas. Located in the folds of the small intestine.

Kidney. Long organ against the dorsal wall of the body cavity. Bird kidneys produce a concentrated urine containing uric acid.

Ureter. Leads into the cloaca. There is no bladder.

Testes. Located at the anterior end of the kidney; small unless the bird is preparing to breed.

Vas deferens. Leads from the testis to the cloaca. There is no penis in the pigeon nor in most birds. (A copulatory organ is present in primitive forms.) The cloacal areas of the male and female are simply pressed tightly together during mating.

Ovary. Only the left ovary is present; it is small unless the bird is breeding.

Oviduct. Again, only the left one is present. If the bird was breeding, there will be eggs in various stages of production within the oviduct. As the fertilized egg passes along, albumin, membranes, and a calcareous shell are added. The hard shell is necessary so that the egg won't collapse when the parent bird sits on it during incubation. All birds lay eggs and development is always **oviparous.**

■ Locate the **heart,** which is underneath the anterior portion of the sternum. You will have to cut away some of the bone. The four chambers are the **right atrium, left atrium, right ventricle,** and **left ventricle.** Birds require a very efficient circulatory system, and the systemic and pulmonary circuits are completely separated. The heart is fully divided into four chambers.

■ Trace the path of a red blood cell from the right atrium to the main artery leaving the heart, using Figure 26-1 as your guide. In birds the main artery, the aorta, has retained only the right branch, which becomes the **dorsal aorta.**

■ Remove one of the wings, and cut through the ribs near the vertebral column to expose the underlying organs.

■ Locate the compact **lungs** in the most anterior and dorsal part of the abdominal cavity, pressed against the dorsal body wall.

The lungs of the bird are unique in that they are connected to a system of **air sacs.** (See text Figure 37-4.) You will not be able to identify air sacs in your dissection. During ventilation, air is drawn through the lungs and into the air sacs, so the lungs do not expand much. During expiration, the air leaves the sacs and enters the lungs. Finally the air leaves after completing a circuit through the more-or-less one-way system. Most of the oxygenation of the blood takes place as the air flows through tiny air capillaries (parabronchi) within the lungs. This respiratory system is very efficient and meets the stringent demands of the bird's circulatory system during flight.

The vocal sounds made by a bird are produced in a special organ, the **syrinx,** which is located at the posterior end of the trachea, where it divides into the two bronchi. The **larynx** is the entrance to the trachea and is not involved in vocalization in birds.

■ Remove one of the lungs and locate the **syrinx** of the pigeon.

The brain of the pigeon has greatly enlarged **cerebral hemispheres,** which permit the complex behavior patterns characteristic of birds, such as courtship, pair bonding, mating, and migration. The **cerebellum** is well developed for the coordination required in flight.

CLASS MAMMALIA

Mammals are the only warm-blooded animals with **hair.** The hair and sweat glands are important in thermoregulation. Their mammary glands produce **milk** which is usually released through the **nipples** to nourish the young during their development. Usually the young are retained within the body of the female during early development and are nourished through the blood vessels of the **placenta.** This organ allows the fetal and maternal circulations to exchange nutrients and wastes during the **viviparous** development of the young within the mother's body. Characteristics of the reptilian ancestors of mammals are sometimes retained, however: certain mammals lay eggs, some have scaly tails, and many have claws on their hands and feet.

The major orders of mammals are described in your text. Because the variation among the different orders is so great, it is difficult to pick one that is "typical." In this exercise you will concentrate on the features of the rat, but try to keep in mind that the organs and systems that you are studying may be greatly modified in other mammals.

■ If you are studying live rats, observe their behavior while they are being anesthetized by an overdose of barbituate. Notice the sniffing behavior and the gradual loss of coordination. Barbituates and alcohol have a similar effect on the cerebellum and the rat's behavior is similar to that of a person who is very drunk.
■ In the fully anesthetized or preserved rat, note the hair and nipples that characterize all mammals.
■ Note the elongated snout with **vibrissae** (whiskers) used for tactile sensing.

Why is it advantageous to have the vibrissae as far forward as possible?

_____

■ Locate the **lips** and **nostrils.**

Does the **eye** have a nictitating membrane?

_____

■ Find the external ears, or **pinnae** (singular: pinna). The **eardrums** are in a protected position within the skull.
■ Notice the **scales** on the rat's tail.

Are there scales on the legs, as in the bird?

_____

Are there **claws** on the digits of the hands and feet?

_____

■ Locate the **anus,** the posterior opening of the digestive tract.
■ If your specimen is a male, locate the **penis** in the fur-covered **prepuce** or foreskin.

Is the penis directed anteriorly or posteriorly?

_____

■ If your specimen is a female, locate the **vagina** anterior to the anus and the **urinary opening** anterior to the vagina. The urinary and genital systems have separate openings as in human females.
■ Open the rat's mouth and investigate the attachment of the **tongue.**
■ Locate the **glottis,** which opens into the trachea (leading to the lungs), and its protective covering, the **epiglottis.**

Anterior to the anus in the male is the **scrotum** containing the **testes.** The testes are located outside the abdominal cavity because they must be cooler than the body temperature to produce sperm.

What is the function of the epiglottis while the rat is eating?

_____

■ On the roof of the mouth distinguish between the anterior **hard palate** and the posterior **soft palate.** The openings of the nasal passages are covered by the soft palate.
■ Locate the large **incisors,** which are the gnawing teeth characteristic of rodents. These teeth are constantly being worn down so they must grow at a fast rate.

The teeth of mammals show a lot of variation and have become differentiated to serve different purposes. **Incisors** are front teeth adapted for cutting or cropping the food as in humans and deer or for gnawing as in rodents. The **canines** are further back in the jaw and are for biting or holding prey and for tearing flesh as in a carnivore such as a wolf or lion. In herbivores they are greatly reduced and also serve for cropping. In the rear of the jaw are the **premolars** and **molars,** which have a flattened surface and are used to crush and grind the food. Molars are especially prominent in herbivores, which must spend a great deal of time chewing the food before it can be digested properly.

■ Examine the teeth of the skulls on demonstration and compare them to those of the rat.
■ Sometime during this lab, also examine and compare the mammalian skeletons on demonstration.
■ Cut open the skin of the rat over the abdomen from the pelvic girdle to the ribs, and cut sideways to form two flaps. Cut through the abdominal muscles to expose the internal organs.

The anatomy of the internal organs is shown in Figure 21-7. As you study your specimen, try to identify as many of the following organs as possible.

Esophagus. Leads to the stomach.
Stomach. Separated from the small intestine by the pyloric sphincter, a muscular valve.
Small intestine. Tightly coiled and very long compared to the size of the animal. A long intestine is characteristic of herbivores and omnivores like the rat.
Caecum. Enlarged sac at the beginning of the large intestine important in digestion in herbivores such as the horse.
Large intestine. Ends in muscular **rectum,** which probably contains some fecal pellets.
Liver. There is no gall bladder in the rat.
Pancreas. Located in the loop of the small intestine.
Spleen. Dark red organ that is located next to the stomach.
Kidneys. Compact organs in the dorsal part of the abdominal cavity. Urine travels through the **ureter** to the bladder where it is stored. Urine leaves the body through the **urethra,** which also carries sperm in the male. You will have to dissect below the intestine and abdominal membranes to see these structures.
Adrenal glands. Small oval glands at the anterior end of the kidneys.
Testes. Carefully cut open the scrotal sacs and the tough membrane that surrounds the testis. Sperm are stored in the highly convoluted tubules of the **epididymis** and are carried in the **vas deferens** to the urethra.
Seminal vesicles and **prostate.** These glands add fluids to the semen before it passes into the urethra.

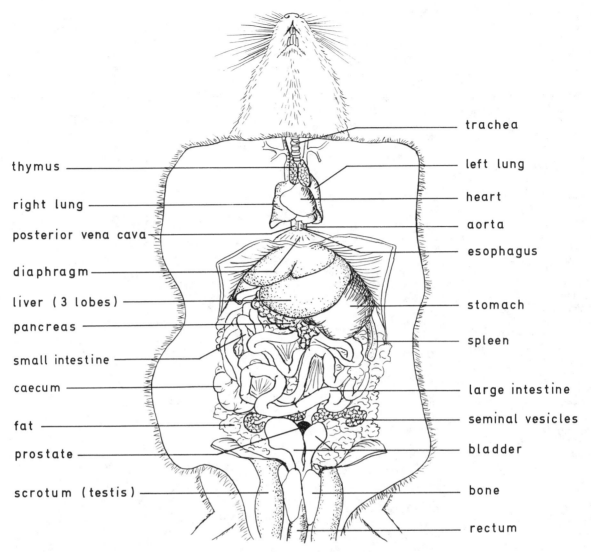

thymus

right lung

posterior vena cava

diaphragm

liver (3 lobes)

pancreas

small intestine

caecum

fat

prostate

scrotum (testis)

trachea

left lung

heart

aorta

esophagus

stomach

spleen

large intestine

seminal vesicles

bladder

bone

rectum

Figure 21-7. Internal anatomy of a male rat. Move the intestine aside to find the organs of the urogenital system.

Ovaries. Pea-sized organs attached to the body wall.
Oviducts. Tightly coiled tiny tubes leading from the ovaries to the horns of the uterus.
Uterus. Consists of two tubes, or **horns,** in which the embryos develop. The horns join together at the posterior end and enter the **vagina.**

If your specimen is a female, is she pregnant?

_____

■ Cut through the sternum and ribs to open the thorax and expose the **trachea;** it is kept open by its cartilaginous rings.
■ Locate the muscular **diaphragm,** which is a sheet separating the abdomen from the thorax. What is the function of the diaphragm?

_____

_____

■ Remove the glandular material anterior to and covering the heart. This is the **thymus gland,** which is im-

portant during the development of the immune system.

The structure of the heart and circulatory system is like that of other mammals. As in birds, the systemic and pulmonary circuits are completely separate because the chambers of the four-chambered heart are completely separate.

■ Identify the four chambers of the heart: **right atrium, left atrium, right ventricle,** and **left ventricle.**
■ Find the **pulmonary artery,** which is the most ventral vessel at the anterior end of the heart and carries blood from the right ventricle to the lungs.
■ Find the **aorta,** which is dorsal to the pulmonary artery. It carries blood from the left ventricle to the body. The aorta is the main artery of the system, and it developed from the left systemic arch that you saw in the frog.
■ Lift the ventricles of the heart to see the **posterior vena cava,** which carries blood from the head and forelimbs to the right atrium.
■ Find the dark **thyroid gland** covering the trachea in the neck region.

■ Locate the **right** and **left lungs.** Unlike those of the bird, they are closed sacs.

Within the lungs, gas exchange takes place across the thin membranes of the tiny air sacs (alveoli) located at the ends of the finely branching air tubes.

The brain of the rat has relatively large cerebral hemispheres. The enlarged olfactory bulbs show that smell is a very important sense in the rat. Vision is poor and unimportant. The visual functions are performed by the rear parts of the cerebral hemispheres.

REVIEW

Review what you have learned in this exercise by making sure that you have some understanding of each of the following structures or terms. If you are not sure of any, refer back to the text of this exercise. You should be able to locate the structures in boldface in any vertebrate in which they occur.

amnion
amniotic egg (cleidoic egg)
analogous structures
anterior
anterior vena cava
anus
aorta
aquatic
artery
atrium
auditory
bladder (urinary)
branchial arteries
caecum
carnivore
cerebellum
cerebrum
claspers
claws
cloaca
colon, or **large intestine**
conus arteriosus
crop
ctenoid scale
dermis
diaphragm
digits
dorsal
ear
endothermic
epidermis
esophagus
Eustachian tubes
external fertilization
eye
fins
gall bladder
gametes
gill slits
gizzard
glottis
gut
heart
herbivore
homologous structures
internal fertilization

intestine (large or small)
jaws
kidney
larva
larynx
lateral line
liver
lungs
milk
mucus
nares or **nostril (singular:naris)**
nictitating membrane
nipples
notochord
olfactory (lobes, bulbs, sacs)
omnivorous
optic
oral (buccal) cavity
ovary
oviduct
oviparous
ovoviviparous
palate (hard or soft)
pancreas
pectoral girdle
penis
pharyngeal gill slits
pharynx
pinna
placenta
placoid scale
posterior
posterior vena cava
pulmonary vein
rectal gland
renal
scales (of epidermis)
sinus venosus
skull or **cranium**
spiracle
spiral valve
spleen

stomach
swim bladder
syrinx
tadpole
teeth (incisors, canines, premolars, molars)
terrestrial
testis
tetrapod, or quadruped
tongue
trachea

tympanic membrane or **eardrum**
ureter
urethra
uterus
vagina
vein
ventral
ventricle
vertebra
vibrissa
viviparous
vomerine teeth

EXPLORING FURTHER

Romer, A. S., and T. S. Parsons. *The Vertebrate Body.* 5th ed. Philadelphia: W. B. Saunders, 1977.

McFarland, William N., F. Harvey Pough, Tom. J. Cade, and John B. Heiser. *Vertebrate Life.* New York: Macmillan, 1979.

Walker, W. F. *Vertebrate Dissection.* 6th ed. Philadelphia: W. B. Saunders, 1980.

Welty, J. C. *The Life of Birds.* 3rd ed. Philadelphia: Saunders College Publishing, 1982.

Journal Articles

Archibald, J. David, and William A. Clemens. "Late cretaceous extinctions." *American Scientist 70(4):* 377, 1982.

Baker, Mary Ann. "A brain-cooling system in mammals." *Scientific American,* May 1979 (#1428).

Buffetaut, Eric. "The evolution of the crocodilians." *Scientific American,* October 1979 (#1449).

Carey, Francis G. "Fish with warm bodies." *Scientific American,* February 1973 (#1266).

Gilbert, Perry W. "The behavior of sharks." *Scientific American,* July 1962 (#127).

Greenwaite, Crawford H. "How birds sing." *Scientific American,* November 1969 (#1162).

Hartline, Peter H., and Eric A. Newman. "The infrared 'vision' of snakes." *Scientific American,* 116, March 1982.

Heller, H. Craig, Larry I. Crawshaw, and Harold T. Hammel. "The thermostat of vertebrate animals." *Scientific American,* August 1978 (#1398).

Johansen, Kjell. "Air-breathing fishes." *Scientific American,* October 1968 (#1125).

Mossman, D. J., and W. A. S. Sarjeant. "The footprints of extinct animals." *Scientific American,* 74, January 1983.

Myers, C. W. and J. W. Daly. "Dart-poison frogs." *Scientific American,* 120, February 1983.

Ostrom, John H. "Bird flight: How did it begin?" *American Scientist 67:*461, 1979.

Russell, Dale A. "The mass extinctions of the late mesozoic." *Scientific American,* 58, January 1982.

Schmidt-Nielsen, Knut. "How birds breathe." *Scientific American,* December 1971 (#1238).

Wann, Langston Jr. "Pterosaurs." *Scientific American,* 122, February 1981.

The Plant Body: Structure and Function

KEY TOPICS

Leaves, stems, woody stems, xylem, phloem, roots, plant nutrition.

INTRODUCTION

Angiosperms are characterized by their **flowers** and their highly efficient **vascular tissues.** The rapid up-take of water and minerals by the **root system** (below ground) and their distribution to the **shoot system** (above ground) allow an angiosperm to maintain large leaves with broad surface areas. The higher rate of photosynthesis carried on by these leaves allows the plant to grow much more quickly than a gymnosperm, and it may reach reproductive maturity in a few weeks. The details of reproduction will be considered later. Here you will study the structure of flowering plants and the important role played by their vascular tissues.

Plants may survive for one, two, or many years. The **annuals** die after a season's growth and allow their seeds to continue the species the following spring. **Biennials** reproduce after two seasons and then die. **Perennials** live on for many years. The body of an annual grows mainly in length, from the tips of its shoot system and from the tips of its roots where actively dividing **meristem** is found. This type of growth is called **primary growth.** Some annuals and most perennials also increase in size sideways. This growth in girth is called **secondary growth** and is due to **lateral meristem.** The stem of some perennials—the trunk of a tree, for example—continues to increase in diameter year after year. Other perennials, such as the chrysanthemum and bulb-forming plants, die back each year and produce little or no secondary growth.

When secondary growth occurs, large amounts of **secondary xylem** called **wood** may be formed. This tissue gives great strength to the stems and roots of **woody plants.** Plants that do not form wood are called **herbs. Secondary phloem** is also produced.

Angiosperm plants show great diversity, but they fall into two main groups: the **monocots** and the **dicots.** These names are derived from the structure of the seed. A monocot has one seed leaf (cotyledon), whereas a dicot has two. The characteristics of the roots, stems, and leaves are also different. Monocots are usually herbs, whereas dicots include both herbs and woody plants. When you finish with the laboratory work in this exercise, state the main characteristics of monocots and dicots in Table 22-2 at the end of this topic.

TRANSPIRATION

When plants are actively photosynthesizing, they need to use water and carbon dioxide. Air must be allowed to enter the leaf interior by opening the **stomata,** and water reaches the leaf by rising through the **xylem** from the roots. When the stomata are open, however, a great amount of water is lost from the leaves, especially on a hot sunny day with the breeze blowing. This lost water must be replaced by rapid uptake from the soil around the roots, or the plant will wilt. The process of losing water by evaporation from the leaves is called **transpiration.** It depends on a continuous column of water molecules from the soil, through xylem vessels, to the leaf. Evaporation is the driving force, pulling on the water column, which is consequently under tension or negative pressure. Thus the plant does not need to expend energy during transpiration.

Demonstrate transpiration by carrying out this simple experiment:

■ Add a drop of dye to a small amount of water in a beaker or flask.
■ Make a clean cut with a sharp razor in the stem of a white flower, such as a daisy or carnation.
■ Place the flower in the beaker, set the beaker in a well-illuminated location, and check the petals from time to time during the laboratory for the presence of the dye.
■ Wait 1-2 hr.
■ After the dye has reached the flower, note which part of the petals stained more darkly.
■ Make a sketch in the space provided in Figure 22-10 at the end of this topic to show the pattern of staining of the petal. Label the part of the petal where transpiration was most rapid.
■ Make a thin cross section of the stem with a sharp razor blade, and examine it under the dissecting microscope.
■ Note the xylem vessels through which the dye rose.
■ Make a sketch of your cross section in Figure 22-10 and label the location of the xylem.

You can also measure the amount of water lost by a plant quantitatively by measuring the rate at which it is taken up by the stem. Record your results in Table 22-3.
■ Assemble the materials shown in Figure 22-1 along with a sharp razor blade.
■ Hold the stem of a plant such as part of a geranium plant beneath the water, and cut the stem off without crushing it.

DO NOT WET THE LEAVES.

■ Hold the piece of rubber tubing under the water, and insert the cut stem into it. (The tubing must be just a bit narrower than the stem.)
■ Immerse the pipet in the pan of water, and attach it to the other end of the tube.
■ Gently squeeze the tubing to expel any air bubbles that might have been trapped below the stem.

IF THE EXPERIMENT IS TO WORK PROPERLY, ALL AIR BUBBLES MUST BE REMOVED.

■ Holding the pipet in a horizontal position, lift the plant and the pipet out of the water, and set the pipet on a flat surface in a good source of light.
■ Record the position of the water column in the pipet every 15 min until transpiration is well established.
■ Calcultate the rate of water uptake by the stem in mL/hr.

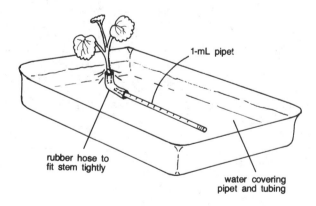

Figure 22-1. Transpiration experiment. Once all air has been excluded from the system by immersing it in water, the plant cutting is lifted out and placed in strong light so that the uptake of water by the stem can be measured.

■ Place the plant in darkness, and continue to follow the uptake of water.
■ Calculate the rate of water uptake by the stem in mL/hr in the dark.

How did the absence of light affect the rate of transpiration?

LEAVES

Types of Leaves

A leaf consists of a flat **blade** (lamina) and a stalk, the **petiole,** which attaches the leaf to the stem. There will be a lateral bud in the leaf **axil** where the petiole joins the stem. Vascular tissue passes through the petiole to enter the midrib of the leaf and the leaf veins. Some leaves are **simple** and consist of just one blade and its petiole, but others are compound and consist of several **leaflets** that share a single petiole. The types of leaves are shown in Figure 22-2.

If it is unclear whether a leaf is a compound leaf or several simple leaves, look for buds. Because the buds are always found on stems, leaves that join without buds in their axils are part of a single compound leaf.

■ Examine the leaves on demonstration, and decide whether each is simple or compound.

The vascular tissue within the leaf is in large bundles called veins. If the veins run from the petiole more or less parallel out to the tip of the leaf, the leaf has **parallel venation.** If there is one main vein with smaller

veins branching off it and running parallel to each other, the venation is **pinnate.** If several main veins radiate out from the petiole and have many smaller branches, the leaf has **palmate venation.** Most monocots have parallel venation, and dicots tend to have pinnate or palmate venation. These types of venation are shown in Figure 22-2.

■ Identify the three types of venation among the leaves on demonstration.

The arrangement of the leaves on the stem may be **opposite,** with two leaves on the opposite sides of the stem; **alternate,** with leaves appearing first on one side and then on the other; or **whorled,** with three or more leaves clustered together. If the leaves are opposite, the twigs and branches will also be opposite because they arise from buds in the leaf axils.

■ Find an example of opposite, alternate, and whorled leaf arrangements among the leaves on demonstration.

Structure of the Leaf

(Refer back to Topic 5 and Figure 5-8 for details.) Because leaves are covered by an impermeable cuticle, access to the leaf interior is through the pores called **stomata.** When the plant has sufficient water but needs more CO_2, the adjacent **guard cells** will open the stomata to permit gas exchange.

■ Obtain a dicot leaf, and study its upper and lower surface under high power in the microscope to locate the stomata.

On which surface are the stomata located?

Are they open or closed?

What ion pump is activated to open the stomata?

The interior of the leaf is the **mesophyll** (= middle leaf) and is fundamental tissue containing mainly parenchyma cells.

■ Review the internal structure of the dicot leaf by examining a cross section of a leaf such as a privet leaf.
■ Locate the **palisade mesophyll** (palisade parenchyma), the **spongy mesophyll** (spongy parenchyma), the **air spaces,** and the stomata leading into them.
■ Identify the **cuticle** that covers the leaf and the cells of the **epidermis** that secrete it.
■ Locate a bundle of vascular tissue, and identify the **xylem** and **phloem.**

The leaves of monocots tend to be long and pointed and oriented vertically. They may not have a palisade layer because the sunlight strikes them at an oblique angle. Often the leaf will be adapted to curl up when the amount of water lost through transpiration becomes too high. The curled leaf keeps the concentration of water vapor inside high, but also cuts down the efficiency of gas exchange. The cross section of a blade of grass that has curled up to prevent water loss is shown in Figure 22-3. Notice that the stomata are all on the inside where there is more water vapor, and that they are located in sunken pits.

SIMPLE LEAVES

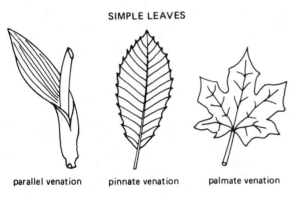

parallel venation   pinnate venation   palmate venation

COMPOUND LEAVES

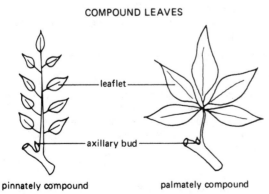

— leaflet —

— axillary bud —

pinnately compound   palmately compound

Figure 22-2. Leaves. A compound leaf has a bud only at its base, not next to its individual leaflets.

Figure 22-3.   A blade of grass in cross section. The leaf is curled and the stomata are located in deep pits to minimize the loss of water.

■ Examine a cross section of a leaf from a monocot such as a lily or oleander.
■ Note where the stomata are located and whether air spaces are present or absent.

Sometimes monocots have a layer of **intercalary meristem** at the base of each leaf. The meristem continues to divide and can replace the leaf tissue as it becomes old, damaged, or cut off by a lawnmower. This is the process that allows grass to be mowed frequently without killing it.

■ Turn to Table 22-1 and fill in the characteristics of monocots and dicots that you have observed. If the potted plants that you studied were not in bloom, consult your text for the difference between monocot and dicot flowers.

STEMS

The Pattern of Stem Growth

Most plant growth is **indeterminate** and stops only when the plant dies. Not all parts of the plant undergo cell division, however. Only certain tissue, called **meristem,** contains actively dividing cells. Meristematic tissue is found only at the tip of the **shoot** (the part above the ground growing upward) and the tip of the **root** (the part underground growing downward). Growth occurs there due to the actively dividing cells of the **apical meristem.** As the shoot grows, it produces not only the lengthening stem, but also **leaves** that branch from the stem and side or **lateral branches.** The point where a leaf or branch joins the stem is called a **node,** and the section of stem between the nodes is called an **internode.**

■ Examine a young plant, such as a bean plant, and locate the nodes and internodes.

■ Examine closely the junction of a leaf or the lateral branch with the stem, and note the **lateral** or **axillary bud** that is found in the axil of the leaf or lateral.
■ Locate the **apical bud** at the tip of the growing shoot.

The Shoot Apex

The apical bud produces a hormone (auxin) that keeps the adjacent lateral buds dormant for a time. Preferential uptake of nutrients and other hormones (e.g., cytokinin) by the rapidly growing apical meristem may also contribute to lateral bud dormancy. This inhibition of the lateral bud development is called **apical dominance.** Eventually the apical bud may grow far enough away so that its influence lessens, and the lateral buds will develop into lateral branches. If the apical bud is removed by a grazing animal or for experimental purposes, it will no longer inhibit the lateral buds, and they will immediately begin to grow.

■ Examine a prepared slide showing the apical bud of a plant such as a lilac or *Coleus* in longitudinal section.
■ Identify the **apical meristem,** where the most actively dividing cells are found.
■ Note the **leaf primordia** adjacent to the meristem; each one (or pair) is attached to the stem at a node, and the small spaces between them are the internodes.
■ Look for **vascular tissue** in some of the older leaf primordia.
■ Lumps of tissue above the leaf primordia are **bud primordia,** which will form the buds that will eventually give rise to new laterals or to flowers.

As the apical meristem grows, the stem between the leaf primordia lengthens and the new leaves become fully developed. The process is something like pulling out the sections of a collapsable telescope, except that the number of sections keeps growing and can be extended indefinitely.

Internal Structure of a Stem

In stems, the vascular tissues are arranged in bundles that may be located around the edge of the stem (in dicots), or scattered throughout the interior of the stem (in monocots). The structure of a dicot stem is shown in Figure 22-4. A dicot stem is compared with a monocot stem in Figure 27-8 in your text.

■ Examine a cross section of the stem of an herb under low power, and locate the **vascular bundles,** the cells of the vascular tissue.

Is the stem from a monocot or dicot?

_____

■ Note the central **pith,** which may have been pulled apart during growth to make the interior of the stem hollow. It is composed of **parenchyma** cells.
■ Note the layer of **epidermis** around the outside of the stem. The epidermis is only a single cell layer thick.
■ Switch to high power, and examine the edge of the stem closely.
■ Note the transparent layer of the **cuticle.** The stem and leaves but not the root are covered with a cuticle formed from the substance **cutin,** which is secreted by the cells of the epidermis.

What is the function of the cuticle?

_____

_____

_____

■ Look for **epidermal hairs** that may be present on the surface of the stem. Hairs usually have a protective function.

■ Study the layer of cells just inside the epidermis. It consists of **collenchyma** cells, which have characteristically thickened corners and act as supporting columns for the stem.

■ Note the inner part of the cortex, which is composed of parenchyma cells.

Some of the stem cells are photosynthetic, and some may contain amyloplasts for storing starch.

■ Examine a single vascular bundle. Locate the larger thick-walled cells of the **xylem** vessels in the inner part and the smaller thin-walled **phloem** tubes in the outer part of the bundle.

■ Locate the cells of the **cambium** between the xylem and the phloem.

■ Locate the thickly packed, darkly staining **fibers** along the outer edge of the vascular bundle. These are heavily walled sclerenchyma cells, which give added strength to the stem.

■ Label the parts of a vascular bundle in Figure 22-4.

The conducting cells of the phloem tissue are the **sieve tube members.** These cells contain living cytoplasm but lack nuclei. Individual sieve tube members are connected end-to-end across perforated plates known as sieve plates. They are closely associated with **companion cells,** which do have nuclei.

■ Locate the small **companion** cells adjacent to the sieve tube members in your slide.

The major function of the phloem is to transport nutrients, often in the form of sucrose, from their **source** (leaves, roots) to **sinks** in the rest of the plant for nourishment (apical buds) or for storage (roots). It can conduct dissolved substances in both directions: Some sieve tubes may be conducting downward while others are conducting different substances upward. In this way, minerals and nutrients can be continuously redistributed among the organs of the plant to meet their changing needs. Conduction in phloem is called **translocation** and requires energy for active transport of sucrose into the veins at the source. The phloem contents are under positive pressure and move rapidly by a **pressure flow mechanism.**

Storage Stems

In some plants, the stem rather than the root is used to store food for the next season. In the potato, for example, part of the stem is a storage organ and also functions in asexual reproduction.

■ Examine a cross section of a potato through one of the "eyes".

■ Note that the eyes are really buds that will send up shoots if the potato is planted in moist soil or exposed to the light. The presence of buds is a distinguishing feature of stems.

You should now be able to list five important functions of stems:

1. _____

2. _____

3. _____

4. _____

5. _____

The Woody Twig

In woody plants, unlike in herbs, the apical meristem has to survive the winter, and the green shoot must be protected from drying out or freezing. The young branches of the plant are called **twigs,** and they become covered with a protective layer of waterproof **cork.** At the end of the growing season, changing environmental conditions cause the terminal bud to cease vegetative leaf produc-

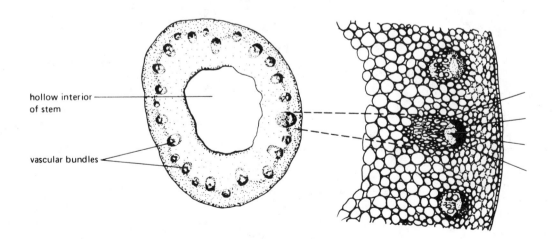

hollow interior of stem

vascular bundles

Figure 22-4. A dicot stem. The many vascular bundles form a ring.

tion and instead form protective **bud scales.** Primary growth of the plant for that season comes to an end. In the spring, the bud scales will fall off, the terminal bud will grow into a new shoot of primary growth, and the "old" twig will now begin secondary growth. It will continue cycle after cycle of secondary growth as long as the plant is alive.

■ Examine the twig of a woody plant such as a hickory tree, and use Figure 22-5 as your guide to its structure.
■ Note the **bud scales** covering the apical bud.
■ Identify the **lateral buds** along the sides of the twig. Those in the older portions of the twig have become latent and will not develop unless the terminal bud is damaged.
■ Just below each bud is a **leaf scar** where the old leaf was once attached. The bud was thus formed in the leaf axil.
■ Look at the leaf scar under the dissecting microscope. The dots within it plugged vascular bundles that once led into the leaf before the leaf was dropped from the tree.

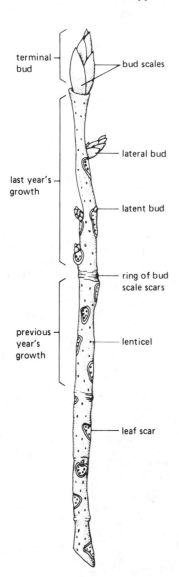

Figure 22-5. A woody twig. This hickory tree grew the length of twig between the ring of bud scale scars and the terminal bud in one season.

■ Locate the **bud scale scars,** which are a ring of wrinkled tissue. This was the position of the terminal bud 1 year before its present position.
■ Look further down the stem to find the next ring of bud scale scars. This was the position of the terminal bud 2 years before its present position.

The point where the twig joins the next larger branch marks the place where it was a lateral bud before it started developing into a new branch.

How many seasons has a twig been growing if it has four rings of bud scale scars between the terminal bud and the branch that it grows from? _____

■ Peel off a bit of the **bark** from the twig, and note that it is much too thick to allow gas exchange. Bark consists of all layers external to the vascular cambium. (See Figure 22-7).
■ Look for small rough spots on the surface of the bark called **lenticels,** and examine one with the dissecting microscope.
■ Note that the surface is spongy and not smooth like that of the bark. Its porous structure allows gas exhange between the cells of the stem and the exterior.

The internal structure of a woody twig that has grown for only part of 1 year is not much different from that of a herbaceous dicot. As the twig continues to grow, however, important changes must take place. The meristematic cells of the vascular cambium, located between the primary xylem and phloem in the vascular bundles, continue to divide and produce more vascular cells. As they do so, the vascular bundles become fused into a ring with phloem on the outside, xylem on the inside, and a layer of dividing cambium cells in between. A simplified diagram of this stage is shown in the left part of Figure 22-6.

Secondary growth begins when the vascular cambium becomes active and produces secondary phloem and secondary xylem. The layer of primary phloem is split apart as it is forced outward, and eventually it degenerates. The secondary phloem now functions to transport food. The primary xylem is left behind as the cambium moves outward in a slowly expanding cylinder, leaving the newly formed cells behind. The oldest xylem is in the center of the stem nearest the pith, and the newest is next to the cambium. A diagram showing the structure of a twig that has grown for two seasons, with both primary and secondary growth, is shown on the right in Figure 22-6. The layer of secondary xylem is called **wood,** and the twig now has an annual ring. After another season, it will have another **annual ring** of secondary xylem. The older stems, which you will examine next, may have dozens of annual rings.

Which is "older," outermost xylem next to the vascular cambium or innermost xylem next to the pith?

_____

The Woody Stem

Just as the layer of phloem split apart as the vascular cambium grew outward, so the epidermis split and a mechanism was necessary to keep the outer covering of the stem intact. Some of the cells outside the phloem became meristematic tissue, and formed the cylinder of

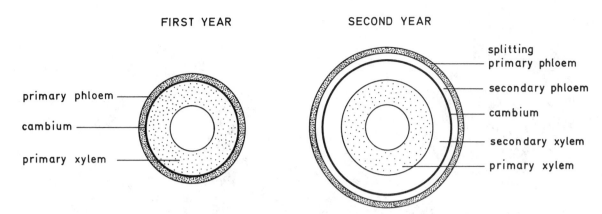

Figure 22-6. New tissue growth in a woody stem. Dividing cells are found only in the cambium.

cork cambium. Cells produced by the cork cambium move outward and secrete the substance **suberin,** which acts to waterproof the surface of the stem. As the layers accumulate, the cells die and form much of the bark of the branch or the tree trunk. The cork cambium and its derivatives are known as the periderm of the stem and provide an actively growing protective covering.

■ Examine a woody stem that is several years old under low power in your microscope.
■ Referring to Figure 22-7, identify the **vascular cambium,** which consists of the flattened cells along the outer edge of the largest annual ring.
■ Note the annual rings of **secondary xylem** inside the vascular cambium.
■ Counting inward from the vascular cambium, note the total number of layers of xylem. (The inner layer nearest the pith is primary xylem.)

The number of layers is equal to the age of this part of the stem in growing seasons.

How old is the stem you are studying?

_____

■ Note the scalloped layer of **secondary phloem** growing from the outer layer of the vascular cambium. This layer is always being split apart as the cambium enlarges.
■ Note the pyramids of tissue within the splits of the phloem. These are called phloem rays.
■ Outside the phloem, locate the **cortex** and the thin layer of **cork cambium** that surrounds it.
■ Note the dead and dying cells on the outside of the cork cambium that will make up the **cork,** or outer bark.
■ The remains of the original epidermis might still be seen on the outermost surface of the bark.

If you were to peel the bark from this twig, it would separate from the stem at the level of the vascular cambium. The bark includes not only cork but also the cork cambium, cortex, and secondary phloem. Removing the bark in this way cuts the supply lines through which the roots receive nourishment from the leaves. If the tree is **girdled** by removing a ring of bark that completely encircles the tree, the roots will starve, and the tree will eventually die. If even a thin strip of bark remains to connect the top and bottom of the stem, however, the roots may receive enough food and the tree may continue to grow.

As the stem grows older, the secondary xylem in the interior no longer conducts sap. It becomes the **heartwood** of the tree. The cells of the heartwood may become filled with metabolic wastes and resins and may turn a darker color than the still-active xylem, the **sapwood.** Heartwood is often the most beautiful and aromatic wood in a tree. Sometimes it starts to rot, or it may be eaten away by insects to make the tree hollow. The physiology is not upset as a result, but the tree is weakened and may split or break under stress.

■ Examine a cross section of an older tree, such as you might come across while splitting firewood.
■ Identify the **bark, sapwood,** and **heartwood,** and indicate the position of the **vascular cambium.**
■ Label these structures in Figure 22-11, at the end of this topic.

How old was your tree when it was cut down?

_____

Wood

What is the botanical term for the tissue that we call wood?

_____

Although the cells of wood are mostly dead, the structure of wood is rather complicated and involves interesting cell adaptations.

GYMNOSPERM WOOD

Tracheids are the only type of conducting cells found in gymnosperms. These cells are primitive because they have a small diameter, and because there are only small pores or pits connecting the cells end-to-end and sideways.

■ Examine in the microscope a cross section of pine wood or a prepared slide showing tracheids.
■ Note the uniform appearance of the tracheids and their small diameter.
■ Note also that the tracheids in each annual ring are somewhat larger toward the center of the tree and smaller and more closely packed toward the outside of each annual ring.
■ Note the very large **resin canals** scattered through the wood.

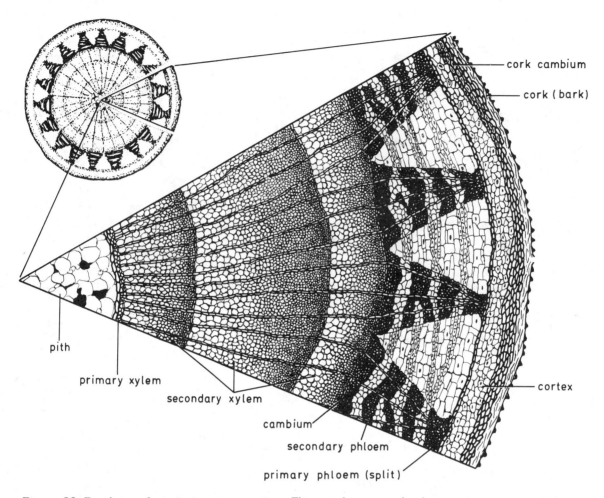

Figure 22-7. A woody twig in cross section. This twig has grown for three previous seasons. It has completed one ring of primary xylem and two rings of secondary xylem.

The inner layer of each ring, the **springwood,** is formed during the spring when the tree is growing faster. The outer layer of **summerwood** is more compact and was formed during the hot, dry months.

ANGIOSPERM WOOD

Angiosperms have developed more efficient conducting cells called **vessel members,** which are stacked vertically to form **vessels.** They have a larger internal diameter and have sometimes completely lost the end walls between the ends of adjacent cells. The wood of these trees is a mixture of fibers, tracheids, and vessel cells.

■ Examine a cross section of angiosperm wood such as maple, elm, or basswood under low power in your microscope.
■ Note the very large vessel members characteristic of angiosperms.

Are the vessels scattered uniformly through the annual ring, or are they concentrated mainly in the springwood?

_____

_____

■ Identify the **tracheids,** which have a much smaller diameter but do conduct some water.
■ Locate the **fibers,** which are very long, thin cells with heavy walls. The presence of fibers makes the wood strong or "hard." Technically (according to the U.S. Department of Agriculture), gymnosperms are softwood and angiosperms are hardwood. Actually, the wood of many gymnosperms is harder than that of many angiosperms: Balsa wood is from an angiosperm but lacks fibers and is extremely soft. The concentration of fibers determines the strength of the wood.

Within the sapwood are two structures containing living cells. Vertical sheets, or **rays,** of living parenchyma cells run out from the center of the tree to connect the living cells of the cambium with the conduits of the xylem in the sapwood.

■ Find the **rays** in the cross section of wood.

There are also columns of living parenchymal cells that secrete **resin,** a sticky, pungent substance that may help protect the wood against physical trauma or damage by insects. Vertical resin canals are very prominent in the wood of gymnosperms, as you saw in the cross section of pine wood.

ROOTS

Types of Root Systems

When a seed germinates, it sends a single **primary root,** or **radicle,** down into the soil. This root sends out side branches called **lateral roots,** and these branch out in turn until a **root system** is formed.

Why must the root develop before the rest of the plant?

_____

_____

If the primary root continues to be the largest and most important part of the system, the plant is said to have a **tap root** system. If many main roots are formed, the plant has a **fibrous** root system. Most monocots, such as grass, and some dicots have a fibrous root system. Some trees, dandelions, and carrots have a tap root.

■ Examine the demonstrations of a fibrous root system and a tap root system.

In Table 22-1 at the end of this topic, describe how well each type of root system is adapted for carrying out the major functions of a root.

Root Tips

Roots, like shoots, typically grow in an indeterminate branching pattern. Meristematic tissue is found only at the tips of the roots.

■ Examine a longitudinal section of a root tip from a plant such as an onion under low power in your compound microscope.
■ Referring to Figure 22-8, identify the **root cap,** the zone of **cell division,** the **quiescent center,** the zone of **elongation,** and the zone of **maturation.**
■ Note the **root hairs** in the zone of maturation. They increase the surface area of the root.

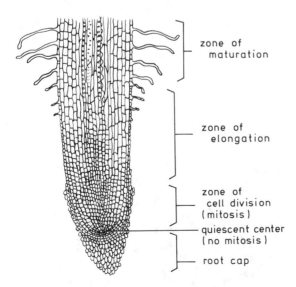

zone of maturation

zone of elongation

zone of cell division (mitosis)

quiescent center (no mitosis)

root cap

Figure 22-8. A growing root tip. Mitosis occurs mainly in the outer columns of the zone of cell division. Cells of the root tip are sloughed off as the root grows through the soil.

■ Switch to high power, and examine the zone of cell division more carefully.
■ Note the many mitotic figures in the columns of **meristem** cells along the sides of the root and the absence of mitosis in the region of the quiescent center.

The new cells formed by mitosis elongate and push the root tip away from the older section of the root. The mature cells remain fixed in position relative to the soil while the tip of the root moves down continuously.

Why are the delicate root hairs found only in the mature part of the root tip?

_____

_____

Why should the foliage of a shrub be reduced after it has lost many root hairs during bare root transplantation?

_____

_____

The inner layer of root cap cells constantly divides to produce more cells. These replace the cells sloughed off from the outer layers of the root cap as the growing root forces its way through the soil.

What is the purpose of having a root cap?

_____

_____

Certain cells of the root cap sense gravity and aid the **geotropic** response so that the root grows downward.

■ Examine a 2-day-old radish seedling that has sprouted.
■ Note the fuzzy appearance of the radicle, which is covered with hundreds of root hairs.

Are the root hairs longer at the top or bottom of the root? _____

How does the growth of the root cause this pattern?

_____

_____

Root Structure

Because a major function of the root is absorption, the surface of young roots is not covered with a waterproof layer but is somewhat permeable to the water and dissolved nutrients with which the root is in contact. Roots also need oxygen to respire and must usually be in contact with air pockets in the soil so that they can carry on gas exchange. The mineral content of the water that is sent to the rest of the plant is controlled to some extent by the layer of endodermal cells that surround the central part of the root. This layer is made waterproof by the **Casparian strip** that surrounds the endodermal cells. The vascular tissue is located within the central region, so that it does not passively take up whatever is in the water around the plant. Thus, the fluid leaving the root in the vascular tissue has passed through living endodermal cells that concentrate certain things needed by the plant.

■ Examine a cross section of a root under low power. Locate the inner **stele,** which is separated from the outer **cortex** by the layer of endodermis.

■ If you are looking at a dicot root, note the X-shaped core of xylem vessels within the stele. Xylem in monocots forms a ring.

■ Use Figure 22-9 to locate the xylem and the **phloem** tissue that make up the vascular tissue.

■ Find the **endodermis,** the layer of cells surrounding the stele and regulating the fluid entering it. Just inside the endodermis locate the cells of the **pericycle,** which retain the ability to divide.

■ Note that the cells making up the cortex all look similar. They are **parenchyma cells** and may contain grains of stored starch within organelles called **amyloplasts.**

■ Study the outermost layer of cells, the **epidermis,** and note that **root hairs** are actually extensions of the epidermal cells.

During primary growth, the root may send out side branches, or **lateral roots.** These begin growing from the meristematic tissue of the pericycle and push their way out through the cells of the cortex into the soil.

■ Examine a cross section of a root, showing a developing lateral.

Does the new root have a root cap? _____

Does it have vascular tissue yet? _____

If the root is from a woody plant, it will form a layer of lateral meristem between the xylem and phloem called the **vascular cambium.** Division of cells within the cambium will allow the formation of secondary xylem and secondary phloem, so that the root can grow in diameter as well as in length.

All roots contain food for their own needs, and the roots of overwintering plants must contain the nutrients to support the growth of new shoots the following spring. Some roots are especially modified to store large amounts of food and, as a result, are popular human food as well.

■ Obtain a piece of a carrot and make a very thin cross section with a razor blade.

■ Place the slice on a slide and add a few drops of iodine stain.

■ After the stain has soaked in for a few minutes, examine the slice under the microscope.

Where are the grains of starch located?

_____

_____

■ While you are waiting for the results of the starch test, make a longitudinal cut through the section of carrot.

■ Note the light-colored ring that divides the inner phloem from the outer xylem.

■ Locate the light-colored streaks from the inner part of the carrot to the edge. These are the connections to the lateral roots that were present along the tap root before it was pulled up out of the ground.

Although nutrients are required for a plant's healthy growth, too much fertilizer can be harmful.

■ Place a piece of carrot root in a solution of 2% ammonium phosphate or ammonium nitrate for 1 hr. and place another piece in distilled water.

■ Describe the condition of the two pieces after 1 hr.

_____

Carrot in 2% fertilizer:

_____

Carrot in distilled water:

_____

If fertilization of plants is overdone, they may be "burned" by the high concentrations of salts and die as a result. Only certain plants such as mangrove are adapted to tolerate high salt concentrations.

■ Note the results of the transpiration experiments, and return all materials and equipment before leaving the laboratory.

EXPLORING FURTHER

Balbach, M. K., L. Bliss, and C. Lawrence. *General Botany: Laboratory Manual.* 6th ed. Philadelphia: Saunders College Publishing, 1982.

Bold, H. C., C. J. Alexopoulos, and T. Delevorya. *Morphology of Plants and Fungi.* 4th ed. New York: Harper and Row, 1980.

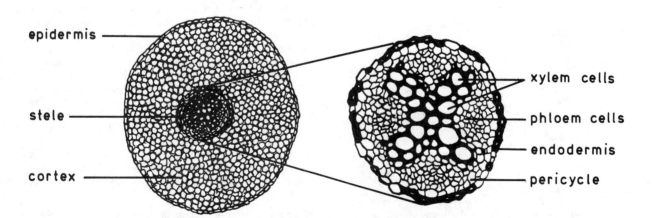

Figure 22-9. A dicot root. The vascular tissue is located within the stele.

Emboden, William A. *Bizarre Plants: Magical, Monstrous and Mythical.* New York: Macmillan, 1974.

Galston, A. W., P. J. Davies, and R. L. Satter. *The Life of the Green Plant.* 3rd ed. Englewood Cliffs, N.J.: Prentice-Hall, 1980.

Jensen, W. A. and F. B. Salisbury. *Botany: An Ecological Approach.* Belmont, Calif.: Wadsworth, 1984.

Lee, A. E., and C. Heimsch. *Development and Structure of Plants: A Photographic Study.* New York: Holt, Rinehart and Winston, 1962.

Raven, P. H., R. F. Evert, and H. Curtis. *Biology of Plants.* 3rd ed. New York: Worth, 1981.

Ray, P., T. A. Steeves, and S. A. Fultz. *Botany.* Philadelphia: Saunders College Publishing, 1983.

Salisbury, F. B., and C. W. Ross. *Plant Physiology.* 2nd ed. Belmont, Ca.: Wadsworth, 1978.

Journal Articles

Albersheim, Peter. "The walls of growing plant cells." *Scientific American,* April 1975 (#1320)

Altshul, Siri von Reis. "Exploring the herbarium." *Scientific American,* May 1977 (#1359).

Biddulph, Susann, and Orlin Biddulph. "The circulatory system of plants." *Scientific American,* February 1959 (#53).

Elias, T. S., and H. S. Irwin. "Urban trees." *Scientific American,* November 1976 (no offprint).

Epstein, Emanuel. "Roots." *Scientific American,* May 1973 (#1271).

Erickson, Ralph O., and Wendy Kuhn Silk. "The kinematics of plant growth." *Scientific American,* May 1980 (#1470).

Folkerts, George W. "The gulf coast pitcher plant bogs." *American Scientist 70(3):*260, 1982.

Fritts, Harold C. "Tree rings and climate." *Scientific American,* May 1972 (#1250).

Galston, A. W., and C. L. Slayman. "The not-so-secret life of plants." *American Scientist 67:*337, 1979.

Heslop-Harrison, Yolande. "Carnivorous plants." *Scientific American,* February 1978 (#1382).

Hitch, Charles J. "Dendrochronology and serendipity." *American Scientist 70(3):* 300, 1983.

Overbeek, Johannes. "The control of plant growth." *Scientific American,* July 1968 (#1111).

Rick, Charles M. "The tomato." *Scientific American,* August 1978 (#1397).

Shepard, James F. "The regeneration of potato plants from leaf-cell protoplasts." *Scientific American,* 154, May 1982.

Tomlinson, P. B. "Tree architecture." *American Scientist 71:* 141, 1983.

Torrey, J. G., and L. J. Feldman. "The organization and function of the root apex." *American Scientist 65:* 334, 1977.

Zimmerman, Martin H. "How sap moves in trees." *Scientific American,* March 1963 (#154).

Student Name _____ **Date** _____

TABLE 22-1. CHARACTERISTICS OF MONOCOT AND DICOT ANGIOSPERMS

Characteristic	Monocots	Dicots
Type of seed leaf (cotyledon)		
Type of leaf venation (vein pattern)		
Arrangement of vascular tissue		
Formation of wood		
Symmetry of flower parts (multiples of 3, 4, and so on)		
Type of root system		

TABLE 22-2. ROOTS

Function	Tap Root	Fibrous Roots
1. Anchoring the plant		
2. Absorbing water and minerals (surface area)		
3. Transport to the stem		
4. Storage of nutrients		

Figure 22-10. Transpiration. Sketch the results from the dye experiment.

Drawing of Petal After Transpiration	**Drawing of Xylem Cross Section After Transpiration**

TABLE 22-3. RESULTS FROM THE TRANSPIRATION EXPERIMENT

	Transpiration in Light			Transpiration in Dark	
Time (min)	*Reading*	*Change (mL)*	*Time (min)*	*Reading*	*Change (mL)*
0					
15					
30					
45					
60					
75					
90					
105					
120					
Average rate = _____ mL/hr			Average rate = _____ mL/hr		

Figure 22-11. A tree trunk in cross section. Label the parts with their correct names.

Reproduction in Seed Plants

OBJECTIVES _____

When you have completed this topic, you should be able to:
1. List the reproductive characteristics that distinguish angiosperms from other seed plants.
2. Given an actual flower or a diagram of a flower, identify it as a monocot or dicot and point out the following parts: sepal, petal, stamen, anther, pistil, ovulary, style, stigma, ovule, pollen.
3. Define pollination and fertilization, and state where they occur in a flower.
4. Explain the role or origin of the following structures and identify them in a microscope slide: microspore, male microgametophyte, pollen grain, pollen tube, megaspore, female megagametophyte, embryo sac, micropyle.
5. Give the botanical definition of a fruit, and name some "vegetables" that are botanically fruits.
6. Given an actual fruit or a diagram, identify the following parts: ovule, locule, endocarp, mesocarp, exocarp, ovulary, attachment sites of old sepals and petals.
7. List or identify the parts of a bean seed and of a corn kernel; state the function or fate of each part.
8. Describe the role of animals in pollination and seed dispersal.
9. State four factors that are important in seed germination.
10. Explain the role of plant hormones in germination, tropisms, and apical dominance.
11. Explain the advantages and disadvantages of asexual reproduction; give an example of asexual reproduction from a root, from a stem, from a leaf, and from an infertile fruit.

KEY TOPICS _____

Flowers, pollen, fruit, seeds, germination, development, plant hormones, asexual reproduction.

INTRODUCTION

As we have already seen in surveying the plant kingdom, most seed plants have dispensed with a free flagellated sperm in their reproductive cycle and have instead developed the pollen grain as a carrier of the male gamete. The process of fertilization leads to the formation of a seed that contains a small embryo and also a source of nutrition within a tough seed coat. The seed is usually resistant to harsh environmental conditions and begins growing only when conditions become favorable.

Angiosperms differ from the other seed plants in that the seeds are formed within **flowers**. In many plants the flowers are showy, or have an odor so that animals are attracted to them and become involved in pollination. The seeds are enclosed within a fruit that may be a source of food for animals. The seeds are then scattered about when the animal feeds or are carried away in its digestive tract and are later expelled far from the parent plant. Thus animals are often an important factor in seed dispersal.

Many angiosperms propagate asexually under appropriate circumstances. If environmental conditions are stable, **asexual reproduction** to produce offspring genetically identical to the parent is favored. This method, however, forgoes the variation associated with sexual reproduction.

215

FLOWERS (See Color Plates 4 and 5)

Angiosperms that are pollinated by animals have several strategies for attracting attention. Their flowers may have large, showy petals, which are brightly colored to attract the notice of potential pollinators. They may even have color patterns that are not visible to us but that attract insects such as bees because some insects can see into the ultraviolet range further than we can. Within the flower there may be nectar, which is an important food source for the pollinators. Some flowers produce volatile chemicals that give the flower a very attractive odor. (Putrid odors that are disgusting to humans may be very attractive to pollinators such as flies.) Many angiosperms have a sort of symbiotic relationship with humans, in which they are protected and propagated in exchange for their production of flowers. Coevolution of flowers and animal pollinators is illustrated in Color Plate 5.

Flowers are modified shoots in which the leaves have become modified to form the flower parts.

■ Obtain a large, simple flower, such as a gladiolus. Cut it from the stem with a razor blade far enough down so that you take all of the green part at the base in addition to the petals.
■ Identify the green **receptacle** at the base of the flower.
■ Carefully dissect the flower from its outer whorls inward. The flower may be enclosed in a green bract, or leaflike part.
■ Note the **sepals,** which make up the outer whorl, called the calyx. They may be green or the same color as the petals. (In the gladiolus, the sepals and petals are so similar that they are collectively called the tepals.)
■ Note the colored **petals,** which make up the **cor-olla** of the flower.
■ Locate the **stamens,** the male reproductive structures that form the next whorl.
■ Locate the **pistil.** It is made up of one or more **car-pels,** which are the female reproductive organs. You will be able to determine the number of carpels later, when you dissect the ovulary.

How many petals, sepals, stamens, and carpels does the flower have?

Petals: _____

Sepals: _____

Stamens: _____

Carpels: _____

Monocots tend to have the flower parts in threes, whereas dicots tend to have four or five of each part.

Considering the other characteristics that distinguish monocots and dicots, as well as the structure of their flowers, do you think this flower is from a monocot or from a dicot? _____

Pollen is formed in the **anther,** which is the top part of the stamen supported by the stalklike **filament.** It is then deposited on the sticky surface of the **stigma** at the top of the pistil during **pollination.** The germinating pollen grain must grow a tube through the **style** of the pistil to the ovulary at its base. The ovules (prospective seeds) within the ovulary are fertilized when the pollen tubes reach them and sperm nuclei enter to unite with nuclei within each ovule.

When you have finished this part of the dissection, label the structures indicated in Figure 23-5 at the end of this topic.

■ Make a cut across the base of the carpels where the green **ovulary** is the widest, as shown in Figure 23-6 at the end of this topic.
■ Make a second cut and remove the slice from the flower.
■ Note the small **ovules** that will mature into seeds; each ovule will be fertilized by one pollen tube.
■ Note the spaces containing the seeds, called **lo-cules.** The number of locules is equal to the number of carpels that make up the pistil.

How many locules (carpels) does the ovulary contain?

_____

■ Identify the wall of the ovulary, which surrounds the locules. It will develop into part of the fruit.
■ Make a sketch of the interior of the ovulary in the space provided in Figure 23-6, and label its internal structures.

There are many variations in flower structure. The flower that you have just studied is **simple** because it contains a single ovulary, and it is **complete** because it contains both stamens and a pistil. A flower such as a daisy is a **composite** flower and consists of many tiny individual flowers. Each white petal is formed by a separate ray flower, and the central disc consists of many other tiny flowers. Sometimes the carpels and stamens are in separate flowers, which are termed **incomplete.** (See Color Plate 4.)

Some flowers are self-fertilizing and have petals that close over the reproductive organs. The anther fertilizes the pistil right next to it, and the closed petals prevent the entry of pollen from another flower carried by wind or insects. Flowers that are normally pollinated by the wind rather than by animals are often inconspicuous and may lack petals altogether. The flowers of many trees and grasses lack petals.

■ Examine other types of flowers that are on demonstration.

In the flower that you studied, the sepals may have been green, or they may have been colored and almost indistinguishable from the petals. In any case, the sepals usually form a whorl of their own outside of the true petals. In some flowers the sepals are large and showy, while the rest of the flower in very inconspicuous. In other flowers, such as the poinsettia, the red "petals" are modified leaves called bracts that surround the tiny flowers in the center.

POLLEN

> *Note:* At the beginning of the laboratory session, set up your demonstration in the following manner.
>
> ■ Obtain a Petri plate of agar or a slide with a drop of 10% sucrose.
> ■ Shake some pollen from the anther of a flower such as gladiolus or *Tradescantia* onto the agar or the drop.
> ■ Cover the pollen, and set it aside in a warm, moist place to allow pollen tubes to develop from the grains of pollen.

The male reproductive organ, the **stamen,** consists of the **anther** (pollen sacs) which is supported by the **filament.**

■ Locate the filament and anther of your flower.
■ Shake a few grains of pollen onto a slide, make a wet mount, and observe the pollen under high power in your microscope.
■ Note the shape of the pollen grains.
■ If the pollen from other sources is available, study it also, and compare the shapes of pollen grains from different sources.

Is all pollen alike?_____

The cells within the anther that undergo meiosis are the **microspore mother cells,** and the haploid cells that are produced are the microspores. This tetrad of microspores will produce four male gametophytes that are parasitic within the anther as they mature into pollen grains. The formation of pollen is shown in Figure 23-1.

■ Examine a prepared slide of an anther of the lily containing pollen tetrads.
■ Look for groups of four cells, which are the tetrads.
■ Examine a slide showing a mature anther that is almost ready to shed pollen.
■ Note that many grains have two functional cells, and there are some mature pollen grains that are dark and opaque.

A single grain of mature pollen contains a generative nucleus and a tube nucleus. The generative nucleus will participate in fertilization. The pollen is deposited on the stigma during pollination and the **tube nucleus** then directs the growth of the **pollen tube,** into which it moves. The generative nucleus divides to form two **sperm nuclei,** which also move out into the tube. Only the sperm nuclei will eventually enter the ovule and contribute genetic material to the new embryo through fertilization. In angiosperms, pollination and fertilization may be separated by a few hours or whatever time it takes for the pollen tube to reach its destination.

■ Examine your demonstration of germinating pollen to see if any pollen tubes have grown.

Are the tubes straight or irregular?_____

If there are no tubes yet, examine the grains again later.

OVULARY

The ovulary at the base of the pistil contains one or more ovules or **megasporangia.** The reproductive cell

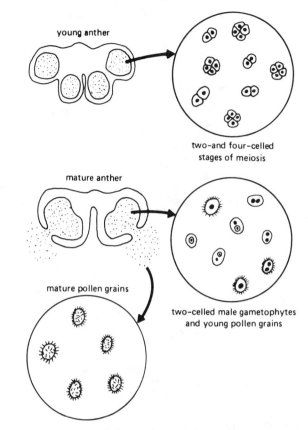

Figure 23-1 Production of pollen grains. A microspore mother cell produces four microspore daughters in a tetrad. Each of the haploid cells gives rise to a pollen grain with its generative and tube nuclei. The mature pollen grain, the male microgametophyte, has a characteristic spiny covering.

within the ovule, called the **megaspore mother cell,** undergoes meiosis to form four haploid cells; only one survives to form the female megagametophyte or **embryo sac.** The exact number of cells forming the gametophyte varies, depending on the species of flower, but there will be one **egg nucleus** and two other nuclei that fuse to form a **central nucleus.** The development of the embryo sac is shown in Figure 23-2.

■ Examine a prepared slide showing the cross section of the ovary of a lily under low power.
■ Referring to Figure 23-2, scan the six ovules of one cross section to locate an **embryo sac,** a large structure with granular cytoplasm. (Many of the ovules will not show an embryo sac because the section was at the wrong level.)
■ When you have located an embryo sac, switch to high power, and note the nuclei within it. Developing sacs will have two or four nuclei, and mature ones will have eight (rarely seen).

Are any of the cells in the embryo sac in the process of dividing by mitosis? _____

Fertilization occurs when the sperm nuclei of the pollen tube enter a pore at the bottom of the embryo sac, called the **micropyle,** and fuse with the nuclei within. One sperm nucleus fuses with the egg nucleus to form the **embryo,** and the second sperm nucleus fuses

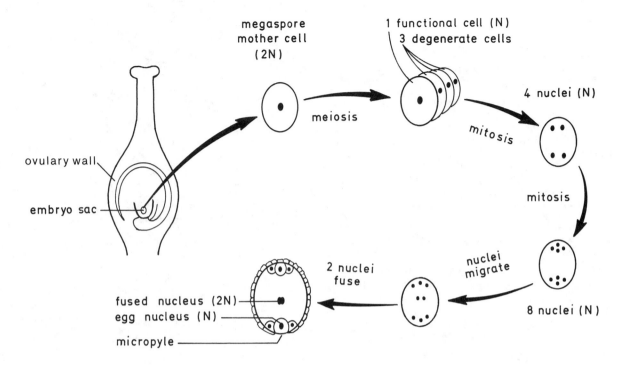

Figure 23-2. Development of the embryo sac. The developmental pattern shown is typical of most flowers. (Development in the lily is more complex.) Note that only some of the ovules will have a visible embryo sac. The embryo sac represents the female megagametophyte and develops from a haploid nucleus.

with the central nucleus to form the **endosperm.** The zygote will be diploid, whereas the endosperm will be triploid or pentaploid. Mitosis then produces the embryo and the tissues of the endosperm. This **double fertilization** occurs only in angiosperms.

Label the important structures in the diagram of fertilization shown in Figure 23-7 at the end of this topic, and give the function or fate of each part listed in Table 23-1.

FRUIT

After fertilization, the ovule develops into a seed, and the entire ovulary matures into the **fruit.** Botanically speaking, a fruit is a ripened ovulary or an ovulary fused with nearby tissue. Ethylene, a plant hormone, promotes fruit maturation or ripening. Various types of fruits are illustrated in Figure 31-19 in your text.

■ Obtain a fruit such as a bean pod. If the fruit was recently picked, you may see old petals and sepals clinging to the end of the pod.
■ Split the pod open and find the seeds. Each one represents an **ovule.**
■ Note that each seed is attached to the pod at a single point.
■ Identify the space surrounding the seeds, known as the **locule.**

How many locules does the bean have?

_____

■ Note the pod, which represents the wall of the ovulary and is called the **pericarp.**

While a bean pod is not very "fruitlike," it is a perfectly good example of a fruit. The pod itself is a com-

TABLE 23-1. FERTILIZATION

Structure	Function or Fate
Egg nucleus	
Central nucleus	
Ovule wall	
1st sperm nucleus	
2nd sperm nucleus	
Micropyle	

pressed version of the kinds of fruits you are used to: it has an inner layer, the **endocarp**; a middle, juicy layer, the **mesocarp**; and an outer layer, the **exocarp.**

■ Make a cut through the pod of the bean, and examine a slice of pod material in the dissecting microscope.

■ Note the lining of the pod, the endocarp, the juicy mesocarp, and the tough outer exocarp.
■ Label the parts if the bean pod shown in Figure 23-8 at the end of the topic. (One ovule failed to get fertilized).

What was the fate of the unfertilized ovule?

_____

_____

A more familiar fruit such as a peach has the same layered structure. The seed is enclosed within a space surrounded by the stony endocarp that we call the pit. The juicy flesh is the mesocarp, and the skin is the exocarp. Label the parts of a peach fruit in Figure 23-8 at the end of this topic.

What specific type of fruit is a peach? _____

Is a strawberry really a berry, botanically speaking?

_____

Sometimes the whole pericarp is reduced to a dry skin that surrounds the seed. This is seen in a wheat grain or in the fruit of a dandelion.

SEEDS

Anatomy

Take a closer look at the structure of a seed by dissecting a bean seed that has been soaked to loosen the skin and soften it. The external structure is shown in Figure 23-3.

■ Note the rough whitish area called the **raphe.** This is the remnant of the stalk that once attached the hilum of the seed to the pod.
■ Examine the seed with your dissecting microscope, and find the tiny opening of the **micropyle.** Pollen entered the ovule through the micropyle.
■ Carefully split the seed into two halves, and refer to Figure 23-3 to identify the parts: **cotyledon, plumule** or **epicotyl, hypocotyl, radicle, foliage leaves.** (Epicotyl is that part above the attachment point of the cotyledons; hypocotyl is that part below.)

The bean is a dicot, and its seed has two cotyledons. The seeds of monocots have only one. The endosperm tissue of the bean has been completely absorbed by the cotyledons.

■ Obtain a soaked corn kernel, and cut it in half as shown in Figure 23-4.
■ Identify the single **cotyledon,** the **endosperm,** the **hypocotyl, epicotyl,** and the **foliage leaves (plumule)** of the embryo. The shoot is covered by a sheath called the **coleoptile.**

In the corn kernel, the cotyledon has absorbed only part of the endosperm tissue, and there is still a substantial amount of endosperm left. The ovulary wall has become the pericarp.

■ Add a few drops of iodine stain to the cut surface of the corn kernel to stain the stored starch.

Does the endosperm or cotyledon contain more stored starch?

_____

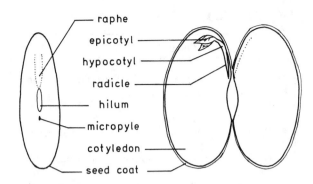

Figure 23-3. A bean seed. The bean on the right has been split open to reveal the embryo (epicotyl and hypocotyl). The apical meristem of the shoot is hidden within the first foliage leaves.

Metabolism

The seed has lost most of its water, and carries on metabolism at a very slow rate. This **dormancy** is maintained by the hormone abscisic acid. Some seeds will be able to germinate under the right conditions, and are **viable** whereas others are **inviable.** It is easy to test for metabolic activity in seeds by soaking them and observing the reduction of a dye by the living tissue. The dye is tetrazolium, which is normally colorless, but turns pink when it is reduced by living tissue.

■ Cut several soaked yellow corn kernels in half, and put them into a test tube.
■ Add enough 0.5% tetrazolium solution to cover the kernels, and set them aside.
■ Observe the cut surfaces from time to time for the production of a pink color.
■ After the pink color is well developed, remove the kernels and examine them to see which part of the seed has the darkest color and therefore the greatest metabolic activity.

Where was there the greatest metabolic activity?

_____

Were any of the seeds totally inactive with the dye (dead)? _____

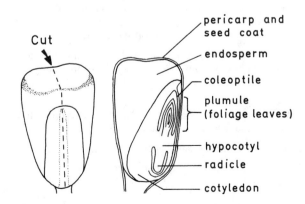

Figure 23-4. A corn kernel. The shoot is covered by the sheath of the coleoptile, and the pericarp has fused with the seed coat.

GERMINATION

Note: At the beginning of the laboratory session, set up your demonstration in the following manner.

■ Obtain a few alfalfa sprouts, a Petri dish, and some filter paper or paper toweling.
■ Cut a circle of toweling to fit the Petri dish, and moisten it with tap water.
■ Place the sprouts on the toweling, and cover the dish.
■ Note the color of the cotyledons and hypocotyls of the sprouts.
■ Place the dish in strong sunlight or artificial light.

Several factors may be important in the process of germination: a period of cold, absorption of water, light, abrasion or digestion of the seed coat, and an increase in the content of the hormone gibberellin. Seeds differ in their requirements, but they all require a supply of water in order to germinate. The absorption of water that starts germination is called **imbibition.**

■ Examine some bean seeds that have been soaked in water overnight, and compare them with dry seeds.

In what two ways does the seed change during imbibition?

_____

_____

During the first days of development, the seed must rely on its own stored food present in its cotyledons. It must reach sunlight and a source of water within a limited time span or it will not survive. In order to increase its chance for success, its growth is closely controlled by hormones.

The level of abscisic acid is high in the seed and maintains dormancy. After imbibition has taken place, gibberellin production increases and stimulates elongation of the stem. Abscisic acid and inhibitory concentrations of auxin in the cells of the root cap cause the root to show **positive geotropism** and to grow downward toward the water. Auxin helps the shoot to show **positive phototropism** and grow up toward the sunlight.

■ Examine some young bean seedlings that have been allowed to sprout on agar plates or paper towels.
■ Note that the hypocotyl has grown downward, whereas the epicotyl has turned up toward the light.
■ Look at the oldest plants, and note how the cotyledons have shriveled up as their food was removed by the embryo. They will soon fall off the plant.

An interesting example of the vital importance of hormone balance can be seen in seedlings that have been kept in complete darkness so that they have become **etiolated.**

■ Examine some etiolated seedlings, and compare them with normal seedlings of the same age.

What color are the seedlings? _____

What is their appearance compared with that of normal seedlings?

_____

Gibberellin secreted by a fungus has long been known to cause "foolish seedling" disease of rice, in which the seedlings grow tall and spindly and then fall over and die. Excessive gibberellin is also responsible for the abnormal growth of etiolated seedlings. During the first days of growth, a seedling must reach the light or it will die. The concentration of gibberellin is high to stimulate rapid growth of the stem while the seedling is in the darkness underground. As soon as it reaches the light, the red wavelengths of light transform the light sensitive protein phytochrome P_{660} to P_{735} and the production of gibberellin falls off as a result. The stem's growth slows down, and normal development follows. If, however, the shoot is unlucky and never reaches the sunlight, the phytochrome stays in the form of P_{660} and continues to stimulate the production of large amounts of gibberellin. The seedling grows and grows until it becomes severely etiolated and dies. A seedling that is being kept in complete darkness can be saved by eradiating it with red light to reduce the amount of P_{660} and decrease gibberellin production.

What other process in angiosperms is under the control of P_{660} and P_{735}? _____

As the seedling emerges into the light, it has the potential for carrying on photosynthesis, and will turn green within a short time. One of the steps in the production of chlorophyll is a photoreaction, which requires light. As long as the seedling is in the dark, the reaction is blocked, and there is no chlorophyll. There is, however, a large amount of the compound preceding the light-sensitive step. When light becomes available, the production of chlorophyll proceeds rapidly, and the seedling turns green, as the chlorophyll builds up.

■ Examine the alfalfa sprouts that you set up at the beginning of the period for signs of greening.
■ If they are not green yet, examine them once more before you leave the laboratory.

How long did it take the sprouts to turn visibly green?

_____

Why is it advantageous for the seedling to postpone formation of chlorophyll until it reaches the light?

_____

_____

_____

_____

ASEXUAL REPRODUCTION

Although there is a great deal of concern about the possibility of cloning human beings, growing clones of plants in the laboratory and in agricultural practice has already become widespread: One or a few meristematic cells can be used to grow plant tissue and even whole plants that are genetically identical to the parent cell and to each other. Asexual or vegetative reproduction is basically the same process. Cells of the parent plant produce progeny that are genetically identical to the parent. Asexual reproduction is a way of life among plants, and often it is the only means by which a plant can reproduce. When a successful plant reproduces asexually, the progeny will most likely also be successful because they will be well adapted to local conditions.

Sometimes plants have it both ways: they produce reproductive organs and seeds so that they have good dispersal and a lot of offspring, but the seeds are genetically identical to the parent and their formation does not involve meiosis. This process of **agamospermy** happens in dandelions, some grasses, and well-adapted plants that have given up sexual reproduction but have retained their reproductive organs. Other plants produce fruits, but have no fertile seeds, and the plants must be propagated asexually. Some examples are the pineapple, banana, and tangelo.

■ Examine the interior of a banana.
■ Note the tiny black dots. These are degenerative ovules that failed to form viable seeds.
■ Examine the various examples of asexual production on demonstration in the laboratory.
■ Match the examples that you see with the corresponding type of asexual reproduction shown in Figure 23-9 at the end of this topic.

Check your demonstrations of pollen tubes and alfalfa sprouts, if you have not already done so, and return all materials. Clean up your work area, and store your microscope properly before leaving the laboratory.

EXPLORING FURTHER

Galston, Arthur W., Peter J. Davies, and Ruth L. Satter. *The Life of the Green Plant.* 3rd ed. Englewood Cliffs, N.J.: Prentice-Hall, 1980.
Hutchinson, J. *The Genera of Flowering Plants.* Vols. I and II. Monticello, N.Y.: Lubrecht and Kramer, 1979.
Peterson, R. T., and M. McKenny. *A Field Guide to Wildflowers of Northeastern and North Central North America.* Boston: Houghton-Mifflin, 1974.

Proctor, M. and P. Yeo. *The Pollination of Flowers.* New York: Paplinger, 1973.
Raven, P. J., R. F. Evert, and H. Curtis. *Biology of Plants.* 3rd ed. New York: Worth, 1981.
Ray, P., T. A. Steeves, and S.A. Fultz. *Botany.* Philadelphia: Saunders College Publishing, 1983.
Salisbury, F. B., and C. W. Ross. *Plant Physiology.* 2nd ed. Belmont, Calif.: Wadsworth, 1978.

Journal Articles

Beard, Benjamin H. "The sunflower crop." *Scientific American,* 150, May 1981.
Chilton, Mary-Dell. "A vector for introducing new genes into plants." *Scientific American,* 50, June 1983.
Cook, Robert E. "Clonal plant populations." *American Scientist 71(3):* 244, May-June, 1983.
Echlin, Patrick. "Pollen." *Scientific American,* April 1968 (#1105).
Grant, Verne. "The fertilization of flowers." *Scientific American,* June 1951 (#12).
Kaplan, Donald R. "The development of palm leaves." *Scientific American,* 98, July 1983.
Koller, D. "Germination." *Scientific American,* April 1959 (no offprint).
Pettitt, John, Sophie Ducker, and Bruce Knox. "Submarine pollination." *Scientific American,* 134, March 1981.
Rick, C. M. "The tomato." *Scientific American,* August 1978 (#1397).
Shepard, J. F. "The regeneration of potato plants from leaf cell protoplasts." *Scientific American,* 154, May 1982.
Swaminathan, M. S. "Rice." *Scientific American,* 80, January 1984.

Student Name _____ **Date** _____

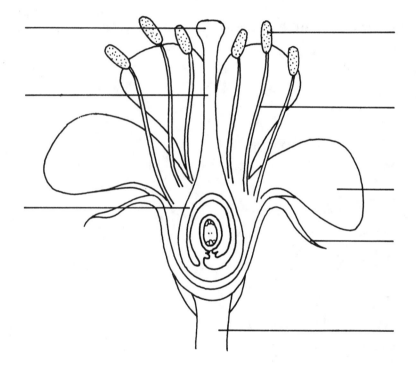

Figure 23-5.   A simple, single flower. Label its parts.

CUTTING THE OVULARY   SKETCH OF OVULARY IN CROSS SECTION

Figure 23-6.   Cutting the ovulary. Make a cross section by cutting at the position shown.

Figure 23-7.   Fertilization. Label the parts indicated.

Student Name _____ **Date** _____

BEAN

PEACH

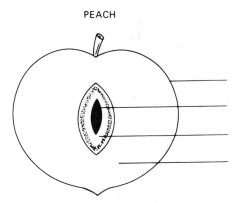

Figure 23-8. Fruits. Label the parts indicated with their correct botanical names.

type: _____

example: _____

type: _____

example: _____

type: _____

example: _____

type: _____

example: _____

type: _____

example: _____

type: _____

example: _____

Figure 23-9. Asexual reproduction. Label each type with its name or description, and note an example.

Skin, Bone, and Muscle

OBJECTIVES _____

When you have completed this topic, you should be able to:
1. Describe the tissues that make up human skin.
2. List the functions of skin in the vertebrate classes.
3. Identify the major bones of the human skeleton and distinguish whether they belong to the axial skeleton or the appendicular skeleton.
4. Describe the major structural differences between bone and cartilage, and give the advantageous properties of each tissue.
5. Identify the major muscles of a vertebrate.
6. Describe the type of movement that is carried out by striated muscle, smooth muscle, and cardiac muscle; give the advantages of each muscle type.
7. Explain what happens when a muscle is given an increasingly intense stimulus.
8. Explain what happens when a muscle is given an increasingly frequent stimulus.
9. Define flexor, extensor, antagonist, reciprocal inhibition, tetany, fatigue, and twitch.

KEY TOPICS _____

Skin, skeleton, joints, smooth muscle, cardiac muscle, striated muscle, antagonistic muscles, muscle physiology.

INTRODUCTION

Muscles are **effectors.** They respond to stimuli detected by other cells. Glands, light organs, and electric organs are also effectors.

The major function of muscles is to move things by changing chemical energy to kinetic energy (motion). **Locomotion** is the most obvious form of movement in which the muscles in cooperation with the skeleton move the whole organism, but muscles also move blood, food, air, and eyeballs; regulate body temperature; and cause countless other physiological changes. Animals always use muscles for locomotion, but not always a skeleton. In invertebrates, muscular contractions often bring about movement of body parts or locomotion by exerting hydrostatic force on body fluids. These fluids must be enclosed in an intact **skin** sufficiently strong to withstand the forces involved. A hydra, a starfish, and an earthworm all move in this fashion. Bristles, fins, feathers, and nails are derived from the skin and also contribute to effective locomotion in many animals.

The skeleton is clearly necessary for muscles to be effective for locomotion in vertebrates, but it also serves other functions. It cradles and protects internal organs, especially the heart and brain, and it supports the body as a whole; antlers help some animals to protect themselves. The long bones are the main blood-generating organs and help maintain the immune system. Bones also serve as a depot for fat and calcium.

Because muscles can react only by contracting and not by "expanding," they must work in pairs and must be attached to the part to be moved, usually a bone. Consider the two bones joined by the fibrous connective tissue of a **ligament** to form a **joint,** as shown in the sketch in Figure 24-5 at the end of this topic.

■ Draw a muscle attached to both bones that will draw them together so that the angle of the joint becomes smaller; this is the **flexor** of the joint. Label the upper attachment point the **origin** (nearest the body) and the lower, the **insertion.** Now draw in the antagonistic muscle that widens the angle of the joint: This is the **extensor.** Label its origin and insertion also.

Are flexors or extensors important when you hit a baseball? _____

Are flexors or extensors important when you pick up a book? _____

227

Other pairs of antagonists work to draw in, raise, twist, or constrict body parts.

Muscles can also work without being attached to bones. When they are in the form of a ring they can contract to close off a tube (pyloric sphincter), or when they are in the form of a tube they can contract in a ring or parallel to the length of the tube to change its shape and force the tube contents to move, as in peristalsis. Cardiac muscle contracts rhythmically for the lifetime even without being stimulated to contract by individual nerve endings. Most of the activities of **smooth** and **cardiac** muscle are not under our conscious control, so we are not as aware of them as we are of **skeletal** muscle.

SKIN

The outer covering of vertebrates is a tough layer that contains both living and dead cells. It protects from abrasion and dehydration; it insulates, especially when it grows hair or feathers; it regulates body temperature through its rich blood supply and sweat glands; and it has nerve endings to detect the stimuli of touch, pressure, temperature, and pain. Glands in the skin secrete protective oils and in certain cases milk for the young.

■ Examine a prepared slide of a cross section of human or mammalian skin.

■ Locate the uppermost **stratum corneum** in which the flattened cells overlap in a protective layer. These cells are dead and consist mostly of the strong structural protein **keratin.** They are continually flaking off and must be replaced from below.

■ Below the stratum corneum find the **stratum basale.** This layer has tightly packed nucleated cells that may contain the pigment melanin found in dark or tanned individuals. At its base is a single layer of cuboidal epithelial cells that constantly divide by mitosis and are pushed upward toward the surface. The **epidermis** of the skin consists of these two strata and is typically about 1 mm thick.

■ Look below the epidermis to see the much thicker dermis where there is a rich blood supply and a thick meshwork of elastic fibers.

■ Scan the slide to find a **hair follicle.** Follicles are actually formed by cells of the epidermis that have grown deep down into the dermis.

■ Notice the coiled glands associated with the hair follicle. Certain **sweat glands** and **oil glands** secrete their products into the follicle. Each hair has a little muscle that can contract to make the hair become erect in case of cold or fright.

■ Scan the slide to find a sweat gland *not* associated with a hair follicle. This type of sweat gland functions only in thermoregulation: It will secrete sweat for evaporative cooling only when the body is overheated.

■ In the lower part of the dermis and below it, notice the round **fat cells** that make up the layer of insulation that covers the body.

SKELETON

The vertebrate skeleton is divided into the **axial skeleton** consisting of the skull, vertebral column, and sternum, and the **appendicular skeleton,** which consists of the pectoral and pelvic girdles and their appendages.

■ Locate the axial and appendicular skeletons in Figure 24-1, which shows the bones of a human being.

■ Study the major bones in Figure 24-1. Then complete Table 24-1 at the end of this topic by matching the technical names of the bones with their common names and deciding whether they are part of the axial or appendicular skeleton.

■ If there are other vertebrate skeletons on demonstration in your laboratory, compare them to each other and to the human skeleton. Some good examples to use are a frog, cat, bat, pigeon, fish, snake, or crocodile.

■ Compare a bipedal animal with one that is quadrupedal.

■ Notice the adaptations of the skeleton for the type of locomotion of the animal.

■ Consider a particular bone such as the femur, ischium, or mandible, and see how it differs in different organisms. Pay particular attention to these features:

Articulation of the spine and skull
Structure of the vertebrae
Ribs
Scapula
Clavicles
Pelvic girdle
Carpals and metacarpals
Tarsals and metatarsals
Phalanges of fore- and hindlimb

Figure 24-1. Human skeleton. Some of the 206 bones (29 in the skull alone).

Your instructor may ask you to make a table showing how these skeletal parts show different adaptations in different organisms.

A typical long bone is shown in Figure 24-2. The ends are covered with smooth **cartilage** (hyaline cartilage) and rub against the cartilage of the adjacent bones. Ligaments hold the bones in place at either end, and the muscles are attached to the bone by **tendons.** During development, there are sections of cartilage within the end of the bone that grow as the bone lengthens. (The very ends of the bone, the **epiphyses,** have to be hard and bony or they would wear away.) When the growing cartilage becomes converted to bone so that the epiphyses and **shaft** (diaphysis) unite, growth in the length of the bone stops.

The hollow interior of the bone is the **marrow** and is filled with blood-forming cells and fat. In mammals, only the very outer shell of the bone is hard, or **compact bone.** The rest is **spongy bone,** which is rich in blood vessels.

MICROSTRUCTURE OF BONE AND CARTILAGE (See Color Plate 2)

Compact Bone

■ Examine a slide of compact bone; this is bone ground thin enough so that light can penetrate. The concentric circles are the **Haversian systems.** Each contains a **Haversian canal** in which there are one or two blood vessels (a large capillary or a small arteriole and a venule) as well as a nerve. The rings are the lamellae, which are rings of the calcium phosphate **matrix** that makes up the substance of the bone. The tiny open spaces around the edges of each circle are the **lacunae,** which contain the bone cells that produced all of the matrix. Tiny canals (canalicules) connect each lacuna with a

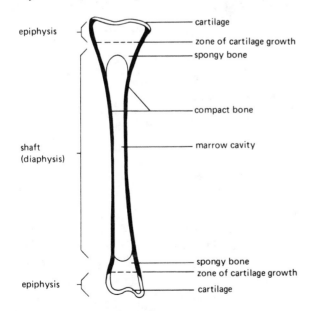

epiphysis — cartilage
— zone of cartilage growth
— spongy bone

— compact bone

shaft (diaphysis) — marrow cavity

— spongy bone
— zone of cartilage growth
epiphysis — cartilage

Figure 24-2. A long bone. During development the bone grows longer in the regions marked with dashes. When the epiphyses and shaft unite, growth stops.

Haversian canal, allowing extracellular fluid to reach and nourish the living cells.

■ Draw a section of the bone in the space provided in Figure 24-5 to show that you understand its structure.

Cartilage

Cartilage differs from bone in that it does not have mineralization in its matrix and it lacks a blood supply.

■ View a slide of cartilage in the microscope. The homogeneous area is the elastic **matrix,** which contains collagen and elastic fibers. The individual cells that secrete the matrix are scattered throughout the matrix in holes called **lacunae.** Each hole contains one or more cells.

■ Examine your own head and the front of your neck, and list four sites where you find cartilage.

1. _____

2. _____

3. _____

4. _____

Where does the cartilage occur in the spinal column?

_____

Where does it occur in the thoracic cage?

_____

What parts of the pelvic girdle are made of cartilage?

_____

MICROSTRUCTURE OF MUSCLE (See Color Plate 3)

Striated Muscle

■ Examine a slide of striated or skeletal muscle in the microscope. Each strand is a muscle **fiber,** a large cell with many peripheral nuclei.

■ What is this kind of cell called? _____

The membrane of the muscle fiber is the **sarcolemma.** Within the fiber are the many longitudinal **myofibrils,** or bundles of thick and thin filaments.

■ Locate a muscle fiber in the slide, and identify some of its nuclei.

The fine striations that give striated muscle its name are the result of the lining up of thick and thin filaments in exactly the same register in many adjacent myofibrils. Striated muscle is found in the voluntary muscles, which move the parts of the body and are under conscious control.

Smooth Muscle

■ View a slide of smooth muscle.

This type of muscle consists of bundles of spindle-shaped cells. Each cell has a central nucleus and is filled with myofibrils. There is no pattern of cross striations. Smooth muscle is designed for slow, sustained contractions.

Where is smooth muscle found?

_____

_____

Cardiac Muscle

■ Examine a slide of cardiac muscle.

This type of muscle is found only in the walls of the vertebrate heart.

Is cardiac muscle striated? _____

Does it have nuclei? _____

What conspicuous features does it show that are not present in smooth or striated muscle?

_____

_____

■ Locate the position of the **sarcolemma.** (This membrane is too thin to see.) The dark bands scattered throughout the tissue are the **intercalated discs,** which are junctions between individual muscle cells.

MUSCLE ANATOMY

Movement of the body parts and locomotion are accomplished by pairs of antagonistic muscles. Because the forces developed are quite large, there must be reflex circuits that inhibit the contraction of a given flexor while the extensor is contracting, and vice versa. This set of reflexes is called **reciprocal inhibition.** Tension on a muscle triggers nerve impulses from **stretch receptors** in the muscle tendons, which provide the brain with information needed to coordinate contraction of a muscle and relaxation of its antagonist.

Study the human muscle pairs shown in Color Plate 6. If the **quadriceps femoris** muscle of the thigh contracted, the leg would be straight at the knee. If the **biceps femoris** contracted, the leg would be bent.

What pair of antagonists control the bending and straightening of the elbow?

_____

_____

What muscle is involved in each of the following activities?

Frowning: _____

Puckering the mouth: _____

Clenching the fist: _____

Lifting a cup of coffee: _____

Pushing a door shut: _____

Rising from a deep knee bend: _____

Shrugging your shoulders: _____

Kicking a ball: _____

The muscles of a frog are shown in Figure 24-3 for comparison. Use this information for your dissection of the leg in the next part of the laboratory.

MUSCLE PHYSIOLOGY

Preparation

SET UP YOUR EXPERIMENTAL APPARATUS BEFORE BEGINNING YOUR FROG DISSECTION.

The **kymograph** is a drum that revolves at a constant rate. Your instructor will give you directions for operating it.

■ Put a clean recording paper around the drum with the shiny side exposed. Lap the left edge of the paper over the right so that the writing pen steps down when the drum is rotating, rather than catching on the edge of the paper.

■ Set up the ring stand as shown in Figure 24-4. Attach a **femur clamp,** a utility clamp with a _clean slide,_ and a muscle lever. The nerve leading to the frog's muscle will lie on the slide and _must be kept moist with frog Ringer's solution at all times,_ or the sensitive nerve cells will quickly die.

■ Set up the signal magnet and the time marker if they are provided with your experimental apparatus.

■ Attach leads to the stimulator or inductorium as shown in Figure 24-4, or follow the directions given for your equipment.

■ Lead 1 connects the signal marker with the 6-V battery and then goes to the MAG terminal of the stimulator.

■ Lead 2 connects the signal marker with the MAG terminal directly.

■ Lead 3 connects the heart clip clamp to the MOD IN terminal.

■ Lead 4 connects the slide and utility clamp with the SYNCH IN terminal. It should be switched to the femur clamp if you wish to stimulate the muscle directly.

WHEN YOUR INSTRUCTOR HAS APPROVED YOUR SETUP, PROCEED WITH YOUR FROG DISSECTION.

■ Locate the **gastrocnemius** muscle and the Achilles tendon that attaches it to the bones of the foot as shown in Figure 24-3. This is the muscle that you will study. Locate the semimembranosus and the vastus externus muscles. Between them is the **sciatic nerve** (not visible in Figure 24-3), which you will stimulate to excite the gastrocnemius muscle.

■ Obtain a pithed frog or pith your own according to your instructor's directions. The procedure for pithing a frog is given in Topic 27.

■ Cut the skin completely around the "waist" of the frog, and pull it off, freeing it from the legs.

■ Using a probe, _carefully_ separate the large muscles (vastus externus and semimembranosus) on the _dorsal,_ medial side of the upper leg. Locate the femur, along which you will find blood vessels and a white or light yellow fiber, which is the sciatic nerve.

■ Use a glass hook to separate the connective tissue from the nerve, and trace it toward the frog's body to the point where it enters the body musculature. Cut the nerve close to that point. (Watch out for the contraction of the gastrocnemius muscle as you make the cut!)

■ Avoid putting any tension on the delicate nerve. Lay the nerve over the lower leg so that it is out of the way.

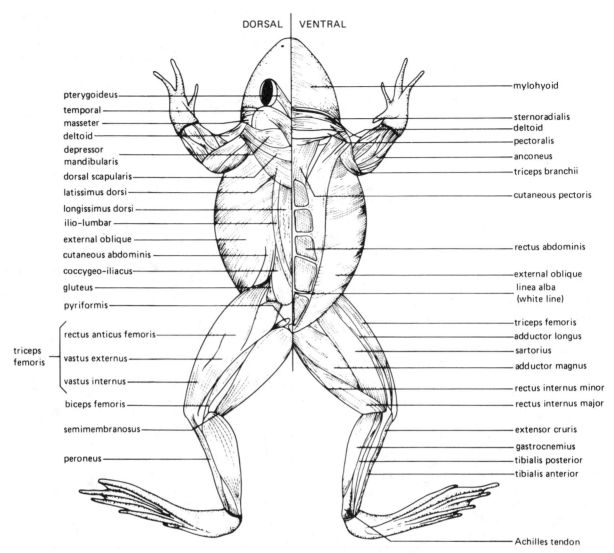

DORSAL | VENTRAL

pterygoideus
temporal
masseter
deltoid
depressor mandibularis
dorsal scapularis
latissimus dorsi
longissimus dorsi
ilio-lumbar
external oblique
cutaneous abdominis
coccygeo-iliacus
gluteus
pyriformis

triceps femoris
— rectus anticus femoris
— vastus externus
— vastus internus
biceps femoris
semimembranosus
peroneus

mylohyoid
sternoradialis
deltoid
pectoralis
anconeus
triceps branchii
cutaneous pectoris
rectus abdominis
external oblique
linea alba (white line)
triceps femoris
adductor longus
sartorius
adductor magnus
rectus internus minor
rectus internus major
extensor cruris
gastrocnemius
tibialis posterior
tibialis anterior
Achilles tendon

Figure 24-3. Frog muscles. Redrawn from Wodsedalek, J. E., and Charles F. Lytle. *General Zoology Laboratory Guide*, 8th ed. © 1981 Wm. C. Brown Company, Publishers, Dubuque, Iowa. Copyright © 1975 by Kendall/Hunt Publishing Co. Reprinted by permission of Kendall/Hunt Publishing Co.)

■ Pull the muscles of the upper leg away from the femur, and cut them off close to the knee.

■ Cut the femur halfway between the hip and knee. Leave enough of a stump to grip with the femur clamp.

■ Trace the broad Achilles tendon around the heel, and cut it free from the bottom of the foot. Free the gastrocnemius from the other muscles and bones of the lower leg.

■ Cut the muscles and bones of the lower leg just below the knee, taking care not to damage the gastrocnemius or the sciatic nerve.

■ Mount your preparation in the apparatus by attaching the femur to the femur clamp and attaching the Achilles tendon to the muscle lever with a heart clip and a piece of thread.

■ Make these adjustments as necessary to get a good recording:

Pen. The ink should be flowing freely to give a good tracing. If not, close the cap of the reservoir bottle, pinch it until the ink flows from the pen, and then loosen the cap slightly while pinching. Adjust the height of the bottle so that ink can flow out.

Heart clip string. Align the muscle and heart clip string so that they are vertical to the muscle lever.

Muscle tension. Raise or lower the muscle lever on the ring stand so that the Achilles tendon is under slight tension.

Pen arm. Move the position of the thread so that the arm responds freely to movement of the muscle.

Kymograph speed. Adjust the rotation rate so that a single twitch gives a record with a recognizable form.

SINGLE MUSCLE TWITCH

Your instructor will give you directions for stimulating the nerve.

KEEP THE NERVE AND MUSCLE WET WITH FROG RINGER'S SOLUTION AT ALL TIMES.

Figure 24-4. Muscle physiology experiment. Apparatus for stimulating a muscle and recording its response on a kymograph. The signal magnet marks the time of stimulation and the time marker shows the duration of the latent period and twitch. Set up the 4 leads according to your instructor's directions.

In Table 24-2, record the stimulus intensity used.

■ Stimulate the muscle through its nerve, wait 15 sec, and repeat.
■ If the tracings are similar, copy the tracing of the **single twitch contraction** in the space provided in Table 24-2.
■ Compare the length of the twitch, beginning at the mark of the signal marker, with the number of cycles in the same interval. Calculate the duration of the twitch in msec according to Table 24-2.

For example, suppose your twitch lasted 12 cycles according to your time marker, and the time marker vibrated at 100 cycles/sec. Then the time that the twitch took would be:

$$\frac{12 \text{ cycles}}{100 \text{ cycles/sec}} = 0.12 \text{ sec} = 120 \text{ msec}$$

If you do not have a time marker, measure the circumference of the drum in cm. Then measure the time in sec for a complete rotation of the kymograph drum. Divide the length by the time in order to calculate the rate of rotation in cm/sec. The time that the twitch took would be:

$$\frac{\text{length of twitch in cm}}{\text{rate of rotation in cm/sec}}$$

The twitch consists of three parts: The **latent period** is the time from stimulus to the beginning of contraction; **contraction** is the period when the muscle is shortening, and **relaxation** is the time during which the muscle is lengthening.

■ Calculate the duration of the latent period, contraction period, and relaxation period for your twitch, and enter the results in Table 24-2.

What chemical events go on during the latent period?

_____

_____

_____

What molecules move to cause the contraction?

_____

Is energy required for the relaxation process?

_____

Did every muscle fiber in the muscle contract during the single twitch? _____

■ Set the stimulator for a higher intensity, and repeat the single twitch.

Did a more intense stimulus cause more intense contraction? _____

Why or why not?

_____

_____

_____

FATIGUE

A muscle can contract indefinitely so long as it has an adequate rest period between twitches. If the stimuli are close together, however, the circulation won't be able to keep pace with the demands of contraction and the muscle will show **fatigue.** Fatigue could occur at the neuromuscular junction or in the muscle.

What substances could run out and thereby cause muscle fatigue?

_____

What substance builds up in the muscle when it is showing fatigue? _____

■ Set the stimulator for multiple shocks at a frequency of 4/sec and an intensity of 3V (0.3V × 10 on the multiplier control). Set the kymograph for slow recording.
■ Stimulate the nerve and record until the contractions are 2 mm high, and then turn off the stimulator.
■ Record the result in Table 24-2.

Was the decrease in the strength of contraction gradual or sudden? _____

■ Test whether the fatigue really occurred in the muscle, or whether it was due to inadequate stimulation of the muscle by the nerve by stimulating the muscle itself directly through the femur clamp using the same intensity of stimulus.

Was the muscle itself fatigued? _____

What causes fatigue at the neuromuscular junction?

_____

_____

■ Stimulate the muscle repeatedly with the same settings that you used for the nerve.

Does the muscle eventually show fatigue at this rate of stimulation? _____

■ Rinse the muscle with Ringer's and give it a 5-min rest.

Temporal Summation

If the muscle is stimulated several times in a row, the intensity of contraction during the twitches may increase. This is called **temporal summation.**

How can the muscle show more contraction on a second or later twitch?

_____

■ Stimulate the muscle repeatedly at intervals shorter than the length of a single twitch.

Do you observe temporal summation? _____

■ Record the results in Table 24-2.

Tetany

Tetany occurs when the stimuli are so close together that the muscle as a whole doesn't have time to relax between twitches and stays contracted. Each individual motor unit twitches, goes through a **refractory period** during which it cannot respond to stimulation, and then twitches again.

■ Set the stimulator so that the frequency of stimuli is the maximum possible.
■ First give the muscle a single stimulus so you have a basis for comparison.
■ Then give the muscle the same strength stimulus at the high frequency, and record the muscle response for several seconds.

■ Record the results in Table 24-2.

Does the muscle show temporal summation at first?

_____

Does the strength of contraction during tetany gradually decrease during the sustained contraction?

_____

When might a tetanic contraction occur in your own body?

_____

When you are finished with your experiment, dispose of the animal remains in the "animal wastes" container, then clean and store your equipment and microscope properly.

EXPLORING FURTHER

Grollman, Sigmund. *The Human Body: Its Structure and Physiology.* 4th ed. New York: Macmillan, 1978.

Schmidt-Nielsen, Knut. *Animal Physiology: Adaptation and Environment.* 3rd ed. Cambridge, England: Cambridge University Press, 1983.

Wilkie, D. R. *Muscle.* New York: St. Martin's Press, 1968.

Journal Articles

Allman, W. F. "Steroids in sports: Do they work?" *Science 83,* 14, November.

Allman, W. F. "Winning recipes." *Science 83,* 90, September.

Cohen, Carolyn. "The protein switch of muscle contraction." *Scientific American,* November 1975 (#1329).

Evarts, Edward V. "Brain mechanisms of movement." *Scientific American,* September 1979 (#1443).

Feld, Michael S., Ronald E. McNair, and Stephen R. Wilk. "The physics of karate." *Scientific American,* April 1979 (#3042).

Lester, Henry A. "The response of acetylcholine." *Scientific American,* February 1977 (#1352).

Napier, John. "The antiquity of human walking." *Scientific American,* April 1967 (#1070).

Rinsler, C. A. "The new and improved chemistry of cosmetics." *Science 82,* 54, April.

Ross, R., and P. Bornstein. "Elastic fibers in the body." *Scientific American,* June 1971 (#1225).

Sonstegard, David A., Larry S. Matthews, and Herbert Kaufer. "The surgical replacement of the human knee joint." *Scientific American,* January 1978 (#1378).

Student Name _____ **Date** _____

TABLE 24-1. COMMON AND SCIENTIFIC NAMES OF SOME HUMAN BONES

Common Names	Scientific Names	Axial	Appendicular
Toe bones			
Neck bones			
Hip bone			
Backbone			
Ankle bones			
Collar bone			
Shoulder blade			
Wrist bones			
Knee cap			
Jawbone			
Shin bone			
Thigh bone			
Foot bones			
Upper arm bone			
Forearm bones			
Bone of calf			
Hand bones			
Finger bones			
Funny bone			
Breast bone			
Tail bone			
Cheek bone			

Figure 24-5. A joint. Add the extensor and flexor muscles with their origins and insertions.

DIAGRAM OF A JOINT

DRAWING OF COMPACT BONE

Student Name _____ **Date** _____

TABLE 24-2. **DATA FROM THE FROG MUSCLE PHYSIOLOGY EXPERIMENT**

Stimulus intensity was: _____

A. DIAGRAM OF A SINGLE TWITCH CONTRACTION:

B. DATA FOR A SINGLE MUSCLE TWITCH:

TIME MARKER CALCULATION

cycles/twitch: _____ cycles

Frequency of time marker: _____ cycles/sec

Duration of twitch = #/frequency: _____ sec = _____ msec

ALTERNATIVE CALCULATION

Rate of drum rotation = $\dfrac{\text{drum circumference: }\underline{\hspace{4cm}}\text{ cm}}{\text{time for one rotation: }\underline{\hspace{3cm}}\text{ sec}}$ = _____ cm/sec

Duration of twitch = length of twitch/rate = _____ sec = _____ msec

Phase	Length of Tracing	Time (msec)
Latent period		
Contraction		
Relaxation		

TABLE 24-2 (Cont.).   MORE DATA FROM THE FROG PHYSIOLOGY EXPERIMENT

C.   DIAGRAM OF FATIGUE:

D.   DIAGRAM OF TEMPORAL SUMMATION:

E.   DIAGRAM OF TETANY:

Processing Food

OBJECTIVES

When you have completed this topic, you should be able to:
1. Describe how a mammal ingests and breaks up its food mechanically.
2. Name the three major classes of food molecules.
3. Describe in general terms what happens to each class of food chemically.
4. Name the parts of the mammalian digestive tract in order, and describe the function of each part in the digestion of each of the macronutrients.
5. List those organs that secrete digestive enzymes, and give the substrates and products of digestion for these enzymes.
6. Describe where in the gut absorption takes place, what substances are absorbed in each place, and what happens to the food after it passes out of the gut lumen into the body.
7. Explain the role of the liver in digestion.
8. Distinguish between: ingestion/digestion; excretion/elimination; bile/enzyme; villus/microvillus; pepsinogen/pepsin; chyme/chylomicron, peristalsis/peritoneum.
9. Describe what happens to each class of food molecules if it is eaten in excess of the body's needs.
10. Explain how the digestive system of a mammalian omnivore (human, pig) differs from that of an herbivore (cow) or carnivore (wolf).
11. Describe the role of symbiotic bacteria in the gut of yourself and of other mammals.

KEY TOPICS

Carbohydrate digestion, protein digestion, lipid digestion, mammalian digestive tract, digestive enzymes, salivary glands, liver, pancreas, omnivore adaptations, gut symbionts.

INTRODUCTION

In this and the following labs you will put together what you learn about animal structure and function by examining a representative mammal, the fetal pig, in some detail. You will be looking at the digestive system, circulatory system, respiratory system, excretory system, endocrine system and reproductive system and you should try to understand how these systems fit together into an integrated organism.

Why a pig?

It turns out that pigs closely resemble humans, anatomically and physiologically. Pigs, like ourselves are omnivores, so their digestive tracts are similar to ours. Their circulatory systems can undergo atherosclerosis, like ours, and so they are used as models in research on the function and diseases of the circulatory system. Special "minipigs" have been developed for laboratory work, because 600 pound porkers are not very practical. Last,

but not least, these pigs are available to us as a by-product of the meat packing industry. When sows are slaughtered, the fetal pigs are discarded, except for those used for biological study (or dog food). Thus the animals are not killed unnecessarily just to obtain the fetal pigs.

The fetal pig develops for 112-115 days before it is mature enough to be born. It will then be about 330 mm long from snout to rump. The pigs usually used for dissection are roughly 102-107 days old.

Since the pig is so like the human, you will most likely find the dissection very interesting once you get underway. It will be a little messy, but this may be your best or only chance to learn firsthand how your body functions in health and disease. In the end, we hope what you learn will be worth the trouble of making a careful dissection.

The fetal pigs have been prepared for dissection by being placed in a preservative such as formalin. (These preservatives are strong and irritating to the hands. Hand

239

cream or lanolin applied to the hands before and after dissection can be helpful.) In addition, these pigs have had their circulatory system injected with colored latex to facilitate blood vessel identification. Veins should appear blue and arteries red, although exceptions occur.

YOU SHOULD NOT WEAR CONTACT LENSES DURING DISSECTION BECAUSE THE FUMES FROM THE PRESERVATIVES WILL IRRITATE YOUR EYES.

Your dissection must be planned and executed *carefully.* Thus it is especially important to read the instructions beforehand. Dissection is a procedure to help you learn the anatomy and structural relationships of the animal. If you do not follow the directions, you may remove, misplace, or lose parts before you have a chance to observe them. Remember that you are going to be using this animal for several laboratory periods, and parts must be preserved *intact* for future study. There are two good rules to keep in mind: Do as little cutting as possible and *never* remove a part unless told to do so. You may be asked to work on your pig together with your lab partner. In that case, each person should do part of the actual dissection to get a feel for the procedures involved. Work slowly at first, and do not hesitate to ask your instructor for advice on how to proceed.

Much of the work of dissection is clearing away connective tissue to expose the organs and free them up so they can be moved. Do not expect all the organs shown in the diagrams to be immediately visible without some probing underneath on your part.

Dissecting Tools

For dissection you will need:

Razor blade (single edge) or **scalpel** to make the initial cuts through the skin. Use these sparingly. Most students tend to be heavy-handed with them and cut too deeply.

Scissors to use for most of the cutting. Use scissors instead of the scalpel whenever possible. Use heavy bone scissors for cartilage and bone. Oil your scissors at the end of each lab to prevent corrosion.

Forceps to use for lifting and moving structures.

Blunt probe to use for lifting parts, separating tissues, and probing ducts.

Fingers can lift, separate, and expose organs far more efficiently than any of the above instruments. Fingers are your best dissecting tools.

Anatomical Terms

You need to know a few adjectives used to denote orientation and direction in anatomical work. Be sure you understand the following and refer back to this list whenever necessary:

Left. The pig's left.
Right. The pig's right.
Anterior. Toward the head.
Posterior. Toward the tail.
Cranial. Toward the head (in humans, the term "superior" is used).

Caudal. Toward the tail (in humans, "inferior").
Dorsal. Toward the back (in humans, "posterior").
Ventral. Toward the belly (in humans, "anterior").
Lateral. Toward the side.
Medial. Toward the midline.
Proximal. Describes the part of a structure nearest a point of reference.
Distal. Describes the part of a structure that is farthest removed from a point of reference.
Pelvic. The hip region.
Pectoral. The shoulder region.

The terms **left** and **right** should be self-evident, but unfortunately these terms lead to more confusion than any of the other terms. It is important that you remember that left and right always refer to the *pig's* left or right, not your own!

MANY MORE TERMS ARE GIVEN IN THE FOLLOWING DIRECTIONS THAN YOU MAY BE EXPECTED TO LEARN.

Your instructor will give you some indication as to how much detail you will be expected to master, depending on the amount of laboratory time spent in dissection. To a certain extent, you will be expected to use your own judgment in deciding what is important. As a rough guide, you should be familiar with the location and function of those structures that are also mentioned in your text.

Care of Your Specimen

Although your specimen is preserved in embalming fluid, it will stay useful for dissection only if it is kept from drying out. It must be kept in a sealed plastic bag containing a little fluid at all times when you are not dissecting. During the laboratory period, you should add a little water or dissecting fluid from time to time to keep the tissues moist and flexible.

COVER THE PIG WITH WET PAPER TOWELS WHENEVER YOU ARE NOT ACTUALLY DISSECTING.

When you are ready to stop the dissection until the next period, make sure the organs are moist before you seal the specimen up in its plastic bag.

EXTERNAL ANATOMY

■ At the sink, remove the pig from its plastic bag and rinse it off under the tap. (Save the bag.) Do not be alarmed at the "drowned rat" appearance of your specimen. Remember that mammals, including humans, are born dripping wet, since they spend the fetal period in a watery environment.

The body of a mammal is divided into a number of regions. The **head** is separated from the **trunk** by the movable neck. The trunk is generally divided into the anterior **thorax** and posterior **abdomen** and **pelvis**. Most mammals have a **tail.**

■ Examine the head and locate the **eyes,** the external ears, or **pinnae** (singular: pinna), the nostrils, and the mouth.
■ Note the paired legs and their various joints.
■ Compare the pig forelimb with your own arm, and try to figure out the corresponding parts.
■ Do the same for the hindlimb.
■ Pick up the pig and manipulate the joints.

Do they move the same way yours do?

_____

■ Notice the toes.

How many are there on each foot? _____

How many toes does the pig actually walk on?

_____

The pig walks on the tip of his toenails, a method of locomotion known as "unguligrade."

How does this differ from the human method of walking?

_____

_____

_____

_____

_____

■ Observe the **umbilical cord** by which the fetal pig was attached to the placenta during development within the uterus.
■ Observe the cut end of the cord, and notice the cut ends of the blood vessels that carried blood containing dissolved nutrients and wastes to and from the placenta of the mother. The human umbilical cord is normally cut at birth, and shrivels up, so all that remains of it is the **navel.**
■ On the ventral surface of the thorax and abdomen find the two rows of **mammary glands.** These glands are one of the distinctive features of mammals. The presence of **hair** is a second distinctive characteristic of all mammals.

Your next task will be to determine the sex of your pig.

■ Raise the tail and observe the **anus,** the posterior end of the digestive tract.
■ If your specimen is a female, there will be a second opening just ventral to the anus, the **urogenital opening.** This is the exit for both the reproductive and excretory systems. Protruding from the urogenital opening in the female is a small, fleshy **urogenital papilla.**
■ If your specimen is male, there is no second opening near the anus. Instead, locate the small **urogenital opening** just posterior to the umbilical cord. The duct leading to it runs forward from between the legs in a long muscular tube, the **penis,** which can be felt under the skin.
■ If your specimen is male, find the scrotal sacs in the area ventral to the anus. The scrotal sacs are not very apparent in the fetal pig. Around the time of birth the testes eventually descend into them.

Is your pig male or female? _____

ANATOMY OF THE DIGESTIVE SYSTEM

■ Place your pig in the dissecting tray so that its ventral side is up.
■ Cut two pieces of string about 2 ft. long.
■ Tie a piece of string securely around the ankle of each of the right legs.
■ Run the two pieces of string under the dissecting tray, and tie them tightly to the ankles of the left legs, thus holding the pig securely in place in the dissecting tray, as shown in Figure 25-1.

If you stretch the legs as far apart as possible at this point, it will be a lot easier to locate the inner organs during your dissection.

The digestive system of the fetal pig consists of the **mouth, oral cavity, pharynx, esophagus, stomach, small intestine,** and **large intestine.** The **salivary glands, liver** and **pancreas** are accessory organs. (See Figure 25-5.) As you study the anatomy of the digestive system you should review the functions of each of these structures. The one-way flow of food from mouth to anus of this **complete digestive tract** allows greatly specialized sections that can act independently of each other. It also allows the animal to continue to eat while previously eaten food is still being digested.

The Mouth and Pharynx

The mouth opens into the oral cavity.

■ Use bone scissors to cut through the corners of the mouth to the back of the jaw, so that the mouth opens widely. (See Figure 25-2.)
■ Note the **hard palate,** which makes up the anterior part of the roof of the mouth. It is made of bone and covered with folds of mucous membrane.

The hard palate separates the oral cavity from the nasal cavities.

string connects forelegs

string connects hindlegs

Figure 25-1. Fetal pig specimen. Stretch the legs as far apart as possible and tie them securely. Remove the pig for storage by slipping the strings out from under the dissecting pan.

Figure 25-2. Cutting the jaw. Use heavy scissors to cut through the jaw cartilage so that the mouth can be fully opened.

■ Note that the membranes continue posteriorly, forming the **soft palate,** which does not contain bone.

In humans, there is a fleshy protuberance from the soft palate called the **uvula.**

■ Locate the uvula *on your neighbor.*
■ Notice the sensory papillae on the surface of the muscular **tongue.** Taste buds within the papillae are responsible for the sensations associated with food ingestion: salt, sweet, sour, and bitter.

How is the tongue attached?

_____

Ducts from the salivary glands enter the rear of the oral cavity and produce **salivary amylase,** which breaks down starch enzymatically during mastication.

What are the products of starch digestion?

_____

What substrate other than starch is required for the reaction?

_____

What is this type of reaction called?

_____

Have any **teeth** erupted from the gums in your specimen? _____

■ Observe the various types of teeth on demonstration.
■ Cut into the gum of the pig along one side, and extract one or more of the developing teeth.
■ Identify a tooth as an **incisor** (for biting, gnawing), **canine** (for stabbing, tearing), or **molar** (for crushing, grinding). Canines are important for carnivores and incisors and molars for herbivores. Omnivores tend to use all three types of teeth.

Describe some digestive and nondigestive uses of teeth:

_____

_____

_____

_____

At the base of the tongue, the oral cavity ends and the **pharynx** begins. The pharynx is the common passageway for the digestive and respiratory tracts because both air and food must pass through this structure. You may have to extend the cuts you made earlier to open the mouth wide enough to see the pharynx and associated structures.

■ At the posterior end of the tongue find a trough-shaped fold of tissue, the **epiglottis.** You may have to reach deep into the pharynx with your probe to locate the epiglottis and pull it out into view. Dorsal to this is an opening, the **glottis,** which leads into the **larynx,** part of the respiratory system. (See Figure 28-3.)

During swallowing the epiglottis forms a kind of lid over the glottis and deflects the food away from the glottis. When the epiglottis fails to do this, the food enters the glottis and choking results.

■ Dorsal to the glottis find the second, wider opening into the **esophagus.**

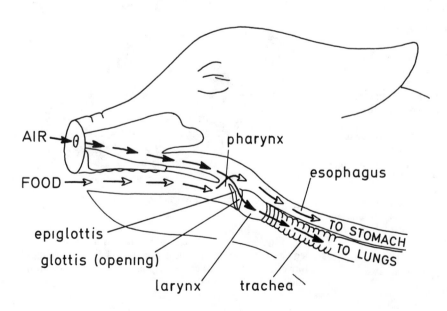

Figure 25-3. The pharynx in action. Air and food passages cross here, and there is some risk that food may enter or block the epiglottis, causing suffocation.

The esophagus is a collapsible muscular tube connecting the pharynx to the stomach. Food enters the esophagus by the reflex swallowing of the pharynx and passes through the esophagus and gut by waves of muscular contraction called **peristalis.**

■ Pass the end of your probe into the glottis and then into the esophagus. Be certain that you can differentiate them. Notice that air entering through the nose must cross the pathway of food during swallowing.
■ Relate Figure 25-3 to your pig to be sure you understand the anatomy of the pharynx.

At this time you will not follow the course of the esophagus as it proceeds through the thorax. It will be easier to study it when you dissect the respiratory system.

The esophagus marks the point at which food has been more or less irreversibly **ingested** or taken into the body by the actions of the teeth, tongue, and pharynx. Next the food will be **digested,** or broken down chemically by hydrolysis into small molecules that can be **absorbed** into the body proper. Some ingested material never becomes part of the body at all; it remains within the **lumen** (interior) of the gut and will be eliminated as waste.

The Abdominal Cavity

■ Look at Figure 25-4 and study the cuts that you are going to make to open the abdominal cavity.
■ With the scalpel or razor blade make a shallow cut from a point about 5 mm anterior to the umbilical cord forward to the most anterior pair of mammary glands.
■ Cut around the umbilical cord on both sides, and continue the two parallel cuts posteriorly, keeping them *outside* the mammary glands.
■ Deepen these cuts carefully until you reach the body cavity. You will have cut deeply enough when you see the dark-colored abdominal organs underneath the transparent membrane called the **peritoneum.**
■ Locate the posterior end of the sternum, or breastbone, and cut laterally on each side following the posterior edge of the rib cage.
■ Make similar cuts just anterior to the hind legs.
■ Now fold out the flaps of the body wall, exposing the abdominal cavity. Its anterior end is bounded by a transverse partition, the **diaphragm.**
■ Pull up and back on the umbilical cord and you will see the **umbilical vein** going to the liver. This vein carries food and oxygen to the fetus from the placenta.
■ Tie the ends of a piece of thread or string to the umbilical vein in two places to form a loop. The vein may now be cut between the ends of the string. The string will let you find the vein easily later on in the dissection.
■ If the body cavity contains much fluid, flush it out with water. During the dissection, paper tissues can be used to soak up any remaining fluid in the body cavity.
■ Examine the lining of the abdominal cavity. This shiny membrane is called the **peritoneum.** The part of the membrane next to the body wall is called the **parietal peritoneum,** while that covering the surfaces of the internal organs is the **visceral peritoneum.** The thin, transparent sheets of tissue that connect the two are called **mesenteries.** The mesenteries suspend and support the visceral organs.
■ Examine the large, dark brown **liver** located just posterior to the diaphragm.

Figure 25-4. Dissection guide. Cut along the dotted lines to open the abdomen of your specimen.

■ Notice that the liver consists of a number of lobes.
■ Lift up the posterior edge of the liver and find the cut end of the umbilical vein anterior to the right side of the liver. (It should be attached to your string.)
■ Just below the entrance of the umbilical vein into the liver you should see the **gall bladder** as a greenish sac embedded in the under surface of the liver.

The liver secretes **bile,** a mixture of **bile salts** (lipids similar to cholesterol) and excreted wastes. (**Excretion** refers to the removal from the body of substances that have entered and been a part of the body cells.) Bile is temporarily stored in the gall bladder and at the appropriate time enters the small intestine where it acts to **emulsify** fats. This breaks the insoluble globs of fat into tiny droplets so that lipid-digesting enzymes have a greatly increased surface area on which to act.

Once food molecules have been digested and absorbed into the blood stream, the liver plays an important role in storing carbohydrates as glycogen and in metabolizing amino acids and lipids.

What are some other nondigestive functions of the liver?

_____

_____

_____

_____

Does the liver secrete any digestive enzymes?

_____

Describe the composition and location of gallstones:

_____
_____

Use Figure 25-5 as your guide in locating the other abdominal organs.

■ With the liver still elevated, identify the **stomach** on the left side of the abdominal cavity.
■ Locate the point near the midline where the esophagus enters the stomach. This is the **cardiac** portion of the stomach. Food from the stomach leaves through the **pyloric** end of the stomach. The flow of food is governed by a circular sphincter muscle called the **pyloric valve.** It releases partly digested food called **chyme** from the stomach into the small intestine.
■ Squeeze the pyloric valve and note how muscular it is.
■ Cut the stomach open lengthwise, and notice the ridges (rugae) on the inside. They serve to increase the internal surface area.
■ Observe the internal entrance of the esophagus and the pyloric valve, which marks the exit into the small intestine.

Are these valves normally open or closed?

_____

■ Notice that the stomach is not empty even though the fetus receives its nourishment from its mother through the umbilical vein. The fetus constantly drinks in the amniotic fluid surrounding it. The contents of the stomach consist of epithelial cells, hair, and other substances from the amniotic fluid.

Cells of the gastric glands, located in the lining of the stomach, secrete **hydrochloric acid, pepsinogen,** and **rennin.** Pepsinogen is an inactive precursor of the enzyme **pepsin,** which hydrolyzes proteins to polypeptides. HCl maintains the acidic conditions in the stomach (pH 1-2) required for pepsin to act. The stomach is protected from digesting itself because the mucosa is alkaline and the cells are tightly pressed together sideways so that acid cannot penetrate the tissue. When the protection fails, a sore called a peptic ulcer results. Rennin hydrolyzes milk protein (casein). Stomach secretions are regulated by the hormone **gastrin** from the stomach's own mucosa.

Does any absorption of food molecules take place from the stomach? _____

How would your own feeding habits have to be modified if your stomach were removed?

_____
_____
_____

■ Note the tongue-shaped **spleen,** which is attached to the stomach by a mesentery. The spleen is part of the circulatory system. In humans it acts as a fine filter to remove debris and possibly harmful bacteria from the blood.

What color is the spleen? _____

■ Identify the anterior end of the **small intestine** leading from the stomach; it is the C-shaped **duode-**

num. This is a very important part of the small intestine because the ducts from the liver, gall bladder, and pancreas enter here. Those from the liver and gall bladder join as the **common bile duct,** which can be seen as a white cord leading from the gall bladder to the duodenum. The **bile** produced by the liver and stored in the gall bladder enters through this duct.

What is the function of bile in digestion?

_____

What is bile made of?

_____

■ If you lift the stomach and press the intestinal mass posteriorly, you will expose the light-colored glandular **pancreas.** (Glandular tissue has the appearance of used chewing gum.) The structural relationship between the duodenum and the pancreas has whimsically been called "the romance of the intestines" because the pancreas lies in the "arms" of the duodenum! The pancreas is connected to the duodenum by two tiny ducts that are too small to be easily seen. The juice secreted by the pancreas enters the small intestine through these ducts. No digestion takes place within the pancreas itself.

The pancreas is also an endocrine gland and secretes the hormones **insulin,** and **glucagon,** which together regulate blood glucose.

What is the major target organ for these hormones?

_____

All major food classes (carbohydrate, protein, fat, and nucleic acid) can be digested by enzymes from the pancreas. These enzymes, as is pepsin, are secreted in an inactive form. **Enterokinase,** an enzyme secreted by the small intestine, activates the protein-digesting enzyme **trypsin** and trypsin in turn activates the other enzymes. A neutral pH is required for activity, so pancreatic juice includes **sodium bicarbonate** to neutralize the acidic chyme entering from the stomach. If secretion of sodium bicarbonate is not sufficient, acid could attack the intestinal lining to cause a duodenal ulcer.

What are the substrates and products of these pancreatic enzymes?

Enzyme	Substrate(s)	Product(s)
trypsin		
chymotrypsin		
carboxy-peptidase		
lipase		
amylase		
RNase		
DNase		

The small intestine itself, in addition to enterokinase, secretes aminopeptidase to hydrolyze small polypeptides

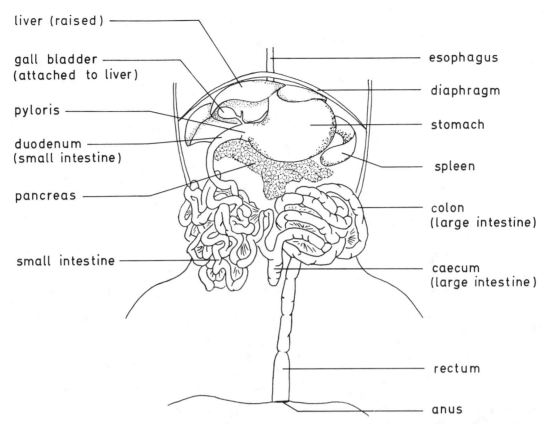

liver (raised)

gall bladder
(attached to liver)

pyloris

duodenum
(small intestine)

pancreas

small intestine

esophagus

diaphragm

stomach

spleen

colon
(large intestine)

caecum
(large intestine)

rectum

anus

Figure 25-5.   Abdominal organs. This diagram shows the approximate location of organs within the abdominal cavity. You will have to lift the liver to see the gall bladder underneath and move aside some of the other organs to see all of them.

and enzymes to digest the disaccharides maltose, sucrose, and lactose. It also secretes two important hormones: **Secretin** stimulates the liver and pancreas to release their secretions, and **cholecystekinin** (CCK) likewise acts on the gall bladder and pancreas. CCK affects hunger centers in the brain to regulate food intake.

■ Trace the rest of the small intestine posteriorly from the duodenum. Notice the great length of the small intestine crowded into the small space. Intestine length tends to be short in carnivores but long in herbivores because plant material is harder to digest and larger amounts must be eaten.

■ Cut the small intestine next to the pyloris and next to the entrance to the large intestine. Dissect it free.

■ Measure its length and compare it with the pig's snout-to-rump length.

Humans, like pigs and rats, are omnivores and have a small intestine of intermediate length. If this length is comparable in pigs and humans, how long would the small intestine be in a person whose sitting height is 1 m?

	Pig	**Human**
Height (length)	cm	1 m
Small intestine	cm	m

■ Cut off a short section of small intestine.

■ Slit it open lengthwise and examine it with a hand lens or under the dissecting microscope.

The velvetlike appearance is due to small projections called **villi,** which greatly increase the interior surface area. The cells on the surface of the villi are in turn covered with a brush border of **microvilli** to further increase the surface area available for absorption. The villi contain capillaries and lymphatic vessels that take up the end products of digestion and circulate them to the rest of the body, especially the liver. Amino acids and sugars enter the blood directly by diffusion or active transport. Amino acids are either used, or immediately metabolized for energy, since little protein can be stored by the body. Carbohydrates can be stored as glycogen in the liver or muscles. Partly digested fats enter the **lacteals** (blind ends of the lymphatic vessels) as tiny droplets called **chylomicrons.** They travel through the lymph and blood to the liver for further digestion. Fats may be metabolized for energy or stored as body fat.

■ Push the intestine to the right side, and relocate the point at which the small intestine enters the **large intestine.** It enters from the side, making a blind pouch called the **caecum.**

The caecum in plant-eating animals is usually large (up to 35 cm long in rabbits) and contains many microorganisms that produce **cellulase,** an enzyme that can digest cellulose. The caecum is of little importance in the pig or human. In humans, the **appendix** is located at the end of the caecum, but it is absent in the pig. The main portion of the large intestine is called the **colon.** It forms a tight double coil and then goes to the dorsal abdominal wall and continues posteriorly along the midline. This type of coiling in the colon is uncommon in mammals. The human colon is shaped like an upside-down U.

What substances are absorbed by the colon?

_____

Does the colon secrete digestive enzymes?

_____

■ Remove a short segment of the colon and cut it open.

How does the inner surface compare with that of the small intestine?

_____

The colon contains a large number of bacteria that are continually being lost in the feces but that are also very important in human nutrition. They synthesize **vitamin K,** which is absorbed from the gut lumen and plays a vital role in blood clotting. Because they lack gut bacteria, newborn babies may be deficient in vitamin K and therefore especially susceptible to bleeding from small wounds.

Later in your dissection you will follow the colon to the **rectum** and **anus** where feces exit from the body. The large intestine both eliminates and excretes since some wastes are undigested food material but others (e.g. bile pigments) have been excreted into its lumen.

The **transit time** of food through the digestive tract can be speeded up if the diet is high in bulk and fiber. This is desireable, since our intestinal bacteria constantly produce **carcinogens** such as nitrites that may lead to cancer of the colon.

HISTOLOGY OF THE INTESTINE

The intestinal wall is made up of four different layers. Review its structure by looking at a cross section of the intestine under low power of the compound microscope. (Refer to Figure 5-5.) The central opening, or **lumen,** has the villi projecting into it.

■ Examine one **villus.** Covering the villus is a layer of epithelial cells called the **mucosa.** Under the mucosa is an area of connective tissue, the **submucosa.**
■ Identify the blood vessels running through the submucosa. The digested food must move from the intestinal lumen, through the mucosa and submucosa into these blood vessels.
■ Locate the **lacteals** or blind ends of the lymphatic vessels.

What kind of food molecules are absorbed by the lymphatic vessels? _____

What are the tiny droplets of this food called?

_____

Where do they go for further processing?

_____

■ Outside the submucosa, locate the **muscularis,** which consists of two layers of muscle: an inner circular layer and an outer longitudinal layer. This arrangement allows the peristaltic contractions of the intestine to move the food through the digestive tract.
■ An **adventitia** of connective tissue covers the muscularis. The outermost tissue is a single cell layer, the **visceral peritoneum.**

Why does the intestine have villi?

_____

What is the function of the goblet cells of the mucosa?

_____

How does the shape of the intestine change when the inner layer of muscles contracts?

_____

_____

How does the shape of the intestine change when the outer layer of muscles contracts?

_____

_____

What tissue supports the blood vessels leading to and

from the intestine? _____

Reminder: When you are finished with your dissection for today, close up the abdomen of your pig and return it and any scraps of tissue to its plastic bag. Seal the bag, label it with your name, and store it properly. Clean your dissecting tools, oil the scissors to prevent rusting, and leave your workplace clean for the next student.

EXPLORING FURTHER

Ganong, W. F. *Review of Medical Physiology.* 11th ed. Los Altos, Calif.: Lange, 1983.
Grollman, S. *The Human Body. Its Structure and Physiology.* 4th ed. New York: Macmillan, 1978.
Guyton, A. C. *Textbook of Medical Physiology.* 6th ed. Philadelphia: W. B. Saunders, 1981.
Morton, John. *Guts: The Form and Function of the Digestive System.* New York: St. Martin's Press, 1967.
Solomon, E. P., and P. W. Davis. *Human Anatomy and Physiology.* Philadelphia: Saunders College Publishing, 1983.

Journal Articles

Bennett, William, and Joel Gurin. "Do diets really work?" *Science 82,* 42, April 1982.
Davenport, H. W. "Why the stomach does not digest itself." *Scientific American,* January 1972 (#1240).
Deutsch, J. A., W. G. Young, and T. J. Kalogeris. "The stomach signals satiety." *Science 201:* 165, 1978.
Fernstrom, John D., and Richard J. Wurtman. "Nutrition and the brain." *Scientific American,* February 1974 (#1291).
Geller, Stephen A. "Autopsy." *Scientific American,* 124, March 1983.
Kappas, Attallah, and Alvito P. Alvares. "How the liver metabolizes foreign substances." *Scientific American,* June 1975 (#1322).
Kretschmer, N. "Lactose and lactase." *Scientific American,* October 1972 (#1259).
Lieber, Charles S. "The metabolism of alcohol." *Scientific American,* March 1976 (#1336).
Moog, Florence. "The lining of the small intestine." *Scientific American,* 154, November 1981.
Scrimshaw, Nevin S., and Lance Taylor. "Food." *Scientific American,* September 1980 (#734).
Scrimshaw, Nevin S., and Vernon R. Young. "The requirements of human nutrition." *Scientific American,* 50, September 1976.

Internal Transport in Vertebrates

OBJECTIVES

When you have completed this topic, you should be able to:
1. Name four functions of the circulatory system.
2. Cite the function of each of the major parts of the circulatory system: heart, arteries, veins, and capillaries.
3. Describe the function of the placenta, umbilical arteries, and the umbilical vein.
4. Trace the path of a blood cell from the umbilical vein to the right atrium of the heart and back to the umbilical artery by the shortest route.
5. Describe the path of blood flow through the four chambers of the heart and the five major vessels connecting to it.
6. Name the parts of the circulatory system that have valves, and state the function of valves in regulating blood flow.
7. Describe the changes in structure and function that occur in these structures when the fetal pig is born: umbilical artery, umbilical vein, hepatic portal vein, ductus venosus, foramen ovale, pulmonary artery, pulmonary vein, ductus arteriosus.

KEY TOPICS

Closed circulatory system, double circulation, mammalian heart, arteries, veins, capillaries, lymphatic system.

INTRODUCTION

The circulatory system of a mammal has four major functions:

1. The transportation of nutrients, gases, wastes, and hormones.
2. The regulation of the pH, water, and salt content of the tissues.
3. The protection of the body by the immune system.
4. The regulation of body temperature.

The **heart** is the pump that forces the blood through the pulmonary and systemic circuits of the circulatory system. The **arteries** are the main vessels carrying blood from the heart to the rest of the body. The arteries end in the tiny **capillaries,** where exchange of nutrients, gases, wastes, and other substances with the tissues can occur. Finally the blood returns from the capillaries of the body to the heart in the large **veins.** Since the blood is contained within vessels or the heart, this is

a **closed circulatory system.** The blood and the capillaries are the physiologically active parts of the circulatory system. The main purpose of the heart and large arteries and veins is simply to move the blood quickly to the capillaries so that exchange can occur there.

THE HEART

Study the diagram of the adult heart in Figure 26-1. This view is from the ventral side and shows the internal structure of the heart.

Adult Heart

■ Use the demonstration heart or a model of the heart to identify the major structures. The ventral side of the heart can be identified easily because it has a diagonal

247

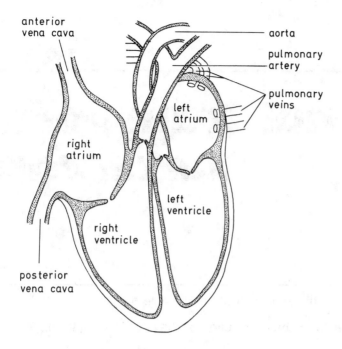

Figure 26-1. Adult heart. Blood from the anterior and posterior venae cavae flows into the right atrium, through the atrioventricular valve (tricuspid) into the right ventricle, and leaves through the pulmonary artery to the lungs. Blood then returns from the lungs in the pulmonary veins, enters the left atrium, passes through the atrioventricular valve (mitral) into the left ventricle, then leaves via the aorta.

line of fat. The dorsal surface is usually flatter and has a short, straight line of fat.

■ Find the ear-shaped **right atrium** and **left atrium** located on either side of the heart. The bulk of the heart consists of the **right** and **left ventricles.**

■ Examine the cut across the base or apex of the heart.

Which ventricle has the greatest muscle mass?

_____

■ Open the cuts in the heart so that you can see these valves:

1. The **tricuspid** valve is between the right atrium and right ventricle.
2. The **mitral** valve is between the left atrium and left ventricle.
3. The **semilunar** valves are at the base of the pulmonary artery and at the base of the aorta.

■ Note the "heart strings" that hold the flaps of the valves in place.

Normal heart sounds are due to to closing of these two sets of valves. A heart **murmur** occurs when the valves do not close completely allowing blood to leak backwards.

■ Note the two large arteries connecting to the heart. They are thick-walled and very muscular.

In which direction does blood flow in these arteries?

_____

The more ventral artery is the **pulmonary artery,** which carries deoxygenated blood from the heart to the lungs. (Note that not all arteries carry oxygenated blood.)

To which chamber of the heart is it connected?

_____

The larger, more dorsal vessel is the **aorta.**

To which chamber of the heart is the aorta connected?

_____

There are three major veins connected to the heart. Because they are thin-walled, they are collapsed in this empty heart.

In which direction does blood flow in each of these veins?

_____

Is the blood flowing in these vessels under high pressure or under low pressure?

_____

■ Find the two large vessels connecting to the right side of the heart. They are the **anterior vena cava** and **posterior vena cava.**

To which chamber of the heart do the anterior and the posterior vena cava connect?

_____

Finally, the **pulmonary veins** come together on the dorsal surface of the heart. They bring oxygenated blood from the lungs back to the heart.

To which chamber do the pulmonary veins connect?

_____

■ Trace the flow of blood from the right atrium to the aorta.

Draw arrows in Figure 26-1 to show the direction that blood flows in each vessel and chamber.

Fetal Pig Heart

Following the dotted lines in Figure 26-2, open the thorax and throat.

CUT CAREFULLY WITHOUT DAMAGING THE UNDERLYING ORGANS AND BLOOD VESSELS.

Figure 26-2. Dissection guide. Cut along the dotted lines to open the thorax and throat regions. Be careful not to damage underlying structures in the midline and shoulder regions.

■ Use your scissors to cut through the bone and cartilage in the center. Be careful that you do not cut into the heart and blood vessels just underneath.
■ Cut along the margin of the rib cage as indicated by the curved line.
■ Touch the throat region of the pig to locate the hard, round larynx, or voice box.
■ Make the necessary cuts to expose the throat region, making sure the larynx is included within the exposed area. (See Figure 26-2.)

Beneath the skin of the throat are muscles and glands. The muscle tissue is mostly in ribbons with the fibers running lengthwise.

■ In the neck region and around the heart, note the large masses of light-colored glandular tissue, the **thymus gland.** This gland is part of the immune system, which produces antibodies as a defense against disease

organisms. It is prominent early in development when the system is being established. Later in life the thymus decreases in size, and it is of little importance in the adult.
■ Locate the **pericardial cavity,** which contains the heart and is lined by the pericardial membrane.
■ Carefully remove the light-colored thymus gland from around the heart and its vessels.
■ Carefully remove the pericardial membrane to expose the heart.
■ Identify the major chambers and vessels of the heart, using Figure 26-3 as your guide; note the light-colored **ventricles** that form the posterior part of the heart and the dark-colored flaps that are the ventral parts of the **atria.** Larger portions of the ventricles are hidden from view.
■ You can cut off the tip of the heart with a razor blade to see the difference in size of the muscles making up the right and left ventricle.

Part of the blood entering the heart follows the pattern that you traced for the adult heart. In the fetal pig, however, there is an opening between the right and left atria called the **foramen ovale.** It allows some of the blood entering the right atrium to pass directly to the left atrium and out through the aorta, instead of first circulating to the fetal lungs.

■ Push the heart posteriorly and clean off pieces of thymus tissue and membrane so that you can see clearly the vessels that arise from the heart.

1. The most conspicuous vessel is the thick-walled, light-colored **pulmonary artery.**
2. Beneath is the slightly larger **aorta,** which is also thick-walled and light-colored.
3. The pulmonary artery is connected to the aorta by the short, thick **ductus arteriosus.** In the fetal stage, most of the blood leaving the heart in the pulmonary artery by-passes the right and left branches of this artery and instead passes through the ductus arteriosus and into the aorta directly.

Why are the lungs by-passed before birth?

_____

_____

_____

_____

_____

_____

Figure 26-3. Fetal pig heart. Ventral view of its external structure. The thick white pulmonary artery is the most prominent vessel leaving the heart.

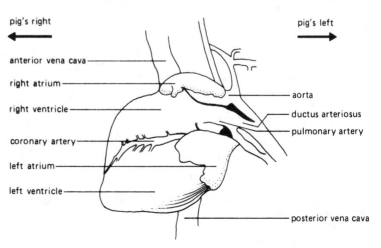

pig's right

pig's left

anterior vena cava
right atrium
right ventricle
coronary artery
left atrium
left ventricle

aorta
ductus arteriosus
pulmonary artery

posterior vena cava

4. Returning to the anterior part of the heart, the large, thin-walled, dark or blue-colored vessel on the right is the **anterior vena cava.** It brings blood from the anterior part of the body to the right atrium of the heart. Lift the posterior tip of the heart to see the **pulmonary veins,** which join together on the dorsal surface of the heart and enter the left atrium.

5. On the right side of the heart is a large blue vessel, which is the **posterior vena cava** and which joins the anterior vena cava in entering the right atrium.

ARTERIES

Arteries are all the vessels carrying blood away from the heart. Remember that the blood carried by arteries is sometimes rich in oxygen and sometimes poor in oxygen. If you have an injected pig, the arteries have been injected with pink latex so that they are easily seen and resistant to breakage. The veins have been injected with blue latex so that you can tell the difference, but sometimes the injection results are not perfect and a certain vessel, the umbilical vein or artery, for example, may be the "wrong color." Ask your instructor for help if you have trouble locating a certain artery or vein. Use Figure 26-4 to identify your pig's arteries.

In cross section, arteries have thick walls that are muscular and have elastic connective tissue. Arteries lose their elasticity with age, leading to **arteriosclerosis.** In the most common form of this disease, **atherosclerosis,** their delicate endothelial linings become covered with lipid deposits. Narrow, hard arteries are likely to become plugged and to then rupture because arterial blood is under very high pressure. When this happens in the brain, nerve cells are destroyed, resulting in a **stroke.**

Pulmonary Artery

■ Locate the branches to the right and left lungs; lift the heart to see them.

What is the main vessel to which the pulmonary artery joins in the fetal pig?

_____

Aorta

■ Note that this vessel arches as it leaves the heart, passes down in the thoracic cavity to the spine, and then runs posteriorly all the way to the umbilical arteries. It is the major artery in both the fetal and adult pig.

■ Locate the following vessels that branch off from the aorta as it passes through the body (see Figure 26-4):

1. **Coronary artery.** The first vessel to branch from the aorta, which supplies blood to the heart itself.

ARTERIES

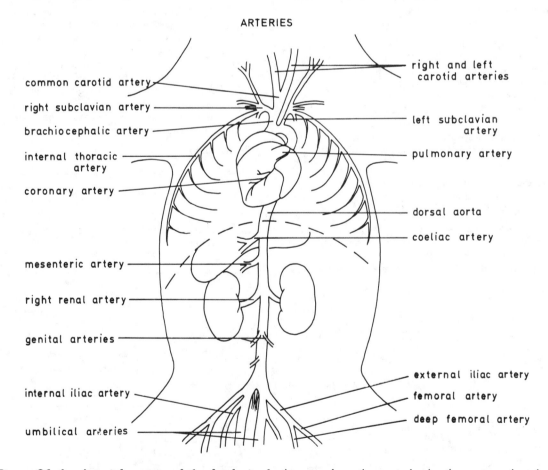

common carotid artery
right subclavian artery
brachiocephalic artery
internal thoracic artery
coronary artery
mesenteric artery
right renal artery
genital arteries
internal iliac artery
umbilical arteries

right and left carotid arteries
left subclavian artery
pulmonary artery
dorsal aorta
coeliac artery
external iliac artery
femoral artery
deep femoral artery

Figure 26-4. Arterial system of the fetal pig. In this view from the ventral side, the aorta arches dorsally, passes beneath the heart, and becomes the dorsal aorta deep within the thorax. The aorta divides to form the prominent umbilical arteries.

(The heart receives no nourishment from the blood passing through its interior.) It is difficult to see the branch point even when you lift the left atrium and look closely. The vessel itself is easy to see on the ventral surface of the heart. When this vessel constricts or becomes blocked by a blood clot (coronary thrombosis) during a heart attack, the oxygen supply to the active heart muscle is interrupted, and some of the muscle tissue dies. If the heart actually stops pumping, cardiopulmonary resuscitation (CPR) may keep the body oxygenated long enough for the damaged heart to be stimulated to resume functioning. If the damage to the heart is extensive, it cannot continue to function and the heart attack will be fatal.

2. **Brachiocephalic artery.** A large branch that divides into the **common carotid artery** and the **right subclavian artery.** Trace the common carotid to its branch point into the right and left carotids, and trace one of the carotids into the throat region. This artery serves the head and neck. The right subclavian sends blood to the right forelimb. The **internal thoracic arteries** send blood to the chest and ribs.

3. **Left subclavian artery.** The branch that leaves the thorax and enters the left forelimb.

■ Push the lungs to the pig's right, and locate the **dorsal aorta** deep in the thoracic cavity next to the vertebral column. Notice that it is still thick-walled and light-colored. Its walls are so thick that the color of the pink latex is not visible. Next to the aorta is the collapsed, flabby, tubular esophagus.

■ Trace the aorta and esophagus posteriorly as they pass through the diaphragm and enter the abdominal cavity.

4. **Coeliac artery.** Branches from the aorta just posterior to the diaphragm and serves the stomach, liver, spleen, and pancreas. Blood pools in the spleen, which is an important part of the circulatory system. It acts as a filter to remove bacteria and dead cells by the action of white blood cells.

5. **Mesenteric artery.** The branches of this artery send blood to the small intestine and to the anterior part of the large intestine.

6. **Renal artery.** The right and left renal arteries send blood to the kidneys. Occasionally you might see a renal artery that is double instead of a single vessel.

7. **Genital artery.** A pair of small genital arteries that branches next, and supply the testes in the male or the ovaries and uterus in the female.

8. **External iliac artery.** A pair of large arteries that supplies the hindlimbs. After each gives off a small branch, it branches into the **femoral artery** and **deep femoral artery.**

9. **Internal iliac artery.** The aorta ends at the spot where the external iliac branches off and it becomes the internal iliac artery for a short distance. The internal iliac in turn splits to form the umbilical arteries.

10. **Umbilical arteries.** These large arteries arise from the internal iliac and carry blood from the fetus to the placenta. Blood in these vessels would be very low in oxygen and nutrients but high in CO_2 and wastes. (Remember that arteries sometimes carry oxygen-rich blood and sometimes oxygen-poor blood.)

You have traced the major arteries as an introduction to the complexity of the circulatory system anatomy. Each artery divides repeatedly into smaller **arterioles** and finally becomes a **capillary bed.** The capillaries join together into larger and larger **venules** and finally return blood to the large veins entering the heart.

COVER YOUR PIG WITH MOIST PAPER TOWELS DURING THE NEXT PART OF THE LABORATORY.

CAPILLARIES

The only purpose of the heart and all of the blood vessels is to provide a constant supply of fresh blood to the body's **capillaries.** The preserved capillaries in your fetal pig are much too small to be seen without special preparation for microscopy. Instead you should look at some living capillaries in which blood is actually circulating to get a feeling for the intense activity that goes on in your **microcirculation.**

Here in the capillaries, which consist of a single layer of endothelial cells, gases and molecules are exchanged between the blood and the tissues. Because the blood is still under fairly high pressure when it enters the capillaries, some of the noncellular fluid (plasma) is forced out into the intracellular spaces around the capillaries so the area for exchange is increased even more. This fluid drains into the **lymphatic system** and is eventually returned to the circulatory system via large lymphatic veins. Blood loses most of its pressure as it passes through the capillaries.

■ Anesthetize a frog according to the directions given by your instructor.
■ Always keep the animal wet with tap water because its moist skin is its major organ of respiration.
■ Wrap a wet paper towel around the frog, leaving the feet exposed, and fasten the animal to a frog board with rubber bands.
■ Spread the foot web over the hole in the frog board so that the toes are wide apart, and pin the foot down with fine insect pins, or use a toe clamp.
■ Place the board on the stage of your compound microscope so that the hole in the board is lined up with the hole in the stage. Your setup should look similar to the one shown in Figure 26-5.
■ Turn on the microscope light, and focus on the foot webbing using scan or low power. You will see lots of star-shaped dark cells: These are the melanocytes that can change shape and alter the frog's color. You will also see a network of fine arterioles and capillaries with rapidly moving blood cells. (If you do not see movement, ask your instructor for help immediately.)
■ Taking care not to scratch the objective with the pins, switch to high power and observe the capillary bed more closely.

How wide is the smallest capillary compared with the width of a red blood cell?

■ Observe the small capillaries. Entrance of blood into a capillary is regulated by a precapillary sphincter muscle.

Does the blood always flow in the same general direction?

Figure 26-5. Frog capillary setup. Keep the frog and the delicate web between its toes moist.

Is the blood flowing in all of the capillaries or only in some?

_____

■ When you are finished, free the frog and return it to the recovery tank.

VEINS

Veins are thin-walled and contain much of the blood. Because the blood in them is normally under very low pressure, veins have valves so that the blood can flow only toward the heart. Movement of the blood is accomplished by pressure of contracting skeletal muscles against the veins. Blood will pool in the legs due to gravity if there is insufficient physical activity. Because veins are not as resilient as arteries, with time they may become stretched out and swollen. They are then called **varicose veins** (e.g., in the legs) or **hemorrhoids** when they occur in the rectum.

Pulmonary Veins

Blood from the right and left lungs drains into the branches of the pulmonary veins. If the lungs are functioning, this blood will be rich in oxygen. You have already seen where the pulmonary veins join and enter the left atrium.

Do the pulmonary veins carry as much blood before birth as they do after birth? _____

The **azygos vein** is also beneath the heart and drains blood from the chest wall into the right atrium. The rest of the venous system is shown in Figure 26-6.

Anterior Vena Cava

■ Locate the vessels leading into the anterior vena cava:

1. **Coronary vein.**
2. **Internal jugular vein.** Parallel to the common carotid and drains the head and neck region.
3. **External jugular vein.** Joins the internal jugular close to the anterior vena cava.
4. **Brachial veins.** The main vessels draining the forelimbs. They join with the external jugulars before entering the anterior vena cava.
5. **Internal thoracic veins.** Carry blood from the chest and ribs.

Posterior Vena Cava

■ Locate the vessels draining the posterior portion of the body, which join the posterior vena cava and include:

1. **External iliac vein.** Drains the anterior part of the hindlimb via the **femoral veins.**
2. **Internal iliac vein.** Drains the posterior part of the hindlimb and joins the external iliacs to form the common iliac. The two common iliacs join to form the beginning of the posterior vena cava.
3. **Genital veins.** Small veins that lead into the posterior vena cava and left renal vein.
4. **Renal veins.** Drain blood from the right and left kidneys.
5. **Hepatic veins.** Veins within the liver that drain into the posterior vena cava just below the diaphragm. (They are hidden within the liver tissue.)
6. **Umbilical vein.** When you originally opened the abdomen, you cut this vessel, which leads from the umbilical cord into the liver (use the string to find the cut ends); one of its branches leads into the hepatic portal system below, and another branch, the ductus venosus, leads directly into the posterior vena cava.
7. **Ductus venosus.** In the fetal pig, part of the blood in the umbilical vein branches off in this vessel and goes directly into the posterior vena cava. This allows some blood rich in oxygen and nutrients to be pumped directly out to the body without passing through a capillary bed (see Figure 26-7).

Hepatic Portal System

A portal system connects two capillary beds, in this case intestinal capillaries and liver capillaries. Blood flows as follows:

heart → arteries → intestine capillaries → **hepatic portal vein** → liver capillaries → veins → heart.

This allows efficient processing of nutrient-rich blood after digestion of a meal.

■ Gently separate the liver and stomach from the small intestine and locate the **hepatic portal vein** draining blood from within the mesentery of the small intestine

VEINS

- external jugular veins
- internal jugular veins
- left brachial vein
- anterior vena cava
- left azygos vein (beneath heart)
- pulmonary veins (beneath heart)
- posterior vena cava
- umbilical vein
- hepatic portal vein
- left renal vein
- left genital vein
- common iliac vein
- external iliac vein
- internal iliac vein

right brachial vein

internal thoracic vein

coronary vein

hepatic veins within liver

femoral vein

deep femoral vein

Figure 26-6. Venous system of the fetal pig. In this ventral view, the major veins leading to the heart are the venae cavae. The pulmonary veins are beneath the heart and the hepatic veins are hidden within the liver.

into the liver. It may not be injected with blue latex in your pig—if not, find it in another specimen.

The structure of the portal system is shown in Figure 26-7.

Veins from the small intestine, large intestine, stomach, and spleen join to form the hepatic portal vein, which carries nutrient-rich blood to the liver after birth. During fetal development the gut has little function, so the hepatic portal system is not important in transport between gut and liver.

How do nutrients enter the fetal circulation?

_____

_____

_____

_____

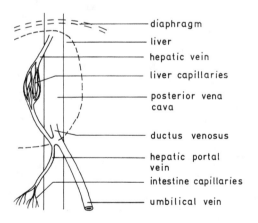

- diaphragm
- liver
- hepatic vein
- liver capillaries
- posterior vena cava
- ductus venosus
- hepatic portal vein
- intestine capillaries
- umbilical vein

Figure 26-7. Hepatic portal system. The hepatic portal system drains from the intestine, stomach, and spleen through the hepatic portal vein into the capillary beds of the liver. In the fetal pig, where the placenta rather than the intestine provides nutrition, the umbilical vein empties partly into the portal vein and partly through the ductus venosus directly into the posterior vena cava.

TRANSFORMATION OF FETAL TO ADULT CIRCULATION AT BIRTH

At the time of birth the connection of the fetus with the placenta via the umbilical cord is broken. The umbilical vein no longer brings blood rich in oxygen and nutrients to the liver, and the umbilical artery does not carry spent blood to the placenta to pick up more oxygen and nutrients and exchange wastes with the maternal circulation.

The fetal circulation responds to these changes in the following way:

1. **Lungs.** When the lungs are ventilated, the pulmonary circuit becomes functional for the first time. Blood leaves the right ventricle through the pulmonary artery, exchanges oxygen and CO_2 in the capillaries of the lungs, and returns to the left atrium via the pulmonary veins. It is now extremely harmful to by-pass the pulmonary circuit. Therefore the foramen ovale seals shut and the ductus arteriosus closes and degenerates.
2. **Digestive System.** Nutrients enter the gut as the piglet suckles and are carried to the liver by the hepatic portal system, which thereby replaces the umbilical vein. The ductus venosus no longer has any function, and both it and the umbilical vein degenerate.
3. **Kidneys.** The umbilical arteries and vein can no longer transport wastes to the placenta for removal from the fetal blood. Therefore, the kidneys now have to fully assume that function. The renal artery and renal vein become fully active.

When you are satisfied with your understanding of the circulatory system, return your pig to its proper storage place or container. Clean your dissecting pan and instruments, and oil your scissors.

EXPLORING FURTHER

See also Topic 25

Prosser, C. L. *Comparative Animal Physiology.* 3rd ed. Philadelphia: W. B. Saunders, 1973.

Singer, C. A. *A Short History of Anatomy and Physiology: From the Greeks to Harvey.* New York: Dover, 1957.

Schmidt-Nielsen, Knut. *Animal Physiology: Adaptation and Environment.* 3rd ed. New York: Cambridge University Press, 1983.

Journal Articles

Jarvik, Robert K. "The total artificial heart." *Scientific American,* 74, January 1981.

Johansen, Kaj. "Aneurysms." *Scientific American,* 110, July 1982.

Kaplan, Norman M. "The control of hypertension: A therapeutic breakthrough." *American Scientist 68:* 537, 1980.

Mayerson, H. S. "The lymphatic system." *Scientific American,* June 1963 (#158).

Schmidt-Nielsen, Knut. "Countercurrent systems in animals." *Scientific American,* 118, May 1981.

Stallones, Reuel A. "The rise and fall of ischemic heart disease." *Scientific American,* 53, November 1980.

Wiggers, Carl J. "The heart." Scientific American, May 1957 (#62).

Winfree, Arthur T. "Sudden cardiac death: A problem in topology." *Scientific American,* 144, May 1983.

Wood, J. E. "The venous system." *Scientific American,* January 1968 (#1093).

Function of the Internal Transport System in Vertebrates

OBJECTIVES

When you have completed this topic, you should be able to:
1. List the major proteins present in the blood plasma and give their functions.
2. List the major types of blood cells in human blood and give their functions.
3. Explain the function of hemoglobin and why it is found within cells rather than free in the blood.
4. Define blood pressure and demonstrate how to measure it.
5. Demonstrate how the beating of the frog heart is regulated by neurotransmitters.
6. Define pulse rate and describe how it is regulated by the nervous system.

KEY TOPICS

Amphibian circulatory system, heart cycle, blood pressure, exercise, blood composition, blood clotting, lymphatic system, immune system, synapses, neurotransmitters, vagus nerve.

INTRODUCTION

In Topic 26 you studied the anatomy of the circulatory system and heart from the point of view of transporting nutrients, wastes, and gases around the body. The circulatory system actually has other important functions. Review its functions by listing the four major ones below:

1. _____
   _____

2. _____
   _____

3. _____
   _____

4. _____
   _____

Several structures other than arteries, veins, capillaries, and the heart are important in the functioning of the circulatory system. The fluid that is lost in the capillaries drains back into the circulation through the **lymphatic system,** which also transports fats that are poorly soluble in water, and includes the lymph nodes, tissues, and lymphocytes of the **immune system.** The **spleen** contributes cells to the immune system and acts as a filter to remove bacteria and foreign substances from the blood. The **bone marrow** forms red and white blood cells, and the **liver** and **thymus** contribute cells to the immune system. The circulatory system does not act alone, but is closely involved with many other organs.

COMPOSITION OF THE BLOOD

Plasma

The liquid part of the blood, called the **plasma,** contains dissolved nutrients, wastes, salts, and the blood proteins, including albumin, globulins, fibrinogen, and lipoproteins. **Albumin** helps maintain the osmotic strength of the blood, and contributes to its buffering capacity. The **gamma globulins** (one group of immunoglobulins) include the variety of antibodies present in the blood at all times. **Fibrinogen** is the structural protein from which clots are formed. It is split by another blood protein, the enzyme thrombin, during the chain reaction of the clotting process. Plasma from which the fibrinogen has been removed is called **serum.** Lipoprotein transports insoluble lipids such as triglycerides and cholesterol.

Blood plasma is a very good buffer and maintains the pH of the blood at around 7.4.

What ion determines the pH of a solution?

_____

Why is it important that pH be kept relatively constant?

_____

_____

_____

The following experiment demonstrates the buffering capacity of blood. Record your results in Table 27-1 at the end of this topic.

■ Obtain two 100-mL beakers. Label them #1 and #2.
■ Add 10 mL of 0.9% NaCl to beaker #1.
■ Add 1 mL of blood plasma and 9 mL of 0.9% NaCl to beaker #2.

AVOID THE RISK OF SERUM HEPATITIS: DO NOT PIPET PLASMA BY MOUTH, AND AVOID CONTAMINATION IF HUMAN PLASMA IS USED.

■ Test the pH of each solution by wetting a glass rod in it, and touching a drop to a piece of pH paper; if pH sticks are used, place one stick into each beaker.
■ If the pH values do not agree, adjust the pH of the solution in beaker #1 by adding 0.05 M HCl or 0.05 M NaOH one drop at a time. Stir the solution and test its pH after adding each drop.

If the pH of the solution in the beaker is too high, should you add HCl or NaOH? _____

■ When both solutions have the same pH, record the value in the table as **initial pH.**
■ Use a pipet to restore the volume of the solution in beaker #1 to 10 mL. Discard the excess solution.
■ Add five drops of 0.1% methyl orange indicator to each beaker.
■ *While counting the drops,* add 0.1 M HCl to beaker #1, one drop at a time, stirring the solution with a glass rod, until there is a definite and *permanent* color change from orange to pink. (This change occurs at a certain pH.)
■ Measure the pH of the solution and record the value under **final pH.**
■ Repeat the procedure for beaker #2, counting the drops needed to reduce the pH to the same value as you did for beaker #1, so that *both solutions are the same color.*

Which solution was more resistant to a change in pH upon addition of acid? _____

How does a buffer react chemically upon the addition of acid or base?

_____

_____

_____

Formed Elements

The three major types of blood cells are the **red blood cells** (erythrocytes), the **white blood cells** (leukocytes), and the **platelets.** Some of these types are illustrated in Figure 27-1 and also in Color Plate 7. To view some of your own blood cells, use the following procedure, illustrated in Figure 27-2.

■ Obtain two clean slides, alcohol, sterile cotton, and a sterile blood lancet in an unopened wrapper.

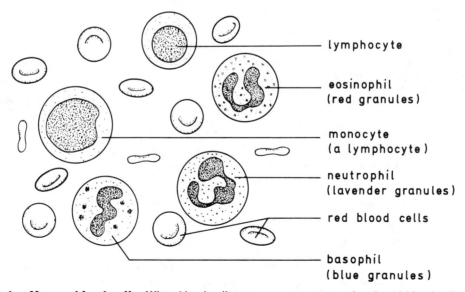

Figure 27-1. Human blood cells. White blood cells are very rare compared with red blood cells (1:700).

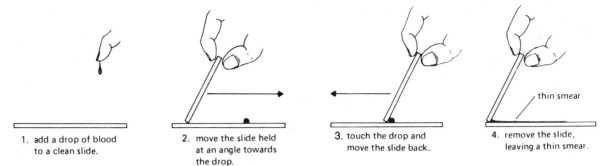

1. add a drop of blood to a clean slide.
2. move the slide held at an angle towards the drop.
3. touch the drop and move the slide back.
4. remove the slide, leaving a thin smear.

Figure 27-2. Blood smear preparation. After the smear has dried, stain the cells with Wright's stain.

AVOID THE RISK OF SERUM HEPATITIS: NEVER USE A PREVIOUSLY USED LANCET. DO NOT TOUCH MATERIALS CONTAMINATED WITH ANOTHER PERSON'S BLOOD.

If you are unable or unwilling to have your finger pricked, work with a partner who doesn't mind, or view a prepared, stained slide.

■ Massage a finger on your left hand if you are right-handed, and ask your partner to wipe it with alcohol and prick it for you or do it yourself.
■ Drip a drop of blood onto one slide.
■ Hold the second slide almost vertical and move it along until it just touches the drop of blood. The drop will spread out along the edge of the second slide.
■ Keep the second slide at an angle, and move it back to smear out the blood into a thin layer. Discard the slide that you used for spreading.
■ Allow the smear to dry, and place the slide on a staining rack.
■ Add enough drops of Wright's stain to cover the surface of the slide, and let it stand for 6 min.
■ Add 10 drops of distilled water, and let it stand for 5 min.
■ Finally rinse the slide with distilled water from a squeeze bottle to remove the dye. Rinse it with more distilled water at the sink, and stand it on end to dry.
■ Examine the dry slide under high power with the compound microscope.

Most of the cells are the pink-staining red blood cells, which have the form of biconcave discs (donuts without the holes).

Do human red blood cells have nuclei?

_____

Where are these cells formed?

_____

What is the respiratory pigment contained within them?

_____

Red blood cells have a limited life span (about 120 days) because they have no nuclei. Old red blood cells are phagocytized in the spleen, and their hemoglobin is degraded in the liver and leaves the circulation as the bile pigments. Much of the iron can be recycled. Insufficient iron intake is one cause of **anemia,** a deficiency of red blood cells in which their concentration falls below the normal level of about 5×10^9 cells per mL. **Polycythemia** is an abnormally large concentration.

Less than 1% of the cells are white blood cells. The **granulocytes** have a grainy cytoplasm. Granulocytes with light pink granules are the **neutrophils.** They phagocytize bacteria and dead body cells. Those with large deep red or orange granules are the **eosinophils,** which increase in number during allergic reactions or during parasite infections. Cells with closely packed blue-violet granules are **basophils** (very rarely seen). They release histamine in response to allergens or tissue injury.

Other white blood cells are **agranulocytes** and have a clear cytoplasm. Small cells with only a thin ring of cytoplasm are the **lymphocytes,** which are important in the response of the immune system. **Mononucleosis** is a disease, probably caused by a virus, that results in an increase in atypical, large lymphocytes. Normal cells with a larger amount of cytoplasm are **monocytes.** They migrate into the tissues where they mature into phagocytic **macrophages.**

Locate 20 or 30 white blood cells and note whether they are granulocytes (grainy cytoplasm, usually pink) or agranulocytes (clear cytoplasm).

Platelets are much smaller than white blood cells. They are very fragile and were probably destroyed during the staining procedure. These are fragments of giant cells found in the bone marrow and are very important during the early stages of blood clotting.

Hemoglobin

The concentration of hemoglobin in red blood cells is very high. That the hemoglobin is packed into these cells is advantageous because otherwise the osmotic concentration of the blood would be extremely high. The environment within the cells can also be closely regulated to control the binding of oxygen to hemoglobin. It is not known why mammalian red blood cells, in contrast to those of other vertebrates, have a biconcave shape and lack nuclei.

HEMOGLOBIN CONTENT

Use the following procedure to measure the hemoglobin content of your blood.

■ Obtain two spectrophotometer tubes, and add 5 mL of distilled water to each one.
■ Wipe your finger with alcohol and carefully prick your finger as you did before (or have your partner take a turn at being pricked).

■ Draw up exactly 0.02 mL of blood in the capillary pipet provided for this purpose.
■ Blow the blood into the water in one of the tubes, and rinse three times with water from the tube.
■ Add 1 drop of concentrated ammonium hydroxide (NH_4OH) to the tube and to a second blank tube.
■ Wait 10 min.
■ Meanwhile, turn on a Spectronic 20 spectrophotometer to warm up, and set the wavelength at 545 nm.
■ With the sample chamber empty, adjust the absorbance to infinity (left knob).
■ Use the blank tube to adjust the **absorbance** to zero (right knob).
■ Determine the absorbance of the solution at 545 nm. Record the value in Table 27-2 at the end of this topic.
■ Calculate the approximate concentration of hemoglobin in your blood by multiplying the absorbance at 545 nm by the factor 28.8. (Hemoglobin concentration is directly proportional to absorbance over a certain range.)

The normal range for hemoglobin concentration is 16 ± 2 g/100 mL for males and 14 ± 2 g for females. Indicate in the table whether your hemoglobin concentration is in the low, normal, or high range. **Anemia** is the condition of having an abnormally low concentration of hemoglobin or red blood cells, and it can be due to a number of different causes, including insufficient iron intake.

SICKLE-CELL HEMOGLOBIN

Persons with sickle-cell anemia have hemoglobin S rather than normal hemoglobin. The hemoglobin contains beta chains with a single amino acid substitution in which glutamic acid is replaced by valine. As a result the hemoglobin has a lowered affinity for oxygen, and the molecules tend to clump together when the concentration of oxygen is very low. During the clumping reaction, the red blood cells are distorted and assume "sickled" shapes.

If you did not study sickle-cell anemia in Topic 11, do so now. Read the section entitled SICKLE-CELL ANEMIA, and complete the exercise at the end of that section.

BLOOD PRESSURE

Blood pressure varies throughout the circulatory system, so it is usually measured in the upper arm for comparison of different individuals. The pressure is the hydrostatic pressure exerted on the walls of the blood vessels by the blood under the force of the contracting heart. It is greatest in the vessels adjacent to the heart, it drops off in the arterioles and capillaries due to the friction caused by the blood moving along the walls, and it is very low in the venules and veins leading back to the heart. Muscular contraction is required to squeeze the blood in the veins from the extremities to the heart because the pressure in these vessels is less than the force of gravity. **Valves** in the veins are extremely important in aiding the return of the blood to the heart, because its pressure is so low.

The blood pressure in the arteries follows a rhythmic cycle with each beat of the heart. When the ventricles contract, exerting the strongest pressure, the resulting high pressure phase is called **systole**. While the heart relaxes, the pressure in the arteries decreases in a low-pressure phase called **diastole**. Blood pressure is always measured at both systole and diastole, and the result is reported as the systolic value/diastolic value. The blood pressure reading is generally higher in older people and lower in people in good physical condition or in athletic training.

Working in pairs, use this procedure to take your partner's blood pressure while he or she is seated. Record your results in Table 27-3 at the end of this topic.

■ Wrap the blood pressure cuff around your partner's upper arm so that it is neither tight nor loose, and secure it with the Velcro fasteners.
■ Squeeze the bulb several times while watching the pressure gauge until the pressure reaches 180-200 mm Hg (760 mm is 1 atm).
■ Place the stethoscope in the hollow at the inner side of the elbow, and be ready to listen for the sound of the pulse.
■ Slowly release the pressure while watching the gauge, and make a mental note of the pressure at which you first hear a single sound with each heartbeat; this is the systolic pressure.
■ Continue to release the pressure until you hear the double sound of a normal heartbeat (lub-dup . . . lub-dup . . .); this is the diastolic pressure.
■ Record the pressure values for systole and diastole, and repeat the measurement twice more to be sure your value is reasonably accurate.
■ Next, ask your partner to lie down and rest for a few minutes. Take the blood pressure three times, and record the results.

Did the value for the blood pressure depend on the position of the subject? _____

■ Repeat the measurement of blood pressure under other conditions.

The blood pressure will usually be higher if the person has recently had a cup of coffee, smoked a cigarette, or been subjected to stress. It is normally regulated by the activity of the autonomic nervous system. If the blood pressure is consistently too high (condition of hypertension), a stroke or small hemorrhage in the brain, or kidney failure may result. Hypertension has many causes, the most common of which is atherosclerosis. If your diastolic blood pressure is above 90 mm, have your blood pressure checked by a health professional. Hypertension can be controlled with drugs or in some cases by conscious effort through biofeedback training.

CAPILLARIES

The active functioning of the blood as a transport tissue goes on only in the capillaries. Here the actual exchange of gases, nutrients, and wastes takes place, and white blood cells can enter and leave the circulatory system. The walls of the capillaries are thin enough so that the cells within them move along in single file.

If you did not see living capillaries in Topic 26 (section entitled CAPILLARIES), carry out the observation of capillaries described there.

HEART RATE

The beating pattern of the heart is not due to nervous stimulation, but is rather due to spontaneous electrical events starting with the pacemaker of the **sino-atrial (SA) node.** The electrical impulse spreads quickly and smoothly through the cardiac muscle of the atria to trigger the **atrioventricular (AV) node,** which in turn stimulates the ventricles to contract. (See text Figure 35-18.) The rate of the intrinsic heartbeat, however, is very responsive to changes in conditions within the body and to external stimuli. It speeds up when the demand for oxygen is high and also under the influence of the hormone **epinephrine** (adrenalin). Epinephrine may be released into the blood by the adrenal gland, and **norepinephrine** is the neurotransmitter of the sympathetic nervous system. The heart rate slows down, especially when we lie down, in response to **acetylcholine,** the neurotransmitter released by the **vagus nerve** (part of the parasympathetic nervous system described in Topic 30). These nervous signals are sent out by the cardiac centers in the brain that constantly monitor stretch receptors in the heart and blood vessels.

Human Heart Rate

■ Place the fingertips of your left hand on your radial artery in the hollow of your wrist at the base of your right thumb. If you have trouble detecting your pulse, use the carotid artery alongside your larynx instead.
■ Count your heartbeats for 3 min, calculate the rate in beats per minute, and record the results in Table 27-4.
■ Jump up and down until you feel out of breath or tired, and again record your heart rate.
■ After your heart rate is back to normal, lie down for 5 min, and measure the rate while resting. Try to relax as fully as possible.

During exercise, epinephrine is released and acts to stimulate the heart rate. Exercise is supposed to benefit your circulatory system because the capillaries in the muscles, especially those of the heart, dilate in order to increase the supply of oxygen to the active tissues. After the exercise is over, the capillaries remain a little bit more open than before so that oxygenation of the tissues is improved all the time. An athlete in top condition will often have a very low heart rate of 50 beats/min or less because the pumping heart meets very little resistance in the peripheral capillaries. In order for the exercise to help significantly, however, the heart rate must reach 150 beats/min for at least a few minutes during each exercise session. Activities such as golf and gardening are just that: they do not increase the heart rate enough to be rated as exercise.

■ During the coming week, test your more strenuous activities to see whether they raise your heart rate to 150 beats/min for a significant period of time.

The Frog Heart

The effects of different factors on the rate at which the frog heart beats will help you understand how the rate is normally adjusted to changing conditions.

Before starting this experiment, you and your partner should have access to all of the following:

Ice bath for the frog
Dissecting needle
Paper towels
Frog Ringer's solution
Scissors
Thread
Forceps
Pipets
5×10^{-5}M acetylcholine
5×10^{-5}M epinephrine
5×10^{-5}M atropine
Electrical stimulator (on *low voltage*)

PITHING THE FROG

■ Chill the frog in ice thoroughly. Remove and pat it dry, and carry out the following steps quickly.
■ Hold the frog firmly in your left hand with its front legs between your middle and ring fingers and the hind legs dangling.
■ Put your index finger over the head, and press down to bend the spinal cord.
■ Run your right index finger along the head until you locate the depression at the base of the skull where the spinal column begins. This is where you will insert the dissecting needle.
■ With a steady hand, insert the needle into the spinal cord, and sever it with a quick side-to-side movement. In this way you will be able to kill the frog as painlessly as possible.

If the frog shows signs of reviving, put it back into the ice bath and repeat the severing of the spinal cord.

■ Push the needle forward parallel with the external surface into the brain. Move it back and forth to sever all connections with the spinal cord so that the frog is neurologically dead.
■ Insert the needle into the spinal cord, and twist it to destroy the cord and the spinal reflexes. The legs will extend sharply as the needle contacts nerves within the cord.
■ When you remove the needle, the legs should be completely limp, and the pithing operation is finished.

EXPOSING THE HEART

■ Lay the frog on its back on a paper towel wet with Ringer's solution. The frog's skin must be kept moist at all times from this point on.
■ Use the forceps to pinch the skin over the abdomen, slightly to side of center, and snip a hole with the scissors.
■ Insert the point of the scissors carefully, being careful not to poke into the abdomen, and make an I-shaped incision by cutting in the order and direction shown in Figure 27-3.
■ Once you can see the underlying muscle, repeat the incision, cutting through the muscle as well. Fold back the flaps to expose the viscera.
■ Note that the beating heart is covered by the membrane of the **pericardium.**
■ Slit the pericardium *carefully* to expose the heart.

Figure 27-3. Frog dissection guide. Keep the frog moist inside and out at all times.

CHECK THAT THE FROG HAS BEEN WARMED UP TO ROOM TEMPERATURE BEFORE BEGINNING YOUR MEASUREMENTS.

■ Record the rate of beating for a 3-min interval, and calculate the beats per minute. Record the results in Table 27-5, at the end of this topic.

You are now ready to study the effect of the drugs and electrical stimulation on the heart.

ACETYLCHOLINE

This neurotransmitter is released by the vagus nerve, which is part of the parasympathetic nervous system. It should have the same effect as electrical stimulation of the vagus itself.

■ Add 3-4 drops of the acetylcholine solution to the fluid around the heart, not to the heart itself.
■ Observe and record the rate of beating for each 15-sec interval until there is a perceptible change.
■ Calculate the beats per minute by multiplying your final value by a factor of 4.
■ Rinse the heart with Ringer's two or three times, removing the fluid from around the heart with a pipet.
■ Give the heart a 5-min rest, and record a normal heart rate before going on.

EPINEPHRINE

This hormone is released into the blood by the adrenal glands and its close relative, norepinephrine is released by the sympathetic nervous system. It prepares the entire body for an emergency "fight or flight" response.

■ Add 2 drops of the epinephrine solution to the fluid around the heart, and observe the effect as you did for acetylcholine.
■ Record the results and allow the rinsed heart to rest.

ELECTRICAL STIMULATION OF THE VAGUS NERVE

Beneath the heart on its dorsal side, locate the bundle of stringlike nerves and connective tissue that joins the sinus venosus as shown in Figure 27-4.

■ Gently draw the bundle to one side with your forceps, and tie a thread to it loosely so that it can be pulled to one side.
■ Take the frog to the stimulator or vice versa. Be sure to keep the frog moist at all times.
■ Turn the stimulator on.
■ Draw the nerve bundle to one side, and touch the points of the electrode to the nerve (*not* to the heart) until there is a change in the rate of the heartbeat. You may have to try several locations along the bundle.

THE TWO POINTS OF THE ELECTRODE MUST NOT TOUCH EACH OTHER.

Figure 27-4. Frog heart. The vagus nerve is important in regulating the rate at which the heart beats.

■ Observe the new rate of beating and record it.

Did the electrical stimulation of the vagus have an effect similar to that of the acetylcholine? _____

■ Allow the rinsed heart to rest until the beat is again close to the normal rate.

ATROPINE

This drug is an alkaloid poison that binds to and blocks the receptors for acetylcholine. It is produced by the deadly nightshade (belladonna) plant as a defense against insect predators. Do not use this drug until you have completed your study of the effects of the neurotransmitters and electrical stimulation.

■ Add 3-4 drops of atropine to the fluid around the heart, and record the new beating rate in Table 27-5.
■ Apply electrical stimulation as you did before, and record the rate during electrical stimulation in the presence of atropine.

How did atropine change the effect of electrical stimulation?

_____

_____

_____

_____

How would atropine affect the functioning of the parasympathetic nervous system?

_____

_____

_____

_____

When you have finished with the frog, dispose of it properly, and clean your dissecting tools for the next student.

EXPLORING FURTHER

See also Topic 25

Erslev, Allan J., and Thomas G. Gabuzda. *Pathophysiology of the Blood*. Philadelphia: W. B. Saunders, 1979.

MacFarlane, R. G. and A. Robb-Smith. *Functions of the Blood*. New York: Academic Press, 1961.

Journal Articles

Allison, A. C. "Sickle cells and evolution." *Scientific American*, August 1956 (#1065).

Adolph, E. F. "The heart's pacemaker." *Scientific American*, March 1967 (#1067).

Axelrod, J. "Neurotransmitters." *Scientific American*, June 1974 (#1297).

Benditt, E. P. "The origin of atherosclerosis." *Scientific American*, March 1967 (#1067).

Cerami, A., and C. M. Peterson. "Cyanate and sickle cell disease." *Scientific American*, April 1975 (#1319).

Comroe, J. H. Jr. "Doctor, you have six minutes." *Science 84*, 62, January-February 1984.

Doolittle, Russell F. "Fibrinogen and fibrin." *Scientific American*, 126, December 1981.

Friedman, Milton J., and William Trager. "The biochemistry of resistance to malaria." *Scientific American*, 154, March 1981.

Hock, Raymond J. "The physiology of high altitude." *Scientific American*, February 1970 (#1168).

Kolata, G. "Fetal hemoglobin genes turned on in adults." *Science 218*: 1295, 24 December 1982.

Karpus, Abraham. "Viruses and leukemia." *American Scientist*: 70(3), 277, May-June 1982.

Mayerson, H. S. "The lymphatic system." *Scientific American*, June 1963 (#158).

Perutz, M. F. "Hemoglobin structure and respiratory transport." *Scientific American*, December 1978 (#1413).

Rodgers, J. C. "Catching cancer strays." *Science 83*: 42, July-August, 1983.

Rose, Noel R. "Autoimmune diseases." *Scientific American*, 80, February 1981.

Schmidt-Nielsen, Knut. "Countercurrent systems in animals." *Scientific American*, 118, May 1981.

Trost, C. "The blue people of Troublesome Creek." *Science 82*: 35, November 1982.

Wessel, Morris A., and A. Dominski. "Our children's daily lead." *American Scientist 65*: 294, 1977.

Zucker, Marjorie B. "The functioning of blood platelets." *Scientific American*, June 1980 (#1472).

TABLE 27-1. PLASMA BUFFERING

Solution	Initial pH	Final pH	Drops HCl Added
Beaker #1 (control)			
Beaker #2 (plasma)			

TABLE 27-2. DETERMINATION OF HEMOGLOBIN CONCENTRATION

Absorbance at 545 nm	
Hemoglobin concentration (Absorbance × 28.8)	g/100 mL
Sex (Male or Female)	
Range (Low, Normal or High)	

TABLE 27-3.   BLOOD PRESSURE

Condition	Reading	Blood pressure Systolic/diastolic
Initial pressure	1	/
	2	/
	3	/
Resting pressure	1	/
	2	/
	3	/
Other condition: _____	1	/
	2	/
	3	/
_____	1	/
	2	/
	3	/

TABLE 27-4.   HUMAN HEART RATE

Condition	Beats/time interval		Beats/min
Initial normal			
Jumping			
Normal			
Lying down			
Other activities: _____			
_____			
_____			
_____			

Student Name _____ **Date** _____

TABLE 27-5. FROG HEART RATE

Condition	Beats/time interval		Beats/min
Initial rate			
Acetylcholine			
After rest			
Epinephrine			
After rest			
Vagus nerve			
After rest			
Atropine			
Atropine + Electrical Stimulation			

Gas Exchange

OBJECTIVES

When you have completed this topic, you should be able to:
1. Distinguish between ventilation (breathing), organismic respiration, and cellular respiration.
2. Give two examples of groups of organisms that use the general body surface for gas exchange.
3. Name some organisms that do not need special structures for gas exchange.
4. Cite one group of organisms that uses internal gills and one group that uses external gills for gas exchange.
5. Explain what a tracheal breathing system is, and state the group of organisms in which it is found.
6. Give the advantages and disadvantages of using air compared with water as a respiratory medium.
7. Describe the structures through which air must travel from the outside to the lungs of a mammal.
8. Explain the function of: the Eustachian tubes, turbinate bones, epiglottis, tracheal cartilage rings, alveoli, and diaphragm.
9. Explain negative pressure breathing in a mammal, describing what happens during inspiration and expiration.
10. Explain positive pressure breathing in a frog.
11. Describe how the rate of ventilation of human lungs is controlled.

KEY TOPICS

Respiratory surface, ventilation, gas exchange, gills, tracheal system, positive and negative pressure breathing, control of human ventilation.

INTRODUCTION

Cells require oxygen as the final electron acceptor in the electron transport system. CO_2 is produced in the Krebs cycle. Thus all aerobic cells need to obtain oxygen and dispose of CO_2.

Unicellular organisms can obtain enough oxygen by simple diffusion and can dispose of their CO_2 and wastes in the same way. All larger and thicker organisms utilize a respiratory system of some sort to ensure that every one of their cells has an adequate oxygen supply. The respiratory system has a large, moist **respiratory surface** across which the actual gas exchange takes place, and a means of circulating air or water next to the respiratory surface. This is the process of **ventilation** or, in the case of air, **breathing.** Animals whose respiratory system is in the form of lungs, gills, and sometimes the body surface, have a circulatory system intimately associated with the respiratory system. The circulatory system carries oxygen from the respiratory surface and distributes it throughout the body. Those organisms with a tracheal system, on the other hand, distribute air directly to all body cells and do not use the circulatory system for gas exchange. Distribution of gases to and from the body's cells is **organismic respiration.** Metabolism of food molecules inside cells uses up O_2 and produces CO_2 in **cellular respiration.**

GENERAL BODY SURFACE

Frogs and many invertebrates use the skin of the **body surface** as a respiratory surface.

How is this surface "ventilated"?

_____

_____

_____

The frog uses its lungs as well as its skin for respiration.

What are some invertebrates that lack respiratory organs and use only the skin?

_____

_____

_____

GILLS

Gills consist of feathery outpocketings that greatly increase the area of the respiratory surface. In some aquatic animals they are external and unprotected, but usually they are protected in some way.

Necturus (Axolotl)

■ Examine the specimen on demonstration. In a living animal the exposed gills are pink.

Why are gills pink or red?

_____

Perch

The gills are protected by a cover called the **operculum,** and water circulates from the mouth through the spaces between the gills and out through the opening of the operculum. The pattern of water circulation through the gills of a fish is shown in Figure 37-3 in your text. Flow of water is opposite or **countercurrent** to that of the blood, so that the greatest possible amount of oxygen diffuses into the blood. The gills themselves are so large that a **gill skeleton** is necessary to give support to the delicate filaments.

■ Examine the gill skeleton of a fish. The spiny anterior protrusions are called **gill rakers** and help keep large particles away from the delicate **gill filaments.**

Water contains much less oxygen than air and the fish must expend considerable energy to ventilate its gills. Being aquatic, however, it does not lose water across its respiratory surface.

TRACHEAL SYSTEM

Insects, centipedes, and millipedes obtain oxygen from air rather than from water. Their respiratory system, the **tracheal system,** is quite different from that of the lungs found in vertebrates: It does *not* depend on the circulatory system. Air enters the body through small openings called **spiracles,** which lead into the **tracheal ducts.** The ducts divide repeatedly into **tracheoles** and finally end in tiny, fluid-filled tubes where gas exchange takes place. The tiny tracheoles extend everywhere in the body, so that no cell is too far away from its air supply.

Figure 28-1 shows how air entering the spiracles reaches a muscle cell. The circulation of air is speeded up in larger, active insects by contraction of the abdominal muscles and flight muscles. Water is lost as air circulates through the tracheal system, so drying out is a serious problem for insects.

■ Examine specimens of a grasshopper or a cockroach. Locate the spiracles along each side of your specimen. The location of grasshopper spiracles is shown in Figure 20-5.

Why does a film of oil quickly kill an insect?

_____

_____

Why is a strong solution of a nontoxic detergent a good insecticide?

_____

_____

■ Remove the dorsal part of the exoskeleton by making cuts along its edges.
■ Locate a **trachea,** the tube leading from a spiracle into the insect's body.
■ Remove a bit of muscle, and tease it apart in a drop of water or Ringer's solution. Observe it under the compound microscope to see the fine tracheal tubes that carry oxygen to all of the muscle cells.

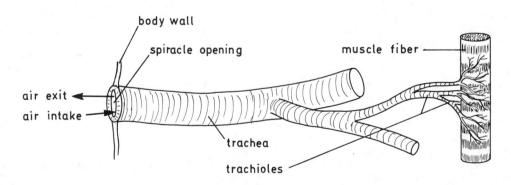

Figure 28-1.   Trachea of an insect. Movements of the body cause the air within the trachea to circulate.

Why does the insect need a circulatory system if it isn't used for gas exchange?

_____

_____

Dispose of your specimen properly and clean your slide and tools before continuing.

What is the role of the hairs, cilia, and mucous lining of the nasal passages?

_____

_____

_____

Do comparable structures play a role in human nostrils?

_____

THE RESPIRATORY SYSTEM OF THE FETAL PIG

In mammals, the lining of the alveoli within the lungs is the respiratory surface where gases can be exchanged. Air is circulated to the alveoli through the nose, pharynx, larynx, trachea, and bronchi during ventilation of the lungs. Air breathers such as the pig trade the advantage of an abundant supply of oxygen in air for the disadvantage of continuous water loss from the large, moist surface of the alveoli.

Nose

■ Examine the external openings (**external nares**) of your pig's snout. Here air enters the nasal passages.
■ Cut across the nose about 1 cm from the tip (see Figure 26-2) with your razor blade or scalpel, and open the cut, or look at the demonstration. Inside you see the curved **turbinate bones,** which help increase the surface area of the passages.

Why is a large surface area needed?

_____

_____

_____

Pharynx

■ Open the pig's mouth and review the location of the **glottis** and **epiglottis.** (See Figure 28-2.) They are located deep in the throat or oropharynx. Air enters the glottis, the opening to the lower respiratory tract, from the opening of the nasopharynx (pharynx above the soft palate). If the epiglottis is not evident, you may have to cut more deeply and fully open the pig's mouth. Use your blunt probe to fish for it, if necessary.

If food accidently enters the glottis, a person may choke and suffocate. Usually the food can be dislodged by using the **Heimlich maneuver.** This involves pressing inward and upward on the diaphragm to force food out of the glottis by air pressure (see text "Focus on Choking," p. 794).

■ Slit the soft palate along its midline, and locate the opening of the **nasal passages.**

A pocket in this part of the pharynx has the openings of the **Eustachian tubes** that lead to the middle ear. They allow pressure within the middle ear to be equilibrated with the pressure outside so that there isn't any strain on the eardrum. Nose and throat infections can spread to the middle ear through the Eustachian tube.

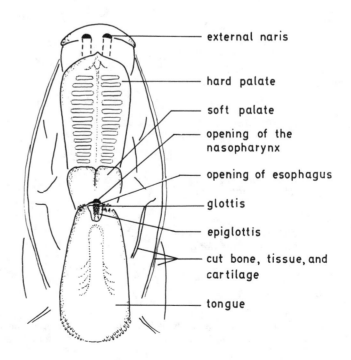

Figure 28-2. Inside the fetal pig's mouth. Cut the jaws open far enough to see the oral cavity and the oropharynx. The glottis is the opening within the folds of the epiglottis. The soft palate must be cut to find the openings of the Eustachian tubes and nasal passages.

Larynx

■ In the region of the larynx, use your probe or fingers to separate the muscles so that the **larynx** itself and the **trachea** posterior to it are exposed. Air passes from the pharynx into the glottis, through the larynx where the vocal cords are located, and through the trachea into the lungs themselves.

■ Notice that the larynx and trachea are hard; the trachea contains rings of cartilage that give it support.

Do the cartilage rings completely circle the trachea?

_____

Why must the trachea be supported by cartilage?

_____

_____

_____

■ Ventral to the trachea near the joining of the neck and trunk, locate a smooth, brownish-colored gland, the **thyroid.** This is an endocrine gland important in regulating the body's metabolism.

■ Locate the **esophagus,** a collapsed flabby tube just dorsal to the trachea. To be sure you locate the right structure, pass a probe into the opening of the esophagus in the pharynx, and feel for it with your fingers beneath

the trachea. Food passes from pharynx to stomach through the esophagus by peristalsis.

■ Cut towards the shoulders as far as necessary to fully open the thorax.

■ Locate the **diaphragm,** a sheet of muscle and tendon that separates the thoracic cavity from the abdominal cavity.

The thoracic cavity is divided into three parts by these membranes:

1. The **right pleural membrane** contains the right lung.
2. The **left pleural membrane** contains the left lung.
3. The **pericardial membrane** surrounds the heart.

Each is a double membrane, lining the organ and the body wall with a very thin space in between called the **pleural cavity** or the **pericardial cavity.** Inflammation of the pleural membranes, **pleurisy,** makes breathing painful and difficult.

■ Remove the remains of these membranes so that the heart and lungs are fully exposed.

The structure of the lower respiratory system is shown in Figure 28-3.

Air from the trachea enters the **bronchi,** which divide into smaller and smaller **bronchioles.** Finally the

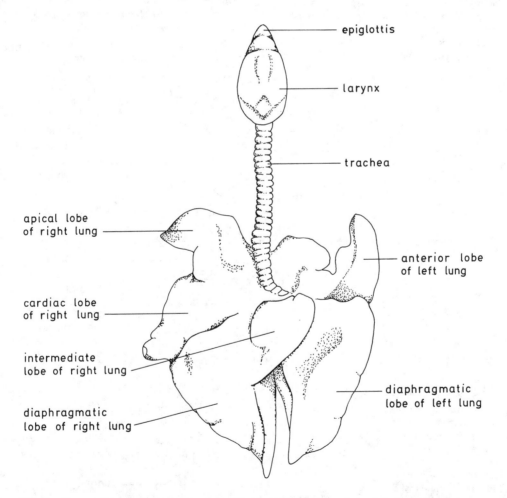

Figure 28-3. Lower respiratory tract of the fetal pig. The bronchi and bronchioles are surrounded by the spongy tissue of the lungs. In the fetal pig, the right lung has four lobes and the left has two (sometimes three).

air ends up in the microscopic, thin-walled, moist sacs called **alveoli.** Their walls are the respiratory surface of the pig. They must be coated with a surfactant to reduce surface tension so they can be easily inflated with each breath. Here gases in the air can be exchanged with gases in the blood of the capillary network because the walls of the alveoli are only one cell thick. Oxygen enters the capillaries by diffusion and facilitated diffusion, and CO_2 crosses from the capillaries into the alveoli.

■ Examine the **lungs** of your pig.

Are the lungs equal in size? _____

The right lung has four lobes and the left lung two or sometimes three. The lungs are filled with fluid in the fetal pig and are much more compact than they will be after they are inflated at birth. The point where the trachea divides into the right and left bronchi is hidden from view beneath the heart and blood vessels.

How does the fetal pig obtain oxygen and dispose of CO_2?

_____

_____

    When you are finished with your dissection for today, store your fetal pig properly, clean your dissecting tools, and oil your scissors.

HOW LUNGS ARE VENTILATED

Vertebrate lungs can be ventilated in two ways. In mammals the lungs are enclosed in the airtight thoracic cavity; enlargement of this cavity creates a **negative pressure** outside the lungs so that air rushes into them. Negative pressure is the same as suction. Air is "pulled" into the

lungs. The frog, on the other hand, uses **positive pressure** from contraction of the oral cavity to "push" air into the lungs. Negative pressure inflation of the lungs is like sucking in on your bubble gum so that it forms a bubble inside your mouth. Positive pressure inflation is like blowing a regular bubble.

Negative Pressure Breathing

Inspiration in mammals is due to expansion of the chest cavity when the rib cage lifts and the diaphragm contracts. Muscles between the ribs and radial muscles in the diaphragm itself must contract for this to happen. The positions of the diaphragm and rib cage during inspiration and expiration are shown in Figure 28-4.

■ Place one hand on your stomach just below your ribs to feel the effect of your diaphragm contracting, and place the other hand on your rib cage.
■ Take a few normal breaths.

Does the rib cage move? _____

Does the stomach move? _____

■ Try to breathe without moving the rib cage at all.
■ Then try not to move your diaphragm.

Can you get enough air using only one set of muscles?

Positive Pressure Breathing

The frog is a good animal to observe using positive pressure breathing because it is easy to see how it is done.

■ Observe the live frog on demonstration when it is out of the water.

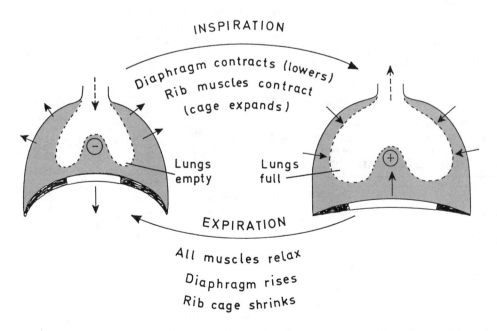

Figure 28-4. Negative pressure breathing. Contraction of rib muscles and diaphragm enlarges the chest cavity creating negative pressure (suction). Ribs rise and the diaphragm lowers while air rushes in during inhalation. Relaxation of muscles causes the ribs to lower and the diaphragm to rise during exhalation, when air is forced out of the lungs under positive pressure.

What movement relating to breathing is most obvious?

A frog can open and close the nostrils and can close off the glottis leading to the lungs. The floor of the mouth can be lowered to draw in air and raised to force air into the lungs. Meanwhile valves in the nostrils must be closed to prevent air from escaping through them while the air is under positive pressure. Air is expelled from the lungs due to their elasticity and to pressure from the abdominal organs. Complete Table 28-1 at the end of this topic to show what happens during inspiration in positive pressure breathing.

HOW THE RATE OF BREATHING IS CONTROLLED

The rate at which you breathe is automatically controlled so that there will be enough oxygen and so that CO_2 will be promptly removed. **Chemoreceptors** in the medulla (part of the spinal cord just below the brain) respond to the pH of the blood. Blood pH will decrease as the CO_2 level increases due to the formation of carbonic acid:

$$H_2O + CO_2 \rightarrow H_2CO_3 \rightarrow H^+ + HCO_3^-$$

As soon as the CO_2 level rises, the receptors detect carbonic acid, and the **inspiratory center** in the medulla speeds up the breathing rate to get rid of the CO_2. *Breathing rate is normally determined by the level of CO_2* rather than that of oxygen, probably because CO_2 is easier for the body to detect. (See Figure 37-11 in your text.) The inspiratory center shuts itself off by sending a message to an **expiratory center,** also in the medulla, via the **pneumotaxic center** in the pons of the brainstem. The expiratory center works by inhibiting the inspiratory center, allowing relaxation of all the muscles involved in inspiration. The inspiratory center is also inhibited by stretch receptors in the lungs that send signals over the vagus nerve to the expiratory center when the lungs are full of air. If the blood oxygen level ever becomes abnormally low, oxygen chemoreceptors in the aorta and the carotid arteries stimulate the inspiratory center, but oxygen concentration does not play a role in normal breathing.

IN THESE EXPERIMENTS, STOP AT ONCE IF YOU BEGIN TO FEEL FAINT. IF YOU HAVE ANY MEDICAL PROBLEM WITH YOUR HEART OR LUNGS, BE A TIMEKEEPER, NOT A SUBJECT.

Work with a partner to make the following measurements:

■ While sitting down and breathing normally, measure the number of breaths per minute three times. Record your results to the nearest half breath in Table 28-2 at the end of this topic.
■ Hyperventilate by breathing as deeply and as fast as you can for 20 breaths. Then breathe normally.

STOP IF YOU FEEL FAINT.

■ Measure your breathing rate for the first minute after you resume breathing and record it.
■ Wait until you are breathing normally again before continuing.
■ Breathe into a plastic bag for 2.5 minutes, and record your breathing rate for each half-minute interval. Calculate breaths per minute for each interval.

STOP IF YOU FEEL FAINT. DO NOT EXCEED 3 MIN.

■ Answer the questions that follow Table 28-2.

When you are finished with your work, return or dispose of all specimens and materials, store your clean dissecting tools, and store your microscope properly.

EXPLORING FURTHER

See also Topic 25

Heimlich, H. J. *Dr. Heimlich's Home Guide to Emergency Medical Situations.* New York: Simon and Schuster, 1980.
Schmidt-Nielsen, Knut. *Animal Physiology: Adaptation and Environment.* 3rd Ed. New York: Cambridge University Press, 1983.

Journal Articles

Avery, M. E., N.-S. Wang, and H. W. Taeusch. "The lung of the newborn infant." *Scientific American,* April 1973 (no offprint).
Comroe, Julius H., Jr. "The lung." *Scientific American,* February 1966 (#1034).
Hong, S. K., and H. Rahn. "The diving women of Korea and Japan." *Scientific American,* May 1967 (#1072).
Johansen, K. "Air-breathing fishes." *Scientific American,* October 1968 (#1125).
Kolata, G. "Cell biology yields clues to lung cancer." *Science 218:* 1 October 1982.
Kylstra, J. S. "Experiments in water breathing." *Scientific American,* August 1968 (#1123).
Naeye, Richard L. "Sudden infant death." *Scientific American,* April 1980 (#1467).

Student Name _____ **Date** _____

TABLE 28-1. POSITIVE PRESSURE BREATHING IN THE FROG.

	Nostrils (Open/Closed)	Glottis (Open/Closed)	Mouth Floor (Raised/Lowered)
1. Air enters mouth.			
2. Air enters lungs.			

3. Finally air leaves the lungs under pressure from the stretched chest wall, and the breathing cycle is ready to start again.

TABLE 28-2. RATE OF HUMAN BREATHING.

STOP IF YOU FEEL FAINT. DO NOT EXCEED 3 MIN BREATHING INTO BAG.

Condition	Time Interval	Breaths	Breaths per Min
Normal	1st min		
	2nd min		
	3rd min		
After hyperventilation	1st min		
Breaths into bag	1st half min		
	2nd half min		
	3rd half min		
	4th half min		
	5th half min		
	6th half min		

Did you feel an urge to breathe right after hyperventilating? _____

Does increased oxygen in your blood affect your breathing rate? _____

Were your breaths deeper or shallower than normal? _____

Did your breathing become more deep or more shallow after breathing into the bag? _____
Why?

_____

_____

There was still oxygen left in the bag. What would have happened if the CO_2 had been removed from each breath that you exhaled?

_____

Excretion and Reproduction

OBJECTIVES

When you have completed this topic, you should be able to:
1. Define the process of excretion in mammals; name the major nitrogenous waste product and the chemical molecules that give rise to it.
2. Describe the nephron, and relate its structure to the internal structure of the kidney.
3. Trace the path of a molecule of urea from the bloodstream to the opening of the urethra.
4. Name and contrast the position and functions of primary sex organs in the male and female.
5. Trace the path an egg follows from its formation to the exterior of the body, assuming no fertilization.
6. Trace the path of sperm cells from their site of origin to the exterior, and give the function of each accessory organ along the way.
7. If copulation and fertilization occur in the pig, state where the semen is deposited, where fertilization occurs, and where development of the young piglets takes place.
8. Describe how fertilization and early development in the human differ from those processes in the pig.
9. Distinguish between: ureter/urethra, ejaculation/fertilization; ovulation/implantation; oviduct/uterine horn; vasectomy/castration.
10. For each of the major types of contraception, explain how the method works, give the exact step in conception that is blocked, and specify the anatomical site where the method has its effect.

KEY TOPICS

Nitrogenous wastes, male urinary system, female urinary system, kidney function, nephron, male reproductive system, female reproductive system, menstrual cycle, gamete formation, fertilization, birth control.

INTRODUCTION

Wastes from within cells are removed from the body in the process of **excretion.** The wastes are chemicals that are formed by the metabolic activity of cells and cannot be gotten rid of except as dissolved substances. In mammals, the main nitrogenous waste is **urea,** a simple molecule formed from CO_2 and ammonia. (See Figure 38-3 in your text.) Nitrogenous wastes are formed whenever proteins or amino acids in the diet or in cells are broken down to carbon skeletons and ammonia in the process of **deamination.** Urea is soluble and relatively nontoxic, so it can be eliminated in urine in a fairly concentrated form. This conservation of water has a price, however, in that ATP energy is required to synthesize urea.

Although the kidney is the main excretory organ, some nitrogenous wastes are also excreted in the sweat, from the lungs, and from the digestive tract.

Food remains that are not and have never been inside of cells are eliminated from the body through the rectum as feces. This process is **egestion** and is basically different from excretion. Excretory wastes from cells of the liver and large intestine do enter the gut, but they make only a small contribution to the fecal wastes.

275

The reproductive system is anatomically associated with the urinary system and, in fact, complete separation of the two is rare among vertebrates. In female and male fetal pigs both systems have a common opening to the exterior, so you will study them both at the same time. You will be responsible for understanding both the male and the female systems, so exchange your pig for one of the opposite sex when you are finished to complete your study of the reproductive system.

The purpose of the reproductive system is to produce **gametes** and to provide a protective environment so that they can meet in **fertilization.** In mammals fertilization restores the diploid number of chromosomes for the next generation, determines whether the individual will be male or female, and triggers the start of development. Fertilization and the establishment of pregnancy is called **conception.**

As you study the anatomy of reproduction, you will also be learning how it is possible to prevent conception, or use **contraception,** in several different ways. Permanent contraception, usually called sterilization, prevents the egg or sperm cells from ever reaching their intended destination. Other methods are temporary and can be started and stopped again whenever desired. The common methods are mechanical, chemical, or hormonal. In many vertebrates other than humans, contraception of some sort is an important part of reproduction. These animals have behavioral or physiological mechanisms for limiting reproduction, whereas human beings must spend millions of dollars to achieve the same end through contraception.

URINARY SYSTEM

■ Push aside or remove the intestines of your pig and locate the large paired **kidneys** (see Figure 29-2 or 29-3). These are reddish organs located deep within the abdominal cavity, underneath the peritoneum on either side of the aorta. They are not enclosed within the peritoneum.

■ Before you clear away the membrane from one of the kidneys, locate the **adrenal gland** pressed against the inner side of its anterior part. This delicate gland is a narrow strip of light brown or yellow tissue and is easily destroyed. The **adrenal medulla** (inner part) is a neuroendocrine organ that secretes epinephrine into the bloodstream, whereas the **adrenal cortex,** or outer part, secretes a variety of steroid hormones.

■ Now, expose the kidney and study its external structure. Identify the following parts:

Renal hilum. Where the blood vessels and **ureter** are attached.
Renal artery. Carries blood from the aorta to the kidney.
Renal vein. Carries blood from the kidney to the posterior vena cava.
Ureter. Hollow tube that carries urine from the kidney to the **urinary bladder.** The ureter is also covered by the peritoneum.

■ Slice through the kidney from right to left with a razor blade, and study the internal structure. (See Figure 29-1.)

Kidney tissue is very rich in mitochondria and has an enormous metabolic rate. Much of its energy is spent **resorbing** molecules from urine or **secreting** molecules into urine. Within the kidney are about one million **nephrons.** The capsules of the nephrons, which receive fluid from blood within the capillaries, are located in the outer part of the kidney, the **cortex.** For each nephron a tubule then passes down into the inner region, or **medulla,** back to the cortex, and finally again into the medulla, where the tubules now join larger **collecting tubules.** The collecting tubules can be seen as rays radiating from the central part of the kidney. They empty into the hollow space, the pelvis, which leads into the beginning of the ureter. The structure of a nephron is shown in Figure 38-13 in your text.

In humans, kidney stones may form within the pelvis of the kidney. During a kidney stone attack, a small stone may become stuck in and block the ureter. Severe pain results as urine pressure builds up behind the stone, creating a medical emergency. In extreme cases, the stone may completely fill the pelvis of the kidney and take the form of a "staghorn."

Figure 29-1. Internal structure of a kidney. The detail shows the position of the parts of a single nephron. Each kidney will have about one million nephrons. Urine flows out of the collecting tubule into the hollow pelvis of the kidney and then exits through the ureter to the bladder. Capillaries permeate the kidney and are closely associated with each individual nephron.

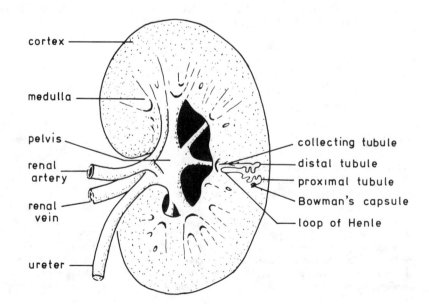

■ Draw a "staghorn" stone within the kidney in Figure 29-1.

■ View the section of kidney cortex on demonstration in the microscope. The larger dark structures surrounded by membranes are the **glomeruli** surrounded by the capsules of the tubules. The round hollow tubes are the **proximal tubules,** and the irregularly shaped tubes are the **distal tubules.**

■ Follow the ureter posteriorly to where it joins the **urinary bladder,** which lies between the umbilical arteries. The structure of the urinary tract is shown in Figures 29-2 and 29-3. After birth, urine leaves the bladder by the urethra.

■ Locate the **urethra,** and clear away enough tissue so that you can see how it disappears deep within the girdle of pelvic bones. You will be able to follow it all the way to the outside when you have finished studying the reproductive system.

The rate at which urine is formed is regulated by the action of anti-diuretic hormone on the collecting tubules (ADH). An increase in this hormone when the body is dehydrated causes the collecting tubules to reabsorb more water, reestablishing homeostasis.

FEMALE REPRODUCTIVE SYSTEM

The gonads, or primary sex organs, of the female are the **ovaries.**

■ Locate these light-colored, small spheres, which are posterior to the kidneys and are held in place by mesenteries. (See Figure 29-2.)

FEMALE

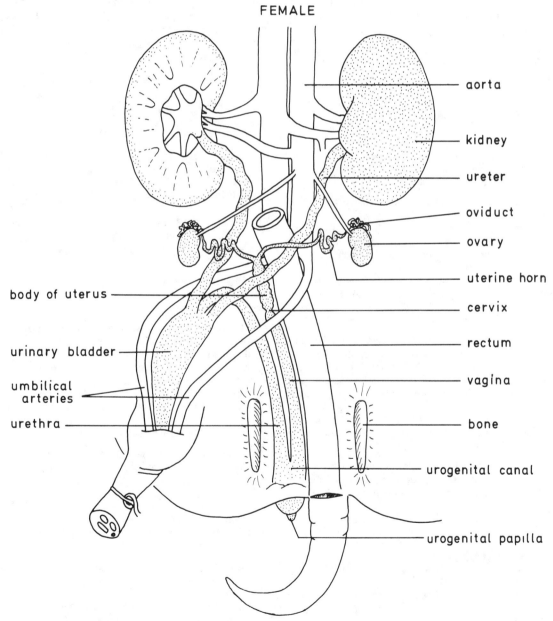

Figure 29-2. Female urogenital system. Dissection of a female fetal pig to show the structures of the urogenital system.

Ovaries have a double function: they contain all the **ova** (egg cells) that the female will ever produce, and they are the endocrine glands that release **female sex hormones** into the bloodstream. Closely attached to the top of the ovary is a *tiny*, twisted white tube.

■ Locate this tube, which is the **oviduct** (also called **Fallopian tube, uterine tube**).

An egg released into the abdomen by the ovary is swept into the open end of the oviduct (ostium) and on down the duct to the uterus by ciliary action. If sperm are present, the egg will be fertilized along the way while it is traveling through the oviduct. The pig's **uterus** is quite different from that of the human. It consists of two long **horns**, in which the developing eggs implant, and a small **body**.

■ Locate the long horns, which are larger than the oviducts, and begin close to the ovaries. Locate the body of the uterus where the two horns join. The body ends at the **cervix**.

The uterus leads into the **vagina**, or birth canal, and the beginning of the vagina can be seen as a constriction marking the cervix within it soon after the uterine horns join.

■ Follow the vagina posteriorly until it disappears into the pelvic girdle.

At this point you should be able to show the rectum, urethra, and vagina all entering the pelvic girdle. It is now necessary to cut through the muscle and the bone of the pelvic girdle to see what happens next.

■ Carefully make a cut with your razor blade along the midline of the pig.
■ Cut almost all the way back to the urogenital papilla.
■ Deepen the cut to the bone, and then cut through the bone, trying not to cut the structures located underneath it.
■ Spread the legs apart, and force the bones of the girdle open to expose the structures within it. Follow the vagina and urethra posteriorly, and see where they join to form the **urogenital canal**.

This canal leads to the urogenital opening of the female pig. As the pig develops, the vagina and urethra become more and more separated so that finally there will be two openings: a ventral one for the urethra and a more dorsal one for the vagina. The rectal opening is most dorsal, just beneath the tail.

On each side of the urogenital opening are the rounded lips, or **labia**. They would have developed into the scrotum if the pig had been male.

■ Slit the side of the urogenital canal, and look on the ventral surface of the canal for the **clitoris**, the female organ that is the counterpart of the male penis.

MALE REPRODUCTIVE SYSTEM

Before starting to dissect, study Figure 29-3 to familiarize yourself with the overall anatomy. Notice that the pathways for urine and sperm join in a common urethra, which passes down through the pelvic girdle, then ventrally and anteriorly along the abdominal wall until it finally exits through the urogenital opening just below the umbilical cord. You will need to dissect quite a bit to see the entire pathway.

■ Raise the flap of abdominal wall where the umbilical cord enters, and relocate the **bladder** between the umbilical arteries.
■ Use your probe to separate the **ureters**, which drain from the kidney into the bladder.
■ If it helps, cut through the middle of the bladder and umbilical arteries, and separate them from the abdominal wall so that you can locate the beginning of the **urethra**, which leads out of the bladder. This area is called the neck of the bladder.
■ Notice the two small tubes that are looped over the ureters and which join the urethra at the bladder neck. They are the **vasa deferentia**, or "tubes," of the male, and carry sperm from the testes to the urethra.
■ To find the **testes**, or male gonads, investigate the scrotum of the pig to see whether they have already moved down from the abdomen, or descended. If not, as is usually the case, they can be found in the groin area, on the inner side of the upper part of the hind leg.
■ Cut through the skin and muscle to locate each testis, which will be enclosed in a tough, white, opaque membrane. Be careful not to cut between the testis and the vas deferens that leads from it.
■ Cut open the outer membrane so that you can see the reddish testis itself.

Like the ovary, the testis has two functions: It will produce the **sperm cells** of the male that enter the vas deferens, and it produces **male sex hormones**, chiefly **testosterone**, that determine the sex of the pig and allow it to function sexually. Covering part of the testis is a whitish mass of tightly coiled tubules, the **epididymis**. Sperm cells produced in the testis pass into the coils of the epididymis where they are stored before entering the vas deferens.

■ Dissect as much as you need in this area to show the path of the vas deferens leading from the testis to the urethra.

Each vas deferens passes from outside the abdomen through the abdominal wall to the inside through the **inguinal canal**. In humans this canal is a weak spot and may rupture or split open, forming a hernia. Testes, like kidneys, are outside the peritoneum. When the testis is within the scrotum, it is supported by a ligament and has its own blood vessels leading to and from the abdomen: The vessels, ligament, and vas deferens form the **spermatic cord** from which the testis is suspended.

■ Follow the vas deferens to the bladder, and observe where it enters the urethra.

The situation here is very complicated and is diagrammed in Figure 29-4 from underneath (dorsal view).

■ Pull the bladder toward you, and try to locate the following structures on the *dorsal* side:

Seminal vesicles. Small, paired, light-colored glands that branch off from the urethra just posterior to the vasa deferentia.

Prostate. Very small, light-colored, smooth, round gland at the junction of the seminal vesicles. It is sometimes too small to be seen.

As sperm cells pass along the urethra, fluids from these glands are released to help make up the **semen**.

MALE

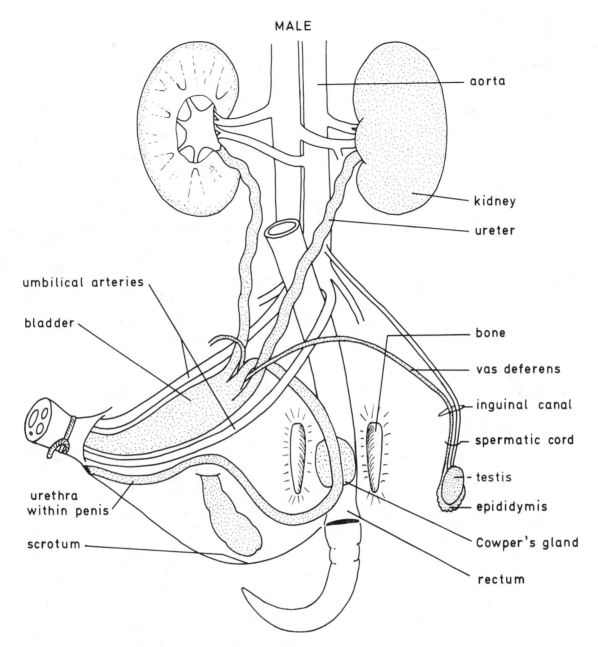

Figure 29-3. Male urogenital system. Dissection of a male fetal pig to show the structures of the urogenital system.

■ Push the flap of abdominal wall containing the umbilical cord to one side: You will need it momentarily.

■ To expose the urethra as it leaves the abdomen, cut through the skin, muscle, and bone of the pelvic girdle slightly to one side of the midline. Try not to cut beneath the bone.

■ Locate the urethra just beneath the bone: It is now quite large and well developed, and is the combined pathway for both the urinary and reproductive systems.

■ Pry apart the bones of the pelvic girdle, and locate the bean-shaped, white **Cowper's glands** (Figure 29-3) on either side of the urethra. They also secrete fluids into the semen.

The urethra leaves the abdomen, and enters the long, muscular **penis** within the abdominal wall.

■ Feel that free strip of abdominal wall to find the penis and dissect it free with your probe. You can now trace the urinary system from the kidney and the reproductive system from the testis through the common urethra to the external urogenital opening.

■ Finally, follow the digestive tract as it exits through the pelvic girdle. The **rectum** lies just dorsal to the urethra and ends in the external opening, the **anus.**

What color is the rectum? _____

Varicose veins within the human rectum are called hemorrhoids.

When you are finished, seal the pig and any extra tissue into the bag, and dispose of it properly. Clean your pan and tools, and oil your scissors for the next student.

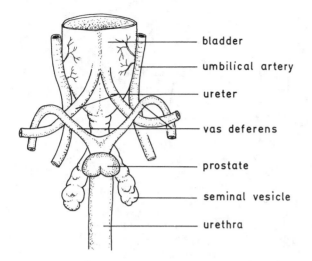

Figure 29-4. Male reproductive system. Dorsal view showing the structures in the region of the neck of the bladder. If you dissect carefully, you should be able to see all of these structures except the prostate, which may be too undeveloped to see.

bladder
umbilical artery
ureter
vas deferens
prostate
seminal vesicle
urethra

HUMAN REPRODUCTION: CONCEPTION

Each human female has about 300,000 eggs that are set aside very early in development, about 3 weeks after conception. Some of these potential eggs mature, one at a time, once the woman is sexually mature. Thus any damage to the eggs or ovaries of a woman, such as from X-rays or toxic chemicals, is permanent. No new eggs can ever be formed. (In the testes, on the other hand, sperm are formed continuously and damaged sperm are quickly replaced.) The physiological conditions that cause eggs to be released and make the reproductive tract receptive to fertilization and implantation of the resulting embryo are under hormonal control. Regular changes in the levels of these hormones cause the events of the menstrual cycle: The egg is released halfway through the cycle, midway between two menstrual periods. (See Figure 29-5.) If you are unsure about the details of the menstrual cycle, you should turn to your text, and review them so that you can understand conception. (See text Figure 43-11.)

The egg cell is rather short-lived once it has been released from the ovary, and conception, or fertilization, normally takes place in the oviduct within half a day of egg release, or **ovulation.** Sperm cells are viable for several days, so regular sexual activity means that the egg has a good chance of being fertilized. In fact, about 80 out of 100 sexually active couples will conceive within a year when no contraceptive is used. This is defined as a conception rate of 80%. A large number of recognized pregnancies, up to 15%, fail to progress normally and end in spontaneous abortion or miscarriage. Usually the embryo is defective in such cases, with about half of the miscarriages due to abnormalities in the chromosomal karyotype.

If a couple had intercourse 2 days before ovulation, could conception occur? _____

If a couple had intercourse 2 days after ovulation, could conception occur? _____

HUMAN REPRODUCTION: CONTRACEPTION

If natural events were allowed to take their course, most women would be pregnant most of the time. In our society, personal freedom, good medical care, improved gen-

Pregnancy

Ovulation, egg released

egg fertilized

1st day of period

egg travels down oviduct

implantation in uterus

continued development

woman suspects pregnancy

Day | 1 | 2 | 3 | 4 | 5 | 6 | 7 | 8 | 9 | 10 | 11 | 12 | 13 | 14 | 15 | 16 | 17 | 18 | 19 | 20 | 21 | 22 | 23 | 24 | 25 | 26 | 27 | 28 | 29 | 30 | 31 | 32 | 33

1st day of period

Ovulation, egg released

1st day of period

No pregnancy

Figure 29-5. Menstrual cycle. If pregnancy occurs, the menstrual period is suspended because the hormone HCG (human chorionic gonadotrophin) from the embryo stimulates the ovary to keep secreting progesterone.

eral health and nutrition, and widespread preference for bottle rather than breast feeding all help contribute to this potentially high pregnancy rate. Of the many ways that pregnancy can be prevented, the only one that is 100% sure is sexual abstinence. Although this method is used to a degree by many societies, it has almost no role in our own. All the other methods of birth control or contraception, including sterilization, do have some finite risk of pregnancy. This risk is given as the chance of pregnancy in a group of couples using the method to prevent pregnancy during the first year of use.* On the average, the couples had a pregnancy rate of 3.7%; they would have expected a rate of about 80% if they had not used any contraception.

Some common methods of contraception are shown in Figure 29-6.

Mechanical Methods

CONDOM

■ Look at the various types of condoms on demonstration.

The rubber sheath is rolled over the penis before intercourse. It prevents sperm from entering the vagina. Thinner condoms are supposed to be more "natural," but are also more likely to break, releasing sperm into the va-

*Table 2 in B. Vaughan, J. Trussell, J. Menken, and E. F. Jones, "Contraceptive failure among married women in the United States, 1970-73," *Family Planning Perspectives* 9:6, 1977.

gina. Lubricants such as Vaseline cause the rubber of the condom to deteriorate and weaken. Condoms are available without prescription and are the only method that gives protection against venereal disease. This method is coitus-related, and requires some practice, care, and self-control when the condom is put on and removed.

Conception rate is 7%. If the condom is used carelessly, the rate will be much higher than if the condom is used carefully with foam.

DIAPHRAGM

■ Look at the one size of diaphragm on demonstration.

This rubber shield is used with spermicidal jelly and inserted into the vagina before intercourse. To be effective, it must fit properly over the cervix (tip of the uterus), so each woman must be individually fitted for her diaphragm by a physician. Diaphragms are available by prescription only and must be used with a spermicidal agent. They also have to be used at the time of intercourse and require practice in learning to insert them properly. Conception rate is 10%.

IUD (INTRAUTERINE DEVICE)

■ Look at the various types on display.

IUDs come in all shapes and sizes. The device is inserted into the uterus through the cervix, and so long as it is in place, it will block pregnancy by preventing implantation of any eggs that happen to be fertilized. An IUD must be inserted by a physician or nurse-clinician, and it can be removed any time the woman desires. It has the great advantage that its insertion is not related to intercourse,

CONTRACEPTIVE METHODS

condom

diaphragm

intrauterine device

contraceptive foam

"the pill"

Figure 29-6. Contraceptive methods. These methods are widely used in the United States. (Courtesy of Planned Parenthood Federation of America, Inc.)

but many women experience undesirable side effects such as cramps, excessive bleeding, and an increased susceptibility to infection. The woman must regularly check the IUD to make sure that it has not been expelled. IUDs are not recommended unless the woman has borne a child, and they have been associated with problems of infertility. Some IUDs contain copper or progesterone to make them even more effective in preventing implantation. The mechanism by which copper inhibits implantation is not known. Conception rate is 3% if the device is not expelled accidentally.

SPONGE

The soft sponge (Today®) is saturated with spermicide and is inserted into the vagina to cover the cervix before coitus. There is just one size and no prescription is necessary. It is effective for over 24 hours, so its use does not have to interfere with sexual foreplay. The main disadvantage is expense—each sponge costs about $1. Conception rate, if the sponge is used properly, is 10-13%. Use of a condom as well is recommended.

Chemical Methods

FOAMS, CREAMS, AND JELLIES

Foams from pressurized cans are put into the vagina with an applicator something like a tampon. Creams are applied in the same way. Foams, as well as creams and jellies, all contain chemicals that effectively kill sperm cells without irritating the vagina. They are available without prescription and must be used each time before intercourse. Some products can be used without a diaphragm, but the effectiveness of all such products can be increased if a diaphragm or condom is used in addition. Jellies are usually designed only for use with a diaphragm. Conception rate is 13%.

FEMININE HYGIENE PRODUCTS (INCLUDING DOUCHES) ARE NOT EFFECTIVE CONTRACEPTIVES.

Hormones

"THE PILL"

The most commonly used birth control pill is a combination of synthetic estrogen and progesterone. It works by blocking the release of anterior pituitary hormones (FSH and LH) that are needed for the egg to mature, be released, and implant properly. (See text Figure 43-11). The pills are taken for 3 weeks to prevent ovulation, and then stopped for 1 week so that a menstrual period occurs. The pill is popular because it is cheap, effective, not used at the time of intercourse, and often makes the menstrual periods less bothersome. On the other hand, some women experience annoying side effects, it must be taken every day, and older women will have an increased chance of blood clots (thromboembolism). Smokers and women over 35 should not use the pill. The pill may also increase the risk of minor vaginal infections, and it does

not prevent venereal disease. Conception rate is less than 2%, and probably 0% if a woman never forgets to take the pills exactly as prescribed.

IMPLANTS

If there is a problem in taking the pill every day, the same effect can be achieved by implanting a capsule under the skin of the arm or thigh. The capsule will slowly release hormones into the body and thereby prevent pregnancy. This method is reversible, but the implant must be inserted and removed by a physician. Implants are less widely used than the other methods.

BREAST FEEDING IS NOT AN EFFECTIVE BIRTH CONTROL MEASURE.

After birth it often takes the woman's hormones and menstrual cycle some time to get back to normal, and ovulation may be inhibited for a few months. This process is so variable, however, that it cannot be relied upon to prevent pregnancy. Some women ovulate very soon after giving birth, and many mothers have become pregnant while they are still nursing.

Surgical Methods

FEMALE STERILIZATION

A surgical incision is made in the abdomen (or vagina) and the uterine "tubes," are cut and tied off. As a result, any eggs released will just degenerate in the far end of the tube and will never be able to reach the uterus. This procedure is easy to do after childbirth but can also be done in nonpregnant women through a very small incision. It has the great advantage of being very effective and having no side effects. On the other hand, it is relatively expensive and is limited to women who do not want (more) children. It can only rarely be reversed. Conception rate is almost 0%. Once in a great while the tubes manage to grow back together.

MALE STERILIZATION

The vasa deferentia, or "tubes," are cut and tied off through a small incision in the scrotum. This procedure can usually be done in the doctor's office and is much cheaper and safer than female sterilization because the testes are outside the abdominal cavity. The other advantages and disadvantages of the two procedures are the same. After sterilization, the man's semen eventually will contain no sperm cells (the stored sperm must first be used up), but otherwise the semen will be the same as before the operation. Sexual functioning is just the same except that the man will not be able to make the woman pregnant. In some cases, the tubes have been surgically rejoined so that the man is again fertile, but this method is at present limited to men who do not plan to have children in the future. Conception rate is almost 0%. The male tubes have an even smaller chance of rejoining than do the female tubes.

Sterilization is not to be confused with **castration,** the removal of the ovaries or testes. These organs must sometimes be removed for medical reasons, such as ovarian or testicular cancer. As a result, the person will no longer produce gametes or sex hormones and a change in secondary sex characteristics may result.

Biological Methods

RHYTHM

The couple using this method tries to predict when the woman will ovulate, and avoids having intercourse around that time. Ovulation is supposed to occur just about 14 days before the next menstrual period begins, but the time between the end of the preceding menstrual period and the time of ovulation tends to be rather variable. If a couple relies strictly on the calendar, the method is quite poor, with a conception rate of roughly 35%. Attention to physiological changes can give some improvement. Hints about the timing of ovulation are sometimes obtained by noting an increase in body temperature and changes in stickiness of cervical mucus. Even under the best of conditions, however, sickness might raise the body temperature, and all sorts of physical and psychological changes will affect the timing of ovulation, so that it will never be possible to predict the correct time with absolute certainty. This method cannot be used by the many women with irregular or somewhat variable cycles, and it always involves periods of sexual abstinence. Conception rate is 7% under the most favorable conditions. Usually the rate is higher than with any other method. Reported success depends strongly on the physiology and motivation of the couple involved.

Pregnancy Termination (Abortion)

Many pregnancies, perhaps 30-60%, end in spontaneous abortions (miscarriages) soon after conception, before the pregnancy is recognized. Usually this results from a defective embryo or imperfect implantation. After pregnancy has been recognized, about 15% of the time there will be a miscarriage and about half of these miscarriages will have abnormal chromosomes.

Induced abortion, carried out by a physician, is not a satisfactory means of contraception by itself because of the strain being pregnant for even a short time puts on the woman's system, and because of the finite risk of infection or other consequence of the procedure. Abortion is, however, a necessary component of contraception because every method used has some risk of pregnancy. There are several types of abortions used, depending on the stage of the pregnancy:

1. A shot of estrogen within 24 hours of unprotected sex will prevent implantation. The side effects are unpleasant.
2. Insertion of an IUD after unprotected sex will prevent pregnancy because several days must elapse before the embryo is ready to implant.
3. Vacuum aspiration, an outpatient procedure in which the cervix is dilated and the embryo removed under suction, can be used for up to 12 weeks.
4. Dilation and curettage (D and C) is used during the first 12 weeks and sometimes later. The cervix is dilated, and the contents of the uterus are scraped out.
5. A saline solution can be injected into the amniotic sac, and as a result, the uterus expels the embryo in a few hours. This more complicated procedure can be used through up to 6 months of pregnancy.
6. Under unusual circumstances, a pregnancy can be ended even later by an operation in which the abdomen is surgically opened and the fetus removed. This is a major operation, but the uterus is not removed as it is in a hysterectomy.

Risk of Complication

Many people do not realize that for women under 40 the overall risk to health of any form of contraception is much smaller than the risk involved if the woman used no contraception and carried each pregnancy that occurred to term. Unprotected women under 25 have a risk of pregnancy-related death of 5 in 100,000 per year, whereas any combination of birth control methods, including IUD, pills, abortion, and so on, has a risk of 1-2 in 100,000 per year. Once a woman has become pregnant, the risk of serious illness or death is much smaller for having an abortion compared with carrying out the pregnancy.

■ Review what you have learned about human reproduction by tracing the path of an ovum and a sperm cell from formation to the site of fertilization.

■ Locate each of the following sites:

Where egg and sperm cells are formed.
Where sperm are deposited.
Where fertilization normally occurs.
Where each of the following acts to interfere with fertilization:
   Male sterilization
   Female sterilization
   Condom
   Foam
   Diaphragm/sponge
   IUD

EXPLORING FURTHER

See also Topic 25

Boolootian, R. A. *Human Reproduction.* New York: John Wiley and Sons, 1971.
Boston Women's Health Collective. *The New Our Bodies, Ourselves.* New York: Simon and Schuster, 1985.
Cox, Klaudia, Ed. *Contraceptive Efficacy Among Married Women in the United States.* National Center for Health Statistics (ser. 23, no. 5), 1979.
Demarest, Robert, and John Sciarra. *Conception, Birth and Contraception.* 2nd ed. New York: McGraw-Hill. 1976.
Ganong, W. F. "Renal Function." *Review of Medical Physiology.* 11th ed. Los Altos, Calif.: Lange Medical Publishers, 1983.
Hatcher, R. A., et al. *Contraceptive Technology 1982-83.* 11th rev. ed. New York: Irvington Publishers, 1982.
Huff, Robert W., and Carl J. Pauerstein. *Human Reproduction: Physiology and Pathophysiology.* New York: John Wiley and Sons, 1979.

Nilsson. L. *A Child is Born*. Rev. ed. New York: Delacorte, 1977.

Turner, C. D., and J. T. Bagnara. *General Endocrinology*. 6th ed. Philadelphia: W. B. Saunders, 1976.

Journal Articles

Gold, Michael. "The baby makers." *Science 85:* 26, April 1985.

Beaconsfield, Peter, George Birdwood, and Rebecca Beaconsfield. "The placenta." *Scientific American,* August 1980 (#1478).

Fuchs, Fritz. "Genetic amniocentesis." *Scientific American,* June 1980 (#1471).

Grobstein, Clifford. "External human fertilization." *Scientific American,* June 1979 (#1429).

Langone, J. "The quest for the male pill." *Discover,* 26, October 1982.

Smith, Homer W. "The kidney." *Scientific American,* January 1953 (#37).

Tieze, C., and S. Lewit. "Legal abortion." *Scientific American,* January 1977 (#1348).

Vaughan, B., J. Trussell, J. Menken, and E. F. Jones. "Contraceptive failure among married women in the United States 1970-73." *Family Planning Perspectives 9:* 6, 1977.

Neural Control: Neurons, Nervous System, and Sense Organs

OBJECTIVES

When you have completed this topic, you should be able to:
1. Describe the basic structure of a neuron.
2. Show in which direction(s), if any, an impulse travels if the neuron is stimulated at any point.
3. Describe the function of a myelin sheath, and give the location of myelinated neurons in the nervous system.
4. Describe the structure of the mammalian brain, and give the functions controlled by the medulla, cerebellum, pons, hypothalamus, pituitary, thalamus, reticular formation, colliculi, and cerebral cortex.
5. Describe the structure of the spinal cord, and give the main types of neurons entering, leaving, or functioning within it.
6. Distinguish between the central/peripheral nervous systems, the somatic/autonomic nervous systems, and the sympathetic/parasympathetic nervous systems.
7. Name the neurotransmitters associated with synapses in each of the following: muscle, sympathetic nervous system, parasympathetic nervous system, brain, and spinal cord.
8. Describe the five main types of receptor cells, and name some sense organs in which each is found.
9. Describe the structure of the vertebrate eye and the types of receptors found in it.
10. Explain how the transducers in the inner ear work.
11. Describe where the proprioceptors are found in the body, and explain their function.
12. Trace the path of the withdrawal reflex when you touch a hot stove.

KEY TOPICS

Neurons, synapses, central nervous system, peripheral nervous system, vision, hearing, taste, smell, touch.

INTRODUCTION

The function of the nervous system is to coordinate the activities of the different parts of the body. **Receptor cells** located in internal and external sense organs send it information, allowing it to respond by means of its **effectors,** which are usually muscles or glands. The nervous system maintains equilibrium, or **homeostasis,** within the body and allows the organism to respond to external stimuli with appropriate **behavior** patterns. In contrast to the endocrine system, which provides slow and long-lasting regulation, the nervous system provides for a rapid response to stimuli.

The **neurons,** or nerve cells, of the vertebrate nervous system are organized into the **central nervous system** and the **peripheral nervous system.** The brain and spinal cord make up the central nervous system (CSN), which receives input from the major sense organs and coordinates most of the body's activities. Many types of **neurotransmitters** (see the following) are active in the synapses of the CNS: acetylcholine, norepinephrine, dopamine, serotonin, epinephrine, GABA, glycine, endorphins and enkephalins.

The **somatic** part of the peripheral nervous system includes the cranial and spinal nerves and their associated sense organs. These nerves control voluntary activities and use acetylcholine as the neurotransmitter. The **autonomic** part of the peripheral nervous system controls those internal functions that are usually carried out at the subconscious level. It includes the **sympathetic** nervous system, which uses norepinephrine as the final neurotransmitter, and the **parasympathetic** nervous system, which uses acetylcholine.

Acetylcholine and norepinephrine are the best understood of the many known neurotransmitters. **Cholinergic neurons** are those that release acetylcholine, and **adrenergic neurons** release norepinephrine.

NEURONS

The neurons that make up the nervous system conduct electrochemical impulses from one site to another through long cell processes. Those processes leading toward the **cell body** are called **dendrites,** and those leading away are called **axons.** Both types of processes usually connect with adjacent neurons by means of junctions called **synapses. Neurotransmitters** are those chemicals mentioned above that conduct nervous signals from one neuron to the next by diffusing in one direction across the gap of the synapse (synaptic cleft). Synaptic transmission is described in Figure 39-11 of your text. Neurotransmitters are removed from the synaptic cleft by enzymes or by reabsorption into synaptic vesicles within the neuron that released them. Dendrites receive stimuli from their synapses, whereas axons stimulate adjacent cells across their synapses. The structure of one type of neuron is shown in Figure 5-4.

■ Examine a prepared slide of neuron.
■ Locate the cell body, nucleus, axon, and dendrites.

Where do impulses reach this cell in the form of neurotransmitter molecules?

_____

Where in a neuron does integration of incoming impulses occur?

_____

Where is an all-or-none action potential generated?

_____

In vertebrates, some axons are surrounded by special Schwann cells, which are filled with a fatty insulating material called **myelin.** The effect of this myelin sheath is to greatly improve impulse transmission along the axon. At intervals along the length of the axon, there are interruptions in the myelin sheath known as the nodes of Ranvier. Instead of traveling at a normal, steady rate, the impulse skips from node to node more efficiently and at a much faster rate by **saltatory conduction.** (See text Figure 39-10.) Myelinated nervous tissue appears white, whereas unmyelinated tissue is gray.

Neurons are supported by cells called **neuroglia** that are very important in nervous tissue, but that do not conduct nervous impulses.

THE CENTRAL NERVOUS SYSTEM

In vertebrates, the nervous system is **bilateral** and shows great **cephalization** in which much of the nervous system, namely the brain and sense organs, is concentrated in the head region.

The Brain

The vertebrate brain is divided into the forebrain, the midbrain, and the hindbrain. In mammals the forebrain is the most prominent part, and it is considerably more developed than it is in lower vertebrates. The external features of a sheep brain are shown in Figure 30-1.

The brain is covered by a triple layer of membranes called the **meninges.** The skull, meninges, and a cushion of **cerebrospinal fluid** protect the brain. The hollow spaces within the brain are called the **ventricles.** Both they and the hollow central canal of the spinal cord are also filled with cerebrospinal fluid.

The **forebrain** consists of the cerebral hemispheres and their underlying parts: the thalamus, hypothalamus, and pineal gland. The **midbrain** in mammals is a small region near the medulla (the anterior and posterior colliculi), which is concerned with certain responses of the eye and ear. The **hindbrain** is the cerebellum, medulla, and pons.

■ Examine a preserved sheep brain, and note the two **cerebral hemispheres,** which are the brain's largest structures. Although the hemispheres appear to be symmetrical here, in humans the two halves differ in size, and some functions are carried out in only one or the other hemisphere.
■ Locate the longitudinal **cerebral fissure** between the two hemispheres.
■ Spread the two hemispheres apart and find the thick **corpus callosum.** It consists of bundles of myelinated and unmyelinated axons, and connects the two hemispheres to each other. It is considered to be **white matter** because of its myelin content.

The cortex (thin outer layer) of the highly convoluted cerebrum contains the **gray matter** of the brain, consisting of cell bodies and unmyelinated axons. Associations, memory, and higher brain functions such as consciousness, language, and abstract thinking are carried on the cerebrum. Conscious sensations reach the **sensory cortex,** and the **motor cortex** controls voluntary movement. The right side of the cortex controls the left side of the body and vice versa.

■ Examine the ventral surface of the brain, and find the **olfactory bulbs** and the **olfactory tracts,** which lead from the chambers of the skull near the nasal passages. These are parts of the forebrain.
■ Find the **optic nerves,** which cross in the **optic chiasma** before entering the brain.

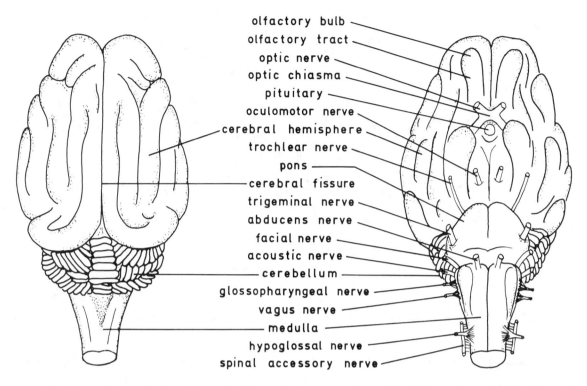

olfactory bulb
olfactory tract
optic nerve
optic chiasma
pituitary
oculomotor nerve
cerebral hemisphere
trochlear nerve
pons
cerebral fissure
trigeminal nerve
abducens nerve
facial nerve
acoustic nerve
cerebellum
glossopharyngeal nerve
vagus nerve
medulla
hypoglossal nerve
spinal accessory nerve

Figure 30-1.   Sheep brain. The cerebral hemispheres are much smaller relative to the rest of the brain than in humans. The pituitary may be missing in your specimen.

■ Posterior to the optic chiasma, look for the **pituitary,** an endocrine and neuroendocrine gland suspended from the hypothalamus of the brain. Secretions from the hypothalamus regulate the release of hormones from the pituitary. (The pituitary gland may be lost or damaged in your sheep brain.)

■ Find the **cerebellum,** which is a rounded structure with a convoluted surface just posterior to the cerebrum. It coordinates muscular movement and is important in maintaining equilibrium.

■ Identify the **medulla,** which is connected to and continuous with the anterior part of the spinal cord. The medulla is the location of vital centers for breathing (in the pons), circulation, and reflexes such as swallowing and vomiting. The medulla and cerebellum both develop from the hindbrain of the sheep embryo.

The internal structures of the brain are shown in Figure 30-2.

■ Examine a sagittal section of the sheep brain and find the location of the pituitary.

■ The dense **hypothalamus,** just dorsal to the pituitary, can now be seen better. It forms the floor of the third ventricle of the brain and is the principle center for regulating the internal organs. In addition to controlling the pituitary, it has centers for hunger, thirst, emotional states, sleep, osmoregulation, sex drive, and body temperature.

■ Just dorsal to the hypothalamus, on the sides of the third ventricle, find the white matter of the **thalamus.** This is an important area for sorting sensory messages before they enter the cerebrum.

■ Locate the **midbrain,** posterior to the thalamus and anterior to the cerebellum. Its two anterior protuberances are the **anterior** (or superior) **colliculi,** which control visual reflexes. The posterior protuberances are the **pos-terior** (or inferior) **colliculi,** which control auditory reflexes. The ventral part of the midbrain, the cerebral peduncles, contains tracts of fibers that conduct impulses anteriorly and posteriorly.

The parts of the brain are connected by various tracts of fibers. The medulla transmits impulses between the spinal cord and the rest of the brain. The **reticular activating system (RAS)** is a complex neural pathway within the medulla and thalamus that communicates with the cerebral cortex. It receives various kinds of sensory input and filters it before it can reach the cortex and be consciously perceived. The RAS also controls the general arousal level of the animal and how strongly it responds to external stimuli. The **limbic system** is located in the forebrain and controls emotional response. It affects sexual behavior, biological rhythms and feelings of pleasure and pain.

Many drugs act by mimicking neurotransmitters in the brain. For example, amphetamine, which is very similar in structure to norepinephrine, interferes with the action of this neurotransmitter, so that the reticular activating system becomes abnormally stimulated. This causes euphoria and hyperactivity.

The Spinal Cord

A cross section of the spinal cord is illustrated in Figure 30-3 and in Figure 39-16 in your text.

■ Examine a slide of the spinal cord in cross section in your dissecting microscope, and orient it so that the **ventral fissure** is toward you.

■ Locate the H-shaped area of **gray matter** around the central canal; it consists mainly of cell bodies.

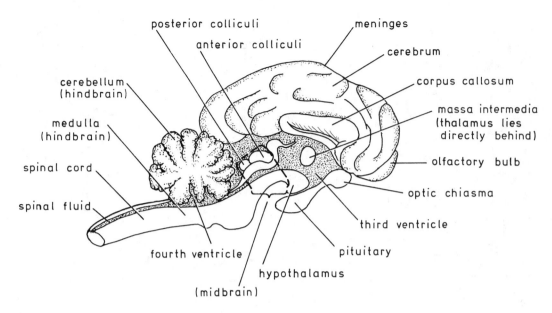

Figure 30-2. Sheep brain in sagittal section. The ventricles of the brain are continuous with the interior of the spinal cord and contain cerebrospinal fluid.

■ Note the **central canal** that is filled with cerebrospinal fluid.
■ Notice the **white matter** that makes up the rest of the spinal cord; it contains axons and dendrites.

How does the arrangement of gray and white matter here compare with the arrangement in the brain?

_____

_____

_____

■ Find the right and left **dorsal roots** through which sensory nerves enter the spinal cord. Each nerve is like a cable containing hundreds or thousands of axons or dendrites. These sensory nerves which carry impulses towards the CNS are **afferent nerves.**
■ Near the dorsal root, find the **dorsal root ganglion,** which contains the cell bodies of the **sensory neurons.**
■ Locate the right and left **ventral roots** through which **motor neurons** carry impulses away from the spinal cord. These motor nerves are **efferent nerves.**
■ Examine the ventral part of the gray matter in the compound microscope.
■ Locate the cell body of a motor neuron—a large, triangular cell that is darkly stained.

What is the function of the motor neurons?

_____

_____

■ Locate an **association neuron** or **interneuron** in the dorsal portion of the gray matter; it will have a more rounded cell body.

What is the function of the association neuron?

_____

_____

■ Find the rounded body of a **sensory neuron** within the dorsal root ganglion.

In which direction does this cell conduct impulses?

_____

■ Examine the white matter to see cross sections of nerve fibers. The dark central part of each fiber is the axon of the neuron, and the space around it is where the myelin is located. (Myelin may be absent as a result of the process of making the slide.) The myelin sheath is surrounded by the membrane of the **neurilemma.**
■ Use the diagram in Figure 30-3 to sketch in a **polysynaptic reflex.** Include the sensory neuron, the association neuron, and the motor neuron in your sketch, and indicate the direction of impulse and synaptic transmission with arrows. Such a reflex action is automatic and depends only on the anatomy of the neuronal circuit involved.

Why is transmission in a polysynaptic reflex one-way?

_____

_____

THE PERIPHERAL NERVOUS SYSTEM

The **somatic nervous system** is the part of the peripheral nervous system concerned with perception of and response to the outside world. It consists of the spinal and cranial nerves and their sensory receptors.

The dorsal and ventral roots join to form a **spinal nerve** (see Figure 30-3). There are 31 pairs of spinal nerves branching from the human spinal cord as shown in Figure 40-18 in your text. The spinal nerves and spinal cord can control reflex behavior without any input from the brain. Normally most responses other than very basic reflexes are modified by impulses from the brain. Only some of the sensory input to the spinal cord will reach the brain.

The major sense organs and heart are served by 12 pairs of **cranial nerves,** which lead directly into the

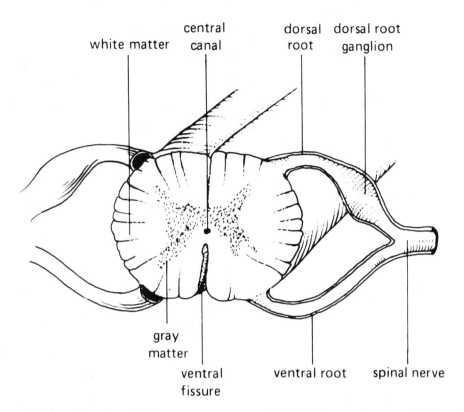

Figure 30-3. Spinal cord. This cross section is at the level of a spinal nerve and shows the dorsal and ventral roots. The white matter containing the axons surrounds the gray matter, which consists of cell bodies.

brain rather than first passing through the spinal cord. They are described in Table 40-3 in your text, and their location is shown in Figure 30-1.

■ Locate as many of these cranial nerves as you can on the sheep brain:

I	Olfactory	sensory	smell
II	Optic	sensory	sight
III	Oculomotor	motor	eye muscles
IV	Trochlear	motor	eye muscles
V	Trigeminal	mixed	face, mouth
VI	Abducens	motor	eye muscles
VII	Facial	mixed	face, tongue
VIII	Auditory	sensory	hearing, balance
IX	Glosso-pharyngeal	mixed	mouth, throat
X	Vagus	mixed	neck, internal organs
XI	Spinal accessory	motor	shoulder muscles
XII	Hypoglossal	motor	tongue muscles

The **autonomic nervous system** is that part of the peripheral nervous system concerned with maintaining homeostasis in the internal environment. It includes ganglia alongside the spinal cord (sympathetic cell bodies) or near target organs (parasympathetic cell bodies) and nerves connecting these ganglia to major organs, blood vessels, and skin. The **sympathetic** division triggers appropriate physiological responses to an emergency situation ("fight or flight" responses). The **parasympathetic** division generally has the opposite effect and stimulates routine activities such as digestion ("relax and digest" responses). The autonomic nervous system usually works without conscious control but can be influenced by the central nervous system. An emergency response, for instance, is often initiated by a terrifying visual or auditory stimulus. In conditioning by **biofeedback,** the responses of the autonomic nervous system are relayed to the conscious level of the CNS, which then allows the brain to exert a positive or negative influence on the response. In this way "autonomic functions" can be brought under conscious control to a certain extent.

SENSE ORGANS

Sense organs contain specialized cells or neurons called **receptors** and **accessory structures** that increase the efficiency of the receptors in perceiving stimuli. Receptors **transduce** physical stimuli into **receptor potentials** and nerve impulses. For example, the eye transduces light into nerve impulses.

The five types of receptors are:

1. **mechanoreceptors,** which respond to movement or physical stress.
2. **chemoreceptors,** which respond to chemical substances.
3. **photoreceptors,** which respond to light.
4. **thermoreceptors,** which respond to heat or cold.
5. **electroreceptors,** which respond to electrical fields.

In this exercise you will be studying the first four types.

The receptors synapse with sensory neurons that carry impulses through nerves to the CNS or to ganglia of the autonomic nervous system, or they carry the impulses themselves. Sensors that detect external stimuli are **exteroceptors** and those that detect movement and position of the body parts are **proprioceptors.**

The action potentials reaching the brain from the various sense organs are all alike. They are perceived as different sensations only because the impulses arrive in different specialized parts of the brain.

The Eye

In the eye, photons of a visual stimulus are transduced into nerve impulses by photoreceptors in the **retina.** In mammals there are two types of receptors: **rods** for perceiving the intensity of light and **cones** for detecting color or wavelength. The cones are concentrated in the **fovea** of the retina, the area of most acute vision. The rods and cones synapse with neurons in the retina, the neurons interact in the initial processing of the visual input, and finally the information is transmitted to the brain via nerve impulses in the optic nerves. The actual transduction process occurs when the photon is absorbed by **retinal,** the vitamin-A-derived part of the visual pigment **rhodopsin** that undergoes a structural change: 11-cis retinal changes to all trans retinal. This change causes a depolarization of the receptor cell membrane and sets up a receptor potential. If enough photons strike the cell, an action potential will result.

The structure of the vertebrate eye is shown in Figure 30-4.

■ Take a preserved sheep eye and note the outer covering, the **sclera,** to which muscles are attached to move the eye.
■ Find the **optic nerve** on the posterior surface.
■ The transparent part of the sclera over the pupil is the **cornea.** The cornea is thicker in the center and acts as a lens to help magnify the image.
■ Beneath the cornea, find the **iris,** which surrounds the opening into the eye, or **pupil.** The amount of light entering the pupil is regulated by the contraction of muscles controlling the iris.
■ Orient the eye so that the optic nerve is to your left and the pupil is horizontal.

■ Cut through the eye with your scalpel from front to back leaving part of the sclera at the bottom intact to hold the halves together.
■ Find the transparent **lens** just behind the pupil. It is hard in a preserved eye, but in life it is flexible and can be thickened or flattened by its associated muscles to focus the image on the retina. In most people over 40, the lens is no longer flexible enough to change shape, and corrective lenses must be worn for close vision.
■ Note the **aqueous fluid,** the fluid material that was contained between the cornea and lens.
■ The main part of the eye is filled with the gel-like **vitreous fluid.**
■ Print something on a scrap of paper.
■ Place a blob of vitreous fluid on the printing.

Does the vitreous fluid contribute to magnification of the image? _____

■ Note the black lining of the sides of the eye. The pigment is located in the **choroid coat,** which also contains blood vessels.
■ Locate the **retina,** which lines the interior part of the eye opposite the pupil. The retina contains the rod and cone receptor cells, and nerve cells.
■ Locate the white area in the retina where the optic nerve leaves the eye. This **blind spot** is filled with nerve fibers and has no receptor cells.

When would the iris be fully open?

_____

When would the iris be tightly closed?

_____

Why is the black lining important?

_____

_____

When light rays pass through the lens of the eye, they are bent so that the image of an object falls on the retina upside down. A thicker lens bends the rays more

Figure 30-4.   The vertebrate eye. Light passes through the transparent cornea and the pupil to the cells of the retina, where its energy is transduced into nerve impulses. The iris regulates the amount of light entering the eye by changing the pupil size.

strongly. The lens of the eye thickens in order to bring nearby objects into focus. The shape of the lens is changed by the contraction of the **ciliary muscle** attached to it. **Accomodation** is the process of adjusting the shape of the lens so that the image falling on the retina is in focus. When the lens fails to focus properly, a person may be nearsighted, farsighted, or astigmatic (see text Figure 41-27).

■ Sketch an object in front of the eye shown in Figure 30-4, and show how its image would fall on the retina.

If the object were moved farther from the eye, would the lens have to thicken or flatten to keep the image in focus? _____

Why don't you see objects upside down?

_____
_____

The Ear

The structure of the human ear is shown in Figure 30-5. The outer ear is the part you are already familiar with: It consists of the **pinna** and the **external canal.** Water in the external canal gives you the sensation of "water in the ear," and too much ear wax in this canal will interfere with the transmission of sound to the **eardrum** or **tympanic membrane** at its inner end.

What is the function of the pinna?

_____

■ Study the features of the middle ear and inner ear in a cutaway model.

The **middle ear** consists of the space between the eardrum and the cochlea of the inner ear, and contains three small bones that conduct the sound. It is connected to the pharynx by the **Eustachian tube.**

Why is a connection of the middle ear with the exterior necessary?

_____
_____

Respiratory infections can travel from the throat up the Eustachian tubes and cause painful inflammation and infection of the middle ear.

■ Locate the **cochlea** in the inner ear. The cochlea contains the organ of Corti, which is the organ of hearing.

If the cochlea were uncoiled, a cross section of it would appear as shown in Figure 30-6.

Within the cochlea there are three fluid-filled canals: the **vestibular canal,** which connects to the oval window, the **cochlear canal,** and the **tympanic canal.** Sound waves reaching the oval window set up vibrations within the vestibular canal that then travel back through the tympanic canal to the round window. Indirect vibrations are set up in the cochlear canal, which contains the mechanoreceptor **hair cells** of the **organ of Corti.** Vibrations of the tectorial membrane above these cells cause movements of the gel-like matrix around the hairs and excite the cells by moving the hairs. Impulses from the receptors are transmitted along the basilar membrane on which the cells are located and reach the auditory nerve, which carries them to the brain. Vibrations of different frequencies (pitches) will excite cells at different po-

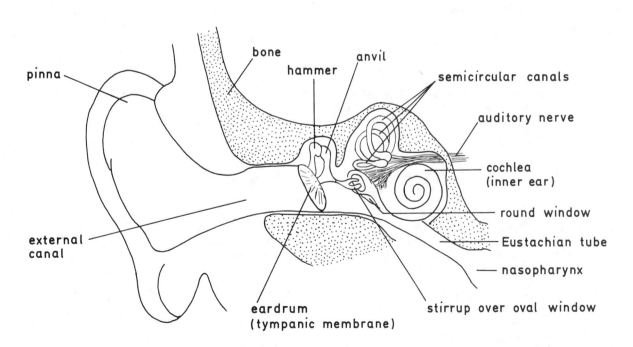

Figure 30-5. The human ear. The mechanical energy of sound waves is transduced into nerve impulses by cells of the organ of Corti within the cochlea. The semicircular canals sense the movement and position of the head and are the organ of equilibrium.

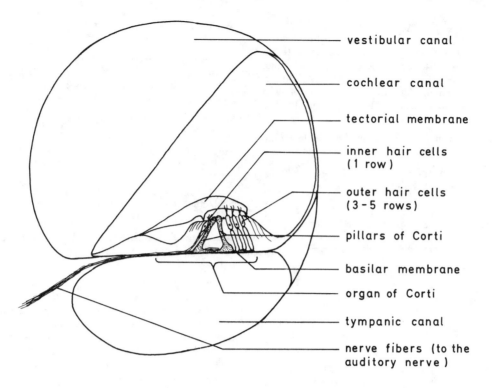

vestibular canal

cochlear canal

tectorial membrane

inner hair cells
(1 row)

outer hair cells
(3-5 rows)

pillars of Corti

basilar membrane

organ of Corti

tympanic canal

nerve fibers (to the
auditory nerve)

Figure 30-6. Cross section of one spiral of the cochlea. Vibrations from the bones of the middle ear travel through the vestibular canal and back through the tympanic canal. The mechanoreceptors that detect the vibrations are located on the basilar membrane of the organ of Corti.

sitions along the membrane, so that pitch as well as intensity can be sensed by the ear. Frequent exposure to loud noise will damage cells at the base of the organ of Corti and result in deafness to high-pitched tones.

■ Examine a microscope slide of the **cochlea;** several sections through the three canals will be visible.
■ Identify the **vestibular, cochlear,** and **tympanic canals** in one section.
■ Locate the organ of Corti between the basilar membrane and the tectorial membrane.

A second part of the inner ear, the **labyrinth,** has nothing to do with hearing, but also contains hair cells, which are mechanoreceptors. This organ of equilibrium consists of fluid-filled **semicircular canals** that are stimulated when the fluid flows through them in either direction. Each canal has an ampulla (sac) in which fluid pressure against a projecting cupula is detected by its hair cells. (See text Figure 41-12.) The semicircular canals are in three planes and allow the organ to sense **acceleration** (change in speed or direction) of the head as it is turned.

At the base of the semicircular canals are two sacs, the **sacculus** and the **utriculus,** which are also fluid-filled and contain crystals of calcium carbonate (otoliths). The crystals rest on a bed with sensory hair cells (cupula) and change position slightly as the head is moved. The pattern of cells being stimulated while the head is at rest in any position allows the organ to sense the **resting position** of the head relative to the force of gravity.

The sense of resting position in humans is very weak, as any scuba diver can testify, and is easily overridden by visual cues. The sense of movement is much stronger. When it conflicts with the visual cues, as during a boat trip or plane flight, the result is the nausea of motion sickness.

HUMAN SENSORY PERCEPTION

The Blind Spot

■ Obtain a sheet of white paper, and mark on it a heavy black cross and a heavy black dot about 8 cm apart.
■ Cover your left eye, and hold the paper at arm's length with the dot at the left and the cross at the right.
■ Stare hard at the dot while you slowly move the paper toward you.
■ Note that the cross is visible at first, disappears completely, and then reappears.

What do you see instead when the cross disappears?

_____

_____

Map your blind spot as follows:

■ Turn the paper sideways so that there is a clear space to the right of the black dot. Lay it flat on the desk.
■ Cover your left eye, and place your right eye about 25 cm from the black dot. Stare at the dot intently while your partner moves a small, brightly colored object (such as a bead on a white pipecleaner) toward the dot from your right side.
■ As soon as the object disappears, tell your partner to stop and mark the position of that edge of the blind spot.
■ Next ask your partner to move the object from the black dot toward the blind spot, and then to stop and mark the spot as soon as the object disappears.
■ Repeat several times, moving the object toward the blind spot from different directions, until your blind spot is well mapped, and then draw in its outline.

Does your blind spot have a regular or irregular shape?

_____

Compare the size and shape of your blind spot with those of other members of the class. The distance from the dot to the blind spot will depend partly on the distance between your eye and the dot.

Why don't you have an empty space in your field of vision all the time?

_____
_____

Explain why we have a blind spot in each eye.

_____
_____

Afterimages

■ Place a small square of solid blue paper or cardboard on a sheet of white paper, and put it under strong illumination.
■ Working with your partner, stare intently at the blue paper while your partner times 60 sec. Then shift your gaze and stare intently at the plain white paper.

Do you see an afterimage? _____

How long did the afterimage last? _____

What color is it? _____

■ Place a small square of solid yellow paper on a white sheet, and repeat your observation.

What color is the afterimage when the object is a yellow square? _____

  While you are staring at the blue square, the cones that are sensitive to the blue light become **adapted** (less responsive), whereas those sensitive to red and green light are unstimulated. Then when you suddenly switch to white light, which contains all three colors, the blue receptors give a response much lower than normal, whereas the red and green receptors give a response stronger than normal. This is exactly the response that occurs with yellow light, and your brain interprets the plain white paper as being yellow. As the receptors return to their normal response levels, the afterimage slowly fades.

Chemoreceptors

Taste is due to **taste receptors** found in taste buds of the tongue papillae (see text Figure 41-17). Smell is due to the **olfactory cells** of the olfactory epithelium located in the roof of the nasal cavity (see text Figure 41-18). Often both taste and olfactory receptors are involved in flavor discrimination.

Record your observations in Table 30-1 at the end of this topic.

TEST A

■ Obtain slices of apple and potato cut to the same size.
■ Close your eyes, pinch your nose shut, and have your partner place one slice on your tongue. Try to detect whether the slice is from an apple or from a potato without moving it around in your mouth and without breathing for 10 sec. Record your identification of the slice as correct (+) or incorrect (−) in Table 30-1.
■ Repeat several times with slices of apple and potato in random order.

TEST B

■ Suck on the slice, and move it around on your tongue. Record your observations.
■ Repeat several times with slices of apple and potato in random order.

Can you distinguish apple and potato by taste alone?

_____

TEST C

■ Blot your tongue dry, and repeat the tests. Record your results in the table.

Is saliva necessary for tasting? _____

TEST D

■ Chew a slice of potato or apple with your nose pinched shut. Record your results.

Can you distinguish apple from potato without olfaction?

_____

TEST E

■ Again chew a slice of apple or potato, but this time breathe through your nose. Record your results.

Is it easier to distinguish them using olfaction?

_____

TEST F

Proceed as follows to map the location of your taste receptors. Your observations will a rough estimate of where the receptors are located, since a single taste papilla or even a single taste bud can respond to more than one of the four basic tastes.

■ Obtain dropping bottles of the following solutions:

5.0% sucrose   (sweet)
10% NaCl   (salty)
0.1% quinine sulfate   (bitter)
1.0% acetic acid   (sour)

■ Open your mouth wide, without sticking out your tongue, and have your partner place a drop of one soluton on spot #1 on the tip of your tongue. Repeat on the side and finally the back as shown in Figure 30-7. Rinse after each drop with plain water.

Figure 30-7. Tongue and taste. Numbers label the spots to be tested.

■ Rate the taste for each drop as absent (0), faint (+), or strong (+ +), and record the results in the appropriate column in Table 30-2 at the end of this topic.
■ Repeat for the other three solutions.

When you finish testing, map your areas sensitive to sweet, salty, bitter, and sour tastes on the outlines in Figure 30-8, at the end of this topic.

Proprioceptors

Proprioceptors in your muscles and joints continuously inform your nervous system about the location of your body and its appendages without visual input. These are mechanoreceptors such as muscle spindles (movement), Golgi tendon organs (tendon stretching), and joint receptors (ligament movement). A certain posture can be maintained by reflexes involving antagonistic muscle pairs and their proprioceptors. Test the effectiveness of proprioception alone in maintaining balance and in motor coordination by performing these actions with your eyes closed. Record the results in Table 30-3 at the end of this topic.

TEST A

■ Stand with your feet together and arms at your sides. Have your partner measure the extent of swaying and your success in attempting to compensate for it.

TEST B

■ Stand on one leg with your arms extended. Have your partner time how long you can stand on one leg with your eyes closed, then repeat with your eyes open.

How important is visual input in supplementing your proprioceptors?

Other proprioceptors (kinesthetic receptors) allow detection of movement of body parts without the benefit of visual input. Test your kinesthetic sense as follows.

TEST C

■ Close your eyes, and extend your arms fully to the sides at shoulder height.

■ Move your arms together without bending your elbows, and attempt to touch your index fingers side to side.
■ Have your partner measure how far apart your fingers are if your fingers fail to touch.

TEST D

■ Close your eyes, and extend your arms sideways at shoulder height, but this time bend your elbows sharply so that your index fingers point at each other.
■ Move the fingers together unti they touch.
■ Have your partner measure how far apart your fingers are if they fail to touch.

Thermoreceptors

Thermoreception in mammalian skin is due to free nerve endings and specialized **Krause's corpuscles** (other sense organs in the skin detect touch, and free nerve endings detect pain.)

MAPPING THERMORECEPTORS

■ Stamp a grid on a hairless part of your forearm, or draw one 3 × 3 cm marked off with a grid 0.5 × 0.5 cm.
■ Have your partner hold a probe in a boiling water bath, dry it, and quickly touch it *lightly* to one point on the grid while you look the other way.
■ Indicate whether you felt a sensation of warmth, and if so, record the result on the grid in Table 30-4 at the end of this topic.
■ Repeat for the other points on the grid, and calculate the number of heat-sensitive points per square centimeter in this area of skin. Next, place a probe in a bath of ice water, dry, and touch it to one point on the grid. Record whether there was a sensation of cold.
■ Repeat for the other points on the grid, and calculate the number of cold-sensitive receptors per square centimeter.

Which type of receptor is more concentrated in this area of skin? _____

HABITUATION

■ Obtain three beakers; fill one with cold water, one with warm water, and one with lukewarm water.
■ Place the index finger of your left hand in the beaker of warm water and the index finger of your right hand in the beaker of cold water. Then count to 60.
■ Now place both fingers in the beaker of lukewarm water.

What sensation do you feel with your left finger?

_____

What sensation do you feel with your right finger?

_____

Explain your sensations.

_____

_____

When you are finished with this lab, return all materials and store your microscope properly.

EXPLORING FURTHER

See also Topic 25

Grollman, S. *A Laboratory Manual of Mammalian Anatomy and Physiology*. 4th ed. New York: Macmillan, 1978.

Jones, D. G. *Neurons and Synapses*. Baltimore: E. Arnold, 1981.

Katz, B. *Nerve, Muscle and Synapse*. New York: McGraw-Hill, 1966.

Shepherd, Gordon M. *Neurobiology*. Oxford: Oxford University Press, 1983.

Journal Articles

Scientific American: The September 1979 issue is devoted to the brain.

Arnold, A. P. "Sexual differences in the brain." *American Scientist 68:* 165, 1980.

Axelrod, J. "Neurotransmitters." *Scientific American*, June 1974 (#1297).

Bloom, Floyd E. "Neuropeptides." *Scientific American*, 148, October 1981.

Constantine-Paton, Martha, and Margaret I. Law. "The development of maps and stripes in the brain." *Scientific American*, 62, December 1982.

DiCara, L. Y. "Learning in the autonomic nervous system." *Scientific American*, January 1970 (#525).

Dunant, Yves, and Maurice Israël. "The release of acetylcholine." *Scientific American*, 58, April 1985.

Favreau, Olga Eizner, and Michael C. Corballis. "Negative aftereffects in visual perception." *Scientific American*, December 1976 (#574).

Hodgson, E. S. "Taste receptors." *Scientific American*, May 1961 (no offprint).

Hoffman, Donald D. "The interpretation of visual illusions." *Scientific American*, 154, December 1983.

Hudspeth, A. J. "The hair cells of the inner ear." *Scientific American*, 54, January 1983.

Jacobs, B. L., and M. E. Trulson. "Mechanisms of action of LSD." *American Scientist 67:* 396, 1979.

Jones, M. D. Jr., *et al.* "Oxygen delivery to the brain before and after birth." *Science 216:* 324, 16 April 1982.

Jouvet, Michel. "The states of sleep." *Scientific American*, February 1967 (#504).

Land, Edwin H. "The retinex theory of color vision." *Scientific American*, December 1977 (#392).

Lassen, Niels A., David H. Invar, and Erik Skinhoj. "Brain function and blood flow." *Scientific American*, October 1978 (#1410).

Llinas, Rodolfo R. "Calcium in synaptic transmission." *Scientific American*, 56, October 1982.

Morell, Pierre, and William T. Norton. "Myelin." *Scientific American*, May 1980 (#1469).

Nathason, J. A., and P. Greengard. "Second messengers in the brain." *Scientific American*, August 1977 (#1368).

Oscar-Berman, M. "The neuropsychological consequences of long-term chronic alcoholism." *American Scientist 68:* 410, 1980.

Owens, D. Alfred. "The resting state of the eyes." *American Scientist 72 (4):* 378, July 1984.

Parker, Donald E. "The vestibular apparatus." *Scientific American*, 118, November 1980.

Poggio, Tomaso, "Vision by man and machine." *Scientific American*, 106, April 1984.

Pribram, K. H. "The neurophysiology of remembering." *Scientific American*, January 1969 (#520).

Rushton, W. A. H. "Visual pigments and color blindness." *Scientific American*, March 1975 (#1317).

Schwartz, J. H. "The transport of substances in nerve cells." *Scientific American*, 152, April 1980.

Snyder, S. H. "Opiate receptors and internal opiates." *Scientific American*, March 1977 (#1354).

Tosteson, Daniel C. "Lithium and mania." *Scientific American*, 164, April 1981.

Winter, Peter M., and John N. Miller. "Anesthesiology." *Scientific American*, 124, April 1985.

Wurtman, Richard J. "Nutrients that modify brain function." *Scientific American*, 50, April 1982.

Wu, Chau H. "Electric fish and the discovery of animal electricity." *American Scientist 72 (6):* 598, November 1984.

Student Name _____ **Date** _____

TABLE 30-1. DATA ON TASTE CHEMORECEPTION

Record (+) if the identification is correct, (−) if the identification is incorrect, and (0) if no identification can be made. Space has been provided in each test for up to six sets of observations.

Test		1	2	3	4	5	6
A. No sucking	Apple						
	Potato						
B. Sucking	Apple						
	Potato						
C. No saliva	Apple						
	Potato						
D. Chewing	Apple						
	Potato						
E. Breathing and chewing	Apple						
	Potato						

TABLE 30-2. MAPPING DATA FOR TASTE CHEMORECEPTORS

Rate each drop of solution as either no taste (0), mild taste (+), or strong taste (+ +). Map the results in Figure 30-8.

RECEPTOR	SOLUTION	POSITION ON TONGUE BEING TESTED						
		Front			Side		Back	
		1	2	3	4	5	6	7
Sweet	5.0% sucrose							
Salty	10% NaCl							
Bitter	0.1% quinine sulfate							
Sour	1.0% acetic acid							

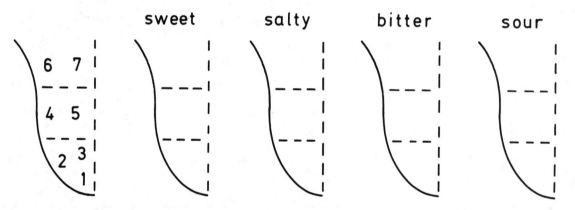

Figure 30-8. Results of taste test. Mark the positive responses for each type of taste receptor where they occurred on the tongue.

Student Name _____ **Date** _____

TABLE 30-3. DATA FOR PROPRIOCEPTION OF STATIC AND DYNAMIC EQUILIBRIUM

Test	Observations
A. Feet together	
B. One leg, eyes closed One leg, eyes open	
C. Touch fingers	Fingers were _____ cm apart
D. Touch fingers	Fingers were _____ cm apart

TABLE 30-4.   DATA ON THERMORECEPTION IN THE SKIN

Warmth Receptors ———————————————————————————————————

concentration: ————/cm²

} .5 cm

Cold Receptors ———————————————————————————————————

concentration: ————/cm²

} .5 cm

Development in Animals

OBJECTIVES

When you have completed this topic, you should be able to:
1. Describe the changes that take place in an invertebrate egg during fertilization and that distinguish an unfertilized egg from a fertilized one.
2. List the four main stages of embryonic development following fertilization.
3. Describe two important ways in which cleavage in a sea urchin embryo (deuterostome) is like that in a human embryo.
4. Correctly explain and use the following words: archenteron (primitive gut), blastocoel, blastopore, blastula, cleavage, gastrula, gastrulation, neurula, neurulation, zygote.
5. Draw a diagram of an embryo containing the three primary germ layers; label the germ layers, blastocoel, blastopore, and gastrocoel (archenteron), and label the embryo with its correct embryological stage.
6. Define embryonic induction and give an example.
7. List or recognize the body parts formed from each primary embryonic germ layer.
8. Define metamorphosis and explain the selective advantage to animals of going through metamorphosis at some stage of the life history.
9. Given a developing chicken egg, open it properly, and decide whether it is 24, 48, or 72 hr old by identifying the features or structures characteristic of that age.

KEY TOPICS

Amniote egg, echinoderms, fertilization, embryonic development, metamorphosis.

INTRODUCTION

You have already studied **meiosis,** the process in which a diploid organism prepares for reproduction by packaging its genetic material into haploid gametes, each of which contains a complete genome, but only part of the parents' genetic material. The reproductive cycle is continued by the process of **fertilization,** in which haploid gametes join to make a diploid **zygote,** thereby restoring the original number of chromosomes. The reproductive cycle is completed when the zygote undergoes **development** into the many-celled adult organism, which becomes sexually mature, undergoes meiosis, and then reproduces in its turn. Today's lab will focus on embryonic development, which begins with fertilization of the egg and ends in the production of a young organism similar in form to the adult. Many developing organisms, including invertebrates such as the sea urchin, insects, and

some amphibians, pass through a developmental stage called the larva, which is different from the adult, but usually exists independently of the parents.

STRUCTURE AND FUNCTION IN THE SEA URCHIN

If live sea urchins are available, your instructor may ask you to complete this section on the sea urchin as a representative echinoderm. Although echinoderm adults are not at all like humans, early development in these organisms is similar to that in humans in several important ways.

■ Observe the sea urchins in the aquarium or supply dish. The spines that cover the top (aboral) surface of the body are mobile, and can pivot on little bumps at the base of each spine.

If the urchin is healthy, the spines will stick straight out.

Can you tell which sea urchins are male and which are female? _____

If the urchins are crawling on the surface of the aquarium, you will be able to see the **tube feet** sticking to the glass and the **mouth,** which is located on the flat underside. (See Figure 31-1.)

■ Use large forceps or wear rubber gloves when you are ready to take one of the animals.

DO NOT TOUCH SEA URCHINS WITH BARE HANDS.

■ Place the urchin in a beaker of sea water or on a Petri dish of sea water with the flat (oral) side down.
■ Observe the animal for a few minutes, and notice the tiny, clear tube feet that extend from between the spines and stick to the surface of the glass.

About how many tube feet does your sea urchin seem to have? _____

■ Place a piece of lettuce or a small object on the surface of the urchin, and wait 5 or 10 min. Then gently try to remove the object.

Does the sea urchin attach its tube feet to the object?

_____

Study Figure 31-1, and note how the **water-vascular system** of radial canals and ampullae connects to all of the tube feet. This is a hydraulic system that allows the feet to be extended by increasing the pressure within the ampulla at the base of each foot. When the foot contacts something, suction can be exerted so that the foot sticks to the object like a tiny suction cup. Each foot can be operated individually. Water circulates into and out of the water-vascular system through a porous plate called the **madreporite,** which is located on the aboral surface. Also located on the aboral surface is the **anus** and the five genital pores through which gametes are released from the gonads into the sea.

The shape of the sea urchin is due to a hard endoskeleton called the **test.** Both the test and the spines are covered by a delicate epidermis. Study the sea urchin test on demonstration, using the dissecting microscope when appropriate.

■ Locate the five **gonopores** on the aboral surface.
■ Notice the tubercles where the spines were once attached.
■ Find the numerous double perforations where the tube feet extended through the test. These occur in five regions that are separated from each other by five sectors in which there were no feet and thus no perforations.

By now you should be able to describe the type of symmetry that the sea urchin shows (twofold/threefold/fourfold/fivefold/sixfold) (bilateral/radial):

_____

■ On the oral surface notice the large opening in the test. This is where the feeding apparatus, called **Aristotle's lantern,** originally protruded through the test, but the membranes holding it together and in position disintegrated when the test was prepared. You can see this structure in your living animal.
■ Again using forceps or gloves, invert the animal so that the flat side is on top. The animal is now upside down from its normal position.
■ Note the feeding structure, Aristotle's lantern, in the center of the oral surface. It contains five teeth that are used to tear the kelp on which the animal feeds, and it is held in place by a membrane that attaches it to the skeleton.

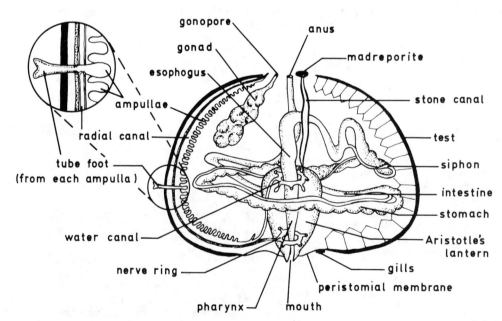

Figure 31-1. **A sea urchin.** Aristotle's lantern is the feeding apparatus used for ingesting kelp and seaweed. The gonads, test (skeleton), and water-vascular system show pentaradial or fivefold symmetry, although diagrammed only once. The many movable spines that cover the surface of the sea urchin are not shown.

The mouth is the opening in the center of the lantern.

■ Take a single tooth from those on demonstration, and study its structure in the dissecting microscope.
■ When you are finished observing the structure of the oral surface, leave your animal upside down for awhile, and observe its response from time to time.

How did your sea urchin react to an upside down situation?

_____

What structures were used in the response?

_____

When you are finished with your sea urchin, return it to the aquarium or supply pan.

SEA URCHIN DEVELOPMENT

During cleavage a single cell becomes many genetically identical cells by the process of repeated mitosis. During this time the embryo shows **growth** in complexity but not in size. Cleavage sets the stage for **morphogenesis,** in which movement of cells occurs to give the organs and organ systems of the embryo their structural form. Meanwhile, cellular differentiation, the specialization of cells for different functions, begins in cleavage and continues throughout development.

Echinoderms and vertebrates are both **deuterostomes** because their pattern of early embryological development shares important features: Cleavage is indeterminate and radial and the primitive mouth develops second, after the anus. Thus the sea urchin is an appropriate choice in which to study early development.

Mature sea urchins are male or female. When the gametes are ripe, they are released through pores on the top (aboral) side of the animal, and fertilization takes place in the sea water.

Is this type of fertilization internal or external?

_____

In the laboratory, the urchins can be induced to release their gametes separately so that fertilization can be carried out and observed under the microscope. If the fertilized eggs are carefully washed and incubated in sea water, they will develop for many days, and will eventually form a larval stage known as the **pluteus.** The pluteus is a free-swimming, feeding organism that eventually attaches to the bottom, and metamorphoses into a tiny sea urchin. Depending on the time of the year, you will use an East Coast sea urchin (*Arbacia*) or a West Coast urchin (*Strongylocentrotus*) to study early development. The schedule for the development of these species is shown in Table 31-1.

Cleavage

Sea urchin eggs are very large cells, so you will have to use a depression slide, or omit the coverslip while you are observing them.

■ Place a drop of stirred sea urchin egg suspension on your slide, and observe it under low power.

What is the diameter of the eggs in μm?

_____

What is the color and texture of the cytoplasm?

_____

What does the cell membrane look like?

_____

■ If you are studying *Arbacia* eggs, add a drop of India ink so that you can see the clear jelly coat surrounding the egg.

About how thick is the jelly coat in μm?

_____

■ Clean the slide and dry it before adding a fresh drop of eggs. Focus on the eggs under low power.

TABLE 31-1. DEVELOPMENT OF SEA URCHIN EMBRYOS

Developmental Stage	*Arbacia punctulata* at 23°C	*Strongylocentrotus purpuratus* at 15°C
Fertilization	0	0
Fertilization membrane forms	1–2 min	1–2 min
First cleavage	50–70 min	90–110 min
Second cleavage	80–110 min	140–170 min
Blastula	5–6 hr	8–10 hr
Hatching of blastula	7–8 hr	18–20 hr
Gastrula	12–15 hr	22–26 hr
Pluteus	24 hr	72 hr
Metamorphosis	2 weeks	2–8 weeks

■ Add a drop of *diluted* sperm cells provided by your instructor. Mix gently with a toothpick while observing in the microscope, and record the time and temperature in Table 31-2 at the end of this topic.

When the sperm cells penetrate the jelly coat, they eventually come into contact with the membrane of the cell. Then one lucky sperm will enter the cytoplasm, leaving its tail behind, and its nucleus will combine with the egg's nucleus to form the new diploid nucleus of the zygote.

You can barely see the individual sperm cells under low power, but you can see right away that something is happening.

What change occurs within 1 or 2 min of adding sperm cells to the eggs?

_____

When the egg cell is stimulated by the arrival of the sperm, a chain of events begins to unfold that is very precise and almost inevitably ends in the production of a normal sea urchin larva. First an electrical reaction begins at the site where the sperm penetrates, and spreads all over the surface of the cell. Then Ca^{++} ions released from this region of the membrane induce changes in the egg cytoplasm, signaling that development should begin. The **vitelline membrane,** which lies between the cell membrane and the jelly coat, separates from the cell membrane and enlarges so that there is a wide space between two membranes. It is now called the **fertilization membrane.** The cell "membrane" now looks double; this is the obvious change that you see whenever fertilization occurs. Any sperm still struggling through the jelly coat are lifted away from their goal and the fertilization membrane provides a protected environment for the developing embryo.

■ Seal your slide of fertilized eggs by applying Vaseline with a toothpick around the coverslip, and set it aside, but observe it every 15 min for the rest of the period. You should see signs of cleavage in about 1 hr. Your instructor may ask you to sample a culture of developing eggs instead of saving the fertilized egg on your slide. Record the age, stage, and appearance of the embryos in Table 31-2 each time you observe them.
■ Take an ordinary slide, and prepare a wet mount of sperm cells from the suspension indicated by your instructor. Observe under high power or oil immersion. Cut down the light by closing the diaphragm.

Are the sperm cells in motion? _____

Can you see the flagella of the sperm cells?

_____

In addition to the nucleus and the flagellum, what organelle is important for sperm cells to carry out their reproductive role? (*Hint:* This organelle provides energy needed in large amounts for sperm motility.)

_____

Once the first division has taken place, cleavage will continue for many cell divisions. In sea urchins cleavage is **indeterminate:** each of the cells formed early in development has the potential to develop into a complete organism. If the daughter cells should happen to separate after the first division, the result would be two identical organisms. (See Figure 44-17 in your text.) When this happens in human development, the result is identical twins. Cleavage is **radial** because each cleavage plane is at right angles to or parallel to the original axis of the zygote. (See Focus on Early Development of *Amphioxus*, p. 959 in your text.) In the sea urchin the yolk is in the form of cytoplasmic granules, so the cleavage furrow can pass completely through the egg, from the animal pole (top) to the vegetal pole (bottom), without difficulty. Study the later stages in cleavage that are available.

How large is the embryo compared to the egg after several divisions?

_____

The **morula** is a solid ball of cells that gradually develops a hollow interior called the **blastocoel.** The embryo is then at the **blastula** stage, and the outer cells are ciliated so that the blastula is motile, and can move about within the fertilization membrane. The human equivalent of the blastula is not motile and is called the blastocyst. It moves along the oviduct by the action of the mother's cilia and implants in the wall of the uterus. After several hours of cleavage, the blastula is fully developed, and "hatches" as the fertilization membrane finally breaks open and releases the embryo. No growth or increase in the amount of cytoplasm has occurred during cleavage. The blastula now enters the next stage of embryonic development.

Gastrulation

During gastrulation the embryo changes from a blastula with one layer of cells into a **gastrula,** which has three layers. In this process cells migrate into the interior of the blastula at a point called the **blastopore,** and form a lining so that the embryo now has two layers: an outer ectoderm and an inner endoderm. The ectodermal cells will form the skin and its derivatives, and give rise to the whole nervous system. The endoderm develops ino the lining of the gut and of certain digestive organs. The space inside both layers is called the **gastrocoel,** or **archenteron,** and will eventually form the lumen of the organism's gut. In deuterostomes, the first opening into the archenteron (blastopore) becomes the anus, and the mouth develops later at the other end of the gut. The cells in the dorsal part of the endoderm form pouches, and bud off to become the cells of the mesoderm. Mesoderm gives rise to the muscle, bone, and some internal organs of the adult. In humans, mesoderm forms in the same way (i.e. by **enterocoely,** another characteristic of deuterostomes, which is explained in text Chapter 24.) The fate of the three germ layers in vertebrates is described in Table 44-1 in your text.

■ Examine a drop of the embryos that have reached the gastrula stage.
■ Record the age of the embryos and their appearance in the table.

Can you see the primitive gut? _____

Neurulation

In vertebrates such as yourself and the chick, the gastrula soon develops a dorsal groove, which pinches off and becomes part of the dorsal nerve cord and the brain. An embryo undergoing this process is at the neurula stage.

Organogenesis

The process of organogenesis in which organs and organ systems are developed will be discussed in the section on the chick embryo where it can be studied more easily.

If older sea urchin embryos are available, you will be able to see a simple digestive system and skeletal system in this case as well.

Metamorphosis

The sea urchin embryo develops skeletal elements, and begins feeding as the **pluteus larva.** (See Figure 31-2.) It continues this existence for up to four months until it finally settles down on the substrate, attaches, and changes into a tiny adult sea urchin. The whole process of **metamorphosis** may take only an hour, and the result is a miniature adult only 1 mm in diameter.

■ Observe the embryos that have reached the pluteus stage.
■ Draw an arrow in Figure 31-2 to indicate the direction in which the pluteus swims.
■ Note the skeletal spines that support the body and arms.
■ Note whether colored pigment granules are present.
■ Identify the complete digestive tract visible through the transparent body of the pluteus.

What is the advantage of a motile larval stage in this species?

_____

_____

CHICK DEVELOPMENT

Fertilization and Early Development

The ovum (egg cell) of a chicken consists of a yellow mass of **yolk** and a small area of yolk-free cytoplasm, the **blastodermic disc,** that will develop into the embryo proper. **Cleavage** and development occur only within the disc, and the yolk supplies required nutrients and energy to support the embryo.

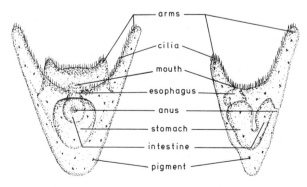

labels: arms, cilia, mouth, esophagus, anus, stomach, intestine, pigment

Figure 31-2. Pluteus larva. The sea urchin larva develops from the zygote within a few days. The motile larva feeds and swims about independently until it settles down and metamorphoses into a tiny adult.

As the egg cell passes through the reproductive tract of the female chicken, it is modified in several ways. A solution of the protein albumin is added to make up the white of the egg. This layer provides physical protection for the delicate embryo, and antimicrobial substances in it protect the embryo from bacterial infection. The albumin itself will provide the chick with a store of amino acids to draw on for protein synthesis, and the liquid is the chick's only source of water. Later on, two membranes and then a porous shell are added. The hard shell protects the embryo and its food supply but also allows gas exchange with the environment.

The egg of a bird is an **amniote** egg. Unlike a fish or amphibian egg, it is fully adapted to terrestrial reproduction. Reptiles and mammals also produce amniote eggs in which the embryo is protected in a miniature watery environment within the amnion membrane.

■ Examine an unfertilized egg on demonstration. Identify the blastodermic disc, which is normally on the upper surface of the yolk.

Is fertilization in the chicken internal or external?

_____

If the egg cell has been fertilized, it will begin cleavage and start to develop right in the hen's oviduct. Since eggs are held there for various lengths of time before being laid, the exact stage of development at the time of laying is different for each individual egg, but usually cleavage, blastula formation, and gastrulation have already been accomplished. Early cleavage in a bird egg is shown on page 961 in your text.

How would an unfertilized egg differ from one that has been fertilized?

_____

Is there any nutritional advantage in eating fertilized eggs?

_____

_____

Cleavage is incomplete in the chick because the yolk is so massive. Early in development, the cells of the **blastodermic disc** split into two layers: The upper layer is the **ectoderm** (epiblast) and the lower layer is the **endoderm** (hypoblast). A thickening, called the **primitive streak,** then develops in the center of the blastoderm. Here cells migrate into the space between ectoderm and endoderm, and form the embryo's **mesoderm.** Mesodermal tissue near the center of the embryo pinches off to form the **notochord** and the pairs of **somites** that lie in rows along each side of the notochord. The notochord induces the ectoderm above it to form a **neural plate.** The plate develops folds, which eventually meet and fuse to form the **neural tube.** The neural tube in turn differentiates into the brain and the spinal cord. Finally the embryo lifts, and the ectoderm folds beneath it so that the embryo is completely covered by ectoderm and the primitive gut is enclosed by the endoderm. These changes are shown in Figure 31-3. When you have time, mark the ectoderm, mesoderm, and endoderm with different colored pencils (blue, red, and yellow, respectively) so that you can follow the developmental process more clearly.

Meanwhile, specialized cells in the area of the blastoderm surrounding the embryo form **blood islands,**

primitive streak
ectoderm
mesoderm
endoderm

neural fold
neural groove
ectoderm
somite
notochord
endoderm

ectoderm
neural tube
somite
notochord
endoderm

ectoderm
neural tube
somite
notochord
lumen of gut
yolk stalk
yolk sac

Figure 31-3. Chick embryo in cross section.
The notochord of the gastrula induces part of the ectoderm to invaginate and form the neural tube. The brain and nervous system will eventually differentiate from the neural tube. You can color-code structures derived from the primary germ layers: ectoderm = blue, mesoderm = red, and endoderm = yellow.

which give rise to extraembryonic blood vessels and blood cells. The embryo develops a primitive heart, and blood soon begins to circulate between the embryo and the surface of the yolk, where capillaries allow gas exchange and absorption of nutrients.

Other cells in the blastoderm grow into protective **extraembryonic membranes.** Although these membranes are not part of the embryo proper, they are vital for its nourishment and development.

1. The **amnion** develops as the inner layer of a fold of tissue growing down over the embryo's head. It meets with another fold growing up over the tail, and fuses with it so that the embryo is completely enclosed in an **amniotic sac,** which is filled with amniotic fluid. The fluid acts as a protective cushion. The growing amnion is visible as a fold of tissue in the 48-hr chick.
2. The **yolk sac** grows out from the primitive gut, and eventually surrounds the whole yolk with a double membrane. Blood vessels in its walls are important for the nutrition of the growing embryo. The blood vessels you will see in the 48- and 72-hr chicks develop in the yolk sac and are important in respiration as well as nutrition at this time.
3. The **chorion** is the outer layer of the fold of tissue that forms the amnion and can be seen at 48 hr. It

will eventually surround the amnion, embryo, and yolk; it protects the embryo and holds it in contact with the yolk. Later it fuses with the allantois to form the **chorioallantoic membrane,** the respiratory organ of the chick during later development. This membrane completely covers the embryo and yolk by day 12 of development.

4. Finally, the **allantois** grows out as a saclike extension of the primitive gut, expands up over the embryo, and eventually surrounds the embryo and yolk with a double membrane: The outer layer of the allantois presses up against the chorion, and the inner layer against the amnion and yolk sac. Because the allantois is richly supplied with blood vessels, it allows gas exchange with the external environment. The wastes that accumulate during development, mostly in the form of uric acid, are stored in the interior of the allantois until the chick hatches. The allantois can be seen as a small sac in the 72- and 96-hr chick embryo.

Living Chick Embryos

Each pair of students will be provided with a chick embryo that has been incubated for 33, 48, or 72 hr. You are responsible for understanding all of these stages, so study the prepared slides or another student's embryo to see all the structures.

Follow steps 1, 2 and 3 in Figure 31-4 to open your incubated egg:

■ Add a little warmed saline (0.9% NaCl) to a finger bowl so that the bottom is just barely covered. (Saline may be omitted if you work quickly.)
■ Take an egg from the incubator or tray, hold it in exactly the same orientation, and carry it carefully to your desk.
■ Turn the egg sideways and wait 1 min for the yolk to adjust.
■ Tap the egg on the edge of the dish until the shell cracks.
■ Holding the egg in the saline, pry the shell apart at its bottom without disturbing the upper surface of the yolk.

If your embryo is 72 hr old, you should see the embryo and its beating heart immediately. If you do not see your embryo, ask your instructor for help. Either the egg failed to develop, or the yolk is turned upside down so that the embryo is hidden.

After you have observed as much structure as you can in the dissecting microscope, remove the embryo from the yolk, and transfer it to a watch glass so that you can see it more clearly. This process (shown in 4-9 of Figure 31-4) is not difficult if you work carefully, but the top of the yolk *must not be covered by saline.**

■ Fold a piece of filter paper in half, and cut out a spoon with a hole just larger than the embryo.
■ Add a teaspoonful of warm saline to a watch glass.
■ Lay the filter paper spoon on the yolk so that the embryo shows through the hole.
■ Press down gently on the paper with your probe, if necessary, so that it is wet all around and sticks to the membranes.
■ Cut the membrane in a circle around the outside of the filter paper to free the embryo.

*Suggested by Professor A. W. Blackler, Cornell University.

Figure 31-4. Handling live chick embryos. The delicate embryo must be kept warm and moist. The egg is opened in physiological saline and the embryo is transferred with a paper spoon.

■ Lift the spoon slowly so that the embryo lifts from the surface of the yolk.
■ Lay the spoon in the watch glass, and observe in the dissecting microscope.
■ A drop of vital stain such as 1% neutral red may be added to bring out more of the embryo's structure.

33-Hour Chick (Figure 31-5)

IMPORTANT FEATURES: 12 somites, heart, vitelline veins, notochord, neural tube, optic vesicles, blood islands.

This embryo is a streak in the center of the blastodermic disc, and you will have to transfer it to a watch glass to see much.

■ The brain has begun to differentiate, and the **optic vesicles** are developing.

■ The **vitelline veins** have joined to form the primitive **heart** and there are about 12 somites along the sides of the **notochord.** The heart might be feebly contracting, but there is no blood flow yet.
■ If you are looking at a stained slide, notice the **blood islands** in the blastodermic disc outside of the embryo itself. They will give rise to the blood cells and some of the vessels. Because the tail region develops more slowly than the head region, it may still show the primitive streak that was the very first sign of development.
■ The **amnion** and **chorion** are beginning to develop as a fold of tissue growing down over the head region. It will eventually contact the posterior fold to enclose the embryo.
■ Finally, you may be able to see the foregut, which is growing toward the head region from underneath the embryo as an outpocketing of the endoderm. It will later extend toward the tail region as well.
■ Examine the demonstration of a vertebra to be sure

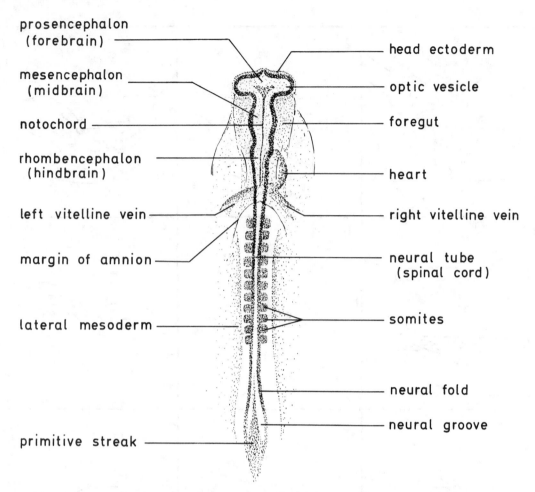

Figure 31-5. Whole mount of a 33-hour chick embryo. The anterior end of the neural tube has begun to differentiate while the posterior end has not yet formed from the neural groove.

that you understand the relationship of the notochord and the spinal cord. The notochord gives rise to intervertebral discs, and the spinal cord of the neural tube runs through the opening in the vertebra.

What structures arise from the somites?

_____

_____

■ Quiz your partner on the structures in Figure 31-5.

48-Hour Chick (Figure 31-6)

IMPORTANT FEATURES: 28 somites, eye with lens, distinct telencephalon and diencephalon, aortic arches, vitelline arteries, amnion and chorion.

This embryo has started to twist to the right so that the head region is now lying on the chick's left side. This is the process of **torsion,** which will continue until the whole embryo is lying on its left side. At the same time, the embryo is curling up in the process of **flexure** so that the neural tube takes the shape of a question mark, with a bend in the region of the hindbrain. The forebrain has formed the **telencephalon** and **diencephalon.**

How many somites are still showing their dorsal sides?

Blood circulation usually begins at about the 16-somite stage.

■ If you are viewing a living embryo, look for contractions of the heart and circulating blood.
■ Trace the flow of blood from the **ventricle** of the heart through the **aorta,** and then through the **aortic arches** in the region of the pharynx.
■ Identify the parts of the brain: The optic cup has induced the formation of the **lens** of the eye by the ectoderm, and the neural tube has induced the formation of the **otocyst,** or primitive ear. In each case a chemical signal called an **organizer** caused the overlying ectoderm to differentiate into an appropriate structure.
■ Note the **vitelline arteries** growing out over the yolk. They join the vitelline veins in capillary beds on the yolk surface.
■ The margin of the **amnion** and **chorion** can be seen above the vitelline arteries.
■ Quiz your partner on the structures in Figure 31-6.

72-Hour Chick (Figure 31-7)

IMPORTANT FEATURES: 36 somites, extraembryonic circulation in yolk sac, mesencephalon, cerebellum, otocyst, pharyngeal clefts, limb and tail buds.

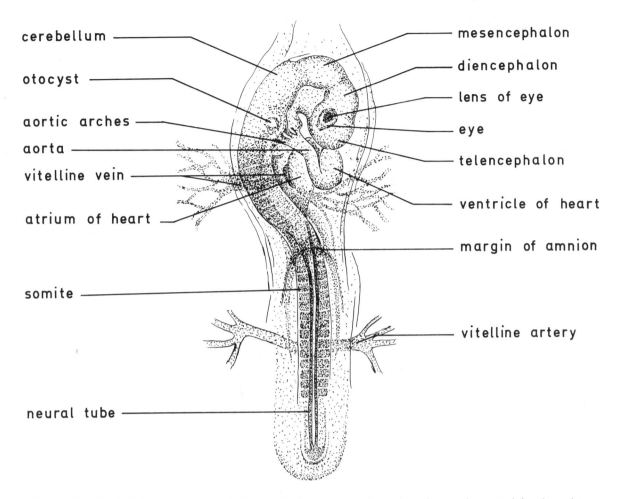

cerebellum

otocyst

aortic arches

aorta

vitelline vein

atrium of heart

somite

neural tube

mesencephalon

diencephalon

lens of eye

eye

telencephalon

ventricle of heart

margin of amnion

vitelline artery

Figure 31-6. Whole mount of a 48-hour chick embryo. The embryo lies partly on its left side and is supported and nourished by an extensive extraembryonic circulation in the yolk sac. The amnion and chorion partly cover the embryo.

The chick is now almost completely on its left side (torsion). Flexure of the brain is prominent, and it is differentiated into distinct regions.

■ Note the optic cup, the lens, and the **octocyst,** or primitive ear. The **atrium** and **ventricle** of the heart are greatly enlarged, and are actively pumping blood through the vitelline and embryonic arteries.
■ There are several **pharyngeal clefts** and **pouches.** These structures appear at some stage in all vertebrate embryos. They are a carryover from the gills of a fishlike ancestor. In terrestrial vertebrates they will give rise to structures such as the middle ear and Eustachian tubes. There are too many somites to count easily (about 36).

What membranes completely enclose the embryo itself?

■ Below the heart you can see the **anterior limb buds,** which will develop into wings, and near the embryo's tail you see the **posterior limb buds,** which will form the legs.
■ You may be able to see the small saclike **allantois** in the region of the posterior limb buds, but it is probably hidden by the tail, and is better seen in later embryos.
■ If you can successfully transfer your embryo to a watch glass, observe circulation in the blood vessels un-

der low power with your compound microscope.
■ Quiz your partner on the structures in Figure 31-7.

96-Hour Chick

IMPORTANT FEATURES: 41 somites, allantois, limb and tail buds.

This embryo has developed about 41 somites, and the yolk is partly covered with prominent blood vessels.

■ The flexure of the body posterior to the brain is now obvious. The eye is easier to see because it is pigmented, but the ear is less distinct because the tissues have become much thicker.
■ Remove the membranes surrounding the embryo so that you can see the heart and limb buds. You can use a probe or teasing needle to straighten out the embryo so that you see the pharyngeal clefts and pouches.
■ The fluid-filled sac at the posterior end is the **allantois.** It will expand and eventually fuse with the chorion, and become the highly vascularized chorioallantoic membrane. This membrane remains close to the porous shell of the egg.

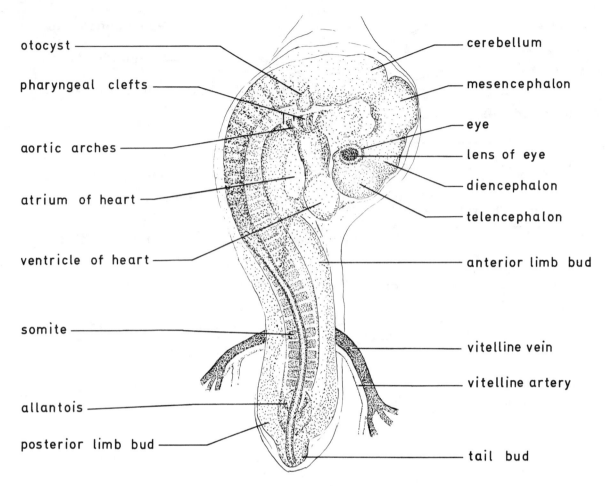

otocyst

pharyngeal clefts

aortic arches

atrium of heart

ventricle of heart

somite

allantois

posterior limb bud

cerebellum

mesencephalon

eye

lens of eye

diencephalon

telencephalon

anterior limb bud

vitelline vein

vitelline artery

tail bud

Figure 31-7. Whole mount of a 72-hour chick embryo. The embryo lies mostly on its left side and the allantois and limb buds are beginning to form.

What are the two functions of the allantois?

_____

_____

When the chick hatches, the chorioallantois will remain behind as a waste-filled membrane stuck to the shell, but its base within the embryo gives rise to the urinary bladder.

Later Development

Your instructor may demonstrate some older living embryos that are even further along in development. All of the major developmental processes happen during the first 6 days of development. The embryo then grows and matures during the rest of the incubation period until it hatches at 21 days, and starts its independent existence as a wobbly, fluffy chick.

■ When you are finished with your work, discard your debris in the EGG WASTES container, clean your dissecting instruments, return the prepared slides, and store your microscopes properly.

EXPLORING FURTHER

Browder, L. W. *Developmental Biology.* 2nd ed. Philadelphia: W. B Saunders, 1984.

Harvey, E. B. *The American Arbacia and Other Sea Urchins.* Princeton, N. J.: Princeton University Press, 1956.

Karp, G., and Berrill, N. J. *Development,* 2nd ed. New York: McGraw-Hill, 1981.

Patten, B. M. *Early Embryology of the Chick.* 5th ed. New York: McGraw-Hill, 1971.

Romanoff, A. J. *The Avian Embryo.* New York: Macmillan, 1960.

Saunders, J. W. *Developmental Biology: Patterns, Problems and Principles.* New York: Macmillan, 1982.

Journal Articles

Bryant, P. J., S. V. Bryant, and V. French. "Biological regeneration and pattern formation." *Scientific American,* July 1977 (#1363).

Davidson, E. H., B. R. Hough-Evans, and R. J. Britten. "Molecular biology of the sea urchin embryo." *Science 217:* 17, 2 July 1982.

De Robertis, E. M., and J. B. Gurdon. "Gene transplantation and the analysis of development." *Scientific American,* December 1979 (#1454).

Epel, David. "The program of fertilization." *Scientific American*, November 1977 (#1372).

Garcia-Bellido, Antonio, Peter A. Lawrence, and Gines Morata. "Compartments in animal development." *Scientific American*, July 1979 (#1432).

Gordon, R., and A. G. Jacobson. "The shaping of tissues in embryos." *Scientific American*, June 1978 (#1391).

Lane, Charles. "Rabbit hemoglobin from frog eggs." *Scientific American*, August 1976 (#1343).

Levi-Montalcini, Rita, and Pietro Calissano. "The nerve-growth factor." *Scientific American*, June 1979 (#1430).

Marx, J. "Electric currents may guide development." *Science 211:* 1147, 13 March 1981.

Peakall, David B. "Pesticides and the reproduction of birds." *Scientific American*, April 1970 (#1174).

Rahn, Hermann, Amos Ar, and Charles V. Paganelli. "How bird eggs breathe." *Scientific American*, February 1979 (#1420).

Shurkin, J. "Operating on the unborn." *Science 83*, 70, May 1983.

Stent, Gunther S., and David A. Weisblat. "The development of a simple nervous system." *Scientific American*, 118, January 1982.

Wolpert, L. "Pattern formation in biological development." *Scientific American*, October 1978 (#1409).

Student Name _____ **Date** _____

TABLE 31-2.   OBSERVATIONS ON SEA URCHIN DEVELOPMENT AT _____ °C

Genus _____

Species _____

Time	Time after Fertilization	Stage	Appearance
	0 min		
	min		
	min		
	min		
	min		
	min		
	min		
	min		
	min		
	min		
	hr		
	hr		
	hr		
	hr		
	hr		
	hr		

Behavior

OBJECTIVES _____

When you have completed this topic, you should be able to:
1. Define orientation, kinesis, sign stimulus, fixed action pattern, ritual, communication.
2. Define taxis and state the three major types of stimuli that result in the response of taxis.
3. Describe an experiment to test for the effectiveness of chemical stimuli in chemotaxis.
4. List the factors involved in fish schooling and describe an experiment to test for each factor.
5. Explain the basis for the stimulus used in the optomotor response experiment.
6. Define agonistic behavior and explain why it is important to survival.
7. Describe the fight and flight components of agonistic displays in the Siamese fighting fish.

KEY TOPICS _____

Scientific method, hypothesis, instinct, learning, territoriality, agonistic displays, courtship rituals, communication.

INTRODUCTION

Behavior is the response of an organism to any internal or external stimulus. In the broadest sense it includes just about anything that the animal or plant does. It is convenient to describe behavior as **innate** when it seems to be an automatic and consistent response to a certain stimulus and **learned** when the response tends to change with experience, so that it becomes more and more appropriate or elaborate when the stimulus has been given many times. Both types of behavior are important in animals with at least moderately complex nervous systems, including humans. In this exercise, you will be studying mainly innate behavior.

Orientation is a type of behavior pattern in which an organism turns its body or moves either toward or away from a certain stimulus. This type of behavior is basic to the success of the animal. Whatever it does, whether it is seeking food, water, sunlight, a mate, interacting with other members of a group, or avoiding predators, there must be some sort of orientation.

Kinesis is a simple type of orientation behavior in which the organism changes its rate of locomotion, but not its direction, in response to the stimulus. If the response is positive and due to kinesis, the animal will slow down its locomotion in the presence of the stimulus and

speed up if the stimulus is absent. In a way, this is a primitive form of seeking behavior: if a necessary environmental condition or factor is missing, the animal moves about quickly, thereby increasing its chances of finding better conditions. If the conditions are favorable, it stays close to that spot by slowing down. For example, an organism that must have a warm environment would move *faster* under cool conditions, but then slow down when warmer conditions were attained by random locomotion.

If the individuals in a culture of *Paramecium* tend to accumulate near a bubble of CO_2 as a result of kinesis, does lower pH make them swim slower or faster?

_____

In organisms that can detect stimuli at a distance, the orientation behavior will be a form of **taxis,** in which there will be a sustained movement either toward or away from the stimulus. This kind of response may be shown for light, heat, cold, moisture, gravity, sound, or chemicals. The response will be termed **phototaxis** if the stimulus is light, **geotaxis** if the the stimulus is gravity, and **chemotaxis** if the response involves a chemical stimulus.

One way in which an organism can show taxis is to

315

try to balance the stimuli reaching a pair of sense organs, such as its photoreceptors or chemoreceptors. If a weaker stimulus reaches the right side, the animal turns to the left until the stimulus on its right increases to the level of the left side (or vice versa). Even if the receptors are very crude, this strategy (called tropotaxis) will allow movement toward or away from the stimulus. If one of the paired receptors is destroyed, the animal will receive no stimulus from the damaged receptor and will continuously move in futile circles *away* from that side. It is trying to increase the stimulus to the damaged side. These futile circular movements are called "circus movements" and are diagnostic for organisms that use tropotaxis.

Many stimuli cause very predictable responses. These stimuli are called **sign stimuli,** or releasers, and the response is called a **fixed action pattern.** The advantage of a fixed action pattern is that an appropriate response can be made quickly and accurately the first time without the need for learning. The disadvantage is that it will occur even if the animal has been tricked by nature or a biologist into making the response under inappropriate conditions. For example, a robin, whose red breast is a sign stimulus warning other males away from its territory, will peck at red feathers that bear no resemblance to another bird. The bird has little control over its fixed action pattern, which is programmed into its nervous system.

In addition to responding to environmental conditions, animals must usually interact with other animals of the same or different species. Interactions between members of the same species, by mutually recognizable visual, auditory, or chemical cues, are called **communication.** Many of the signals used in communication are sign stimuli, which cause very predictable responses in the other individuals.

Sign stimuli are important in courtship, in mating, and in **agonistic,** or **conflict, displays** over territory, food, or mates. Displays are actions that are only indirectly involved in the activity being carried on. The stimuli are often built up into chain reactions called **rituals,** in which the response to a sign stimulus acts as a second sign stimulus, that response as a third stimulus, and so forth. Courtship rituals, for example, ensure coordination of physiological readiness to mate, mating within the same species, and sometimes care of the young.

Agonistic displays allow members of the same species to settle disputes over territory, food, or mates without direct conflict and usually without damage to either party in the dispute. The presence of a competitor will release responses that show the readiness of the opponent to fight. Signs of the intention to fight will cause the opponent either to show its own fight intention or to withdraw. Signs of timidity or **appeasement** will tend to reduce the aggressiveness of the opponent.

The agonistic display will be a mixture of "fight" and "flight" signals, and the proportion of each will be influenced by the **motivation** of the individual. Males will be more motivated to fight when they are in their own territory and when it is the breeding season. They will be less motivated to fight when the female approaches during the breeding season and will therefore be able to begin the courtship ritual. In many species courtship is a means of overcoming the agonistic behavior of the male to the extent that mating is possible.

In carrying out experiments on animal behavior, it is important to avoid **anthropomorphism,** or attributing human emotions and conscious feelings to animals. We cannot know whether an animal is "thinking" or "deciding" but we can obtain objective evidence about how it acts under various conditions. The most reliable evidence about animal behavior is obtained when the animal is observed under a **control situation** and again under an **experimental situation** which differs by a single factor. Quantitative results are obtained, if possible, and enough data is gathered to be statistically meaningful.

In the following experiments, you should clearly state the hypothesis being tested in each case and whether the results support or disprove that hypothesis. Your instructor may ask you to design and carry out experiments to test additional hypotheses.

Hypothesis: A trial, unproved idea put forward as an explanation of data that has been collected; an explanation of cause and effect or of a certain chain of events. It must make predictions that can be tested experimentally.

Example of a hypothesis: "An individual fish schools to make itself inconspicuous to predators."

This hypothesis is an explanation which could be tested by observing the attraction of a school versus the attraction of water plants or another form of refuge. If the fish had no strong preference for the school over the refuge, the hypothesis would be supported.

Example of a non-hypothesis: "An individual fish schools because it likes the company of other fish."

This explanation is anthropomorphic and cannot be tested.

Example of an non-hypothesis: "An individual fish will spend more time on the side of the tank with the school as opposed to the control side with an empty beaker."

This statement is a prediction that can be tested but it is not a hypothesis because it does not attempt to explain anything. The hypothesis being tested in this experiment is: "This species of fish shows schooling behavior." You can turn the hypothesis around and put in into the If . . . Then form, as follows:

IF: "If this species of fish shows schooling behavior...
THEN: "...then an individual fish will spend more time on the side of the tank with the school of fish as opposed to the side with an empty beaker control."

KINESIS IN SOW BUGS

In **kinesis,** the response to a stimulus is movement at a different rate with no directionality. If you correctly analyzed the previous question about *Paramecium*, you predicted that lower pH makes them swim more **slowly,** so that they congregate around a bubble of CO_2. How does that happen? Suppose that the pH is low (acidic) near the bubble due to carbonic acid and high away from the bubble, and the *Paramecium* are initially evenly distributed over both areas. The "basic" individuals will move faster and, on the average, tend to leave the basic area and enter the acidic area at a high rate. The "acidic" individuals will move more slowly and leave the acidic area at a slow rate. The **net movement** of *Paramecium*, will be from the basic area to the acidic area, where they will accumulate. They are **not attracted** to this area, but rather end up there as a result of different rates of locomotion under different conditions.

We shall use sow bugs to demonstrate kinesis. The sow bug is a small terrestrial crustacean often found under rotting wood. Our experiment will investigate its response to moist and dry conditions.

Your instructor has set up an experiment in which one set of 10 sow bugs is in the dry environment of **DISH A** and another set is in the moist environment of **DISH B.** Other conditions that might affect the sow bugs, such as temperature, light, and the physical environment, are the same for both dishes. As a class you will observe the sow bugs every 15 minutes during the experimental period.

■ When it is your turn, count and record the number of moving and stationary sow bugs in dish A. Any animals that are moving their legs but not going anywhere should be counted as stationary because they do not show locomotion.
■ Next count and record the number of moving and stationary sow bugs in dish B.
■ When everyone has had a chance to observe the sow bugs, record the combined class results.

What results would you expect if the sow bugs accumulate in the damp conditions by kinesis?

_____

What results would you expect if the sow bugs accumulate in the dry conditions by kinesis?

_____

Did the class results support either possibility?

_____

TAXIS IN *DROSOPHILA*

You may have noticed during the genetics experiment that the flies had the annoying habit of sitting on the cotton plug of the food vial. This behavior may have been due either to positive phototaxis, negative geotaxis, or both types of taxis.

Phototaxis

■ Place five flies in a clean food vial (without any food), cover it with another clean vial, and tape the vials together as shown in Figure 32-1.
■ Cover the vials with a black paper shield so that only one end is open to the light, and lay it on a horizontal surface.
■ Place a light source near the open end of the tube, and wait 3 min.
■ Quickly remove the shield, and count the flies in each half of the tube; record the results on a properly labeled data sheet at the end of this topic.
■ Tap the flies back into the center of the tube and reverse the tube so that the former right end is now the left end. Replace the shield and light source, which should be exactly as before.
■ Wait 3 min, remove the shield, and count the flies once again.
■ Repeat once more unless your results agreed very well in the first two trials.

Did the flies show phototaxis? _____

If present, was it positive or negative? _____

Why did you have to reverse the vials between trials?

_____

_____

_____

_____

Why did you have to keep the vials horizontal?

_____

_____

Geotaxis

■ Use the same vials or take five new flies, put them in a clean food vial, and tape it end to end to another clean food vial.
■ Let the flies attach to the glass, and then cover the vials completely with a black shield.
■ Hold the vials in a vertical position for 3 min.

Figure 32-1. Phototaxis in *Drosophila*. In this experimental setup, the open ends of the vials are taped together, and the vials are covered with a black shield open to the light at one end only.

■ Quickly remove the shield, and count the flies in each vial. Record the results on your data sheet.
■ Tap the flies to the middle of the tube, cover it with the shield, and hold it in a vertical position, reversing the vials so the one that was held up at first is now down.
■ Wait 3 min, remove the shield, and count the flies in each vial. Record the result.
■ Repeat once more unless your results in the first two trials matched very well.

Did the flies show positive geotaxis or negative geotaxis?

Why did you have to reverse the position of the vials between each trial?

Phototaxis and Geotaxis

Test the relative strengths of the response to light and gravity by opposing these stimuli.

■ Enclose the vials with five flies in the black shield that is open at one end.
■ Hold the vials in a vertical position so that the covered end is the end where you would expect the flies to be under the influence of gravity alone.
■ Hold a light source near the open end of the tube, and wait 3 min.
■ Remove the shield, and count the flies in each vial. Record the results.
■ Repeat two or three more times until you see a definite trend.

Was phototaxis strong enough to overcome geotaxis?

Chemotaxis

Orientation toward volatile substances helps *Drosophilia* locate food and a mate and avoid unpleasant or harmful substances. A simple T-maze for testing chemotaxis is shown in Figure 32-2. The substance to be tested is placed in one vial, the second vial acts as the control, and the flies are placed in the third vial. The progress of the flies can be viewed through the glass.

■ Place some fermenting *Drosophilia* food or fermenting fruit on a small piece of aluminum foil, and put it into vial (a). Attach it to the T-tube.
■ Place a piece of moist filter paper in vial (b) and attach it to the T-tube.
■ Place 12-15 flies in vial (c), and attach it to the T-tube.
■ Watch the flies for 5 min. Record the number of flies in each vial.
■ Record the numbers of flies again after 10 min.

Do you see any trend in the movements of the flies?

■ Put the maze in a dark place for an hour, and record the number of flies in each vial after 60 min.

Did the flies show chemotaxis toward the food?

Figure 32-2. Chemotaxis in *Drosophila*. In the T-maze, vial (a) contains the substance to be tested, and the control vial (b) contains moist filter paper. The flies are introduced into vial (c).

SCHOOLING BEHAVIOR

Animals may gather in a group for different reasons. If they are attracted to the same spot by the presence of food, light, or some external stimulus, the group is called an **aggregate.** If, however, they form a group because they are mutually attracted to one another, the group is called a **school** in the case of fish, and a **herd,** or **flock,** in the case of mammals or birds. In fish, vision, swimming movements in the water, and olfaction may all contribute to keeping the members of the school together, but vision is the most important cue. Schooling fish seem to be attracted to each other mainly by their appearance, and the attraction is strongest for other members of the same species. Schooling is a form of communication between members of the same species, but fish of differing species do sometimes school together as well.

Schooling is very prevalent among all sorts of fish, from very primitive ones to the more advanced species. The members of the school may be better protected from predators than single fish because their swimming motions may appear very confusing to a predator about to strike. They seem to be able to swim more efficiently when spaced out at certain intervals from each other in a school. A predator in a school has a greater chance of locating food than does a lone predator. For plankton-feeding fish, however, food is always present, and there will be less food for each fish in a school than there would be for a single fish. Members of a school can learn from each other more quickly than a single fish can learn, and they do not have to spend energy in locating mates for reproduction.

However, one big disadvantage of schooling behavior is that it has made the fishing industry very successful and efficient and may ultimately lead to the decline or even extinction of many fish species.

Schooling of Fish with Visual Markings

In these experiments you will be testing the role of the visual component in schooling behavior. Because the fish will be separated by a glass barrier, there can be no communication by sound or chemical signals. In many fish, vision is the prime factor in the attraction of schooling fish toward each other, but olfaction and sound seem to help maintain the cohesion of an established school.

BEHAVIOR EXPERIMENTS WILL NOT WORK UNLESS THE ANIMALS ARE TREATED WITH CARE AND PATIENCE.

DO:
1. Always use a net to transfer the fish.
2. Allow time for the fish to adjust to new conditions before beginning your observations.
3. Wash and rinse your hands before reaching into the experimental tanks to place beakers and so on.
4. Treat the fish with care.
5. Report any sick-looking or dead fish to the instructor.
6. Return all fish to the proper tanks when you are finished.

DON'T:
1. Shock or disturb the fish more than necessary for the experiments.
2. Expect the fish to respond instantaneously to a new stimulus.
3. Reach into the stock tanks where the fish are kept.
4. Leave fish in the experimental apparatus or tanks.

Work with a partner and try these tests of schooling behavior. The experimental setups are shown in Figure 32-3 and Figure 32-4. Your instructor may ask you to devise additional experiments on your own.

TANK TEST

In this test, conditions are the same on both sides of the tank, so we predict the test fish should spend the same amount of time on each side.

■ Obtain a stopwatch and a container with a test fish. Wind the watch and practice starting and stopping it a few times.

■ When you gain access to a tank divided into sides A and B (see Figure 32-3), place the fish in the water by submerging the container and drawing it away from the fish. Allow the fish a few minutes to adjust.

■ Then run a 5-min (300-sec) observation period to see whether the fish spends more than half of its time on one side of the tank.

The first partner should start the experiment by starting the stopwatch; the second partner should watch the fish and order the watch stopped during the time when the fish has crossed to the other side of the tank. The first partner should stop the experiment when 5 min have elapsed.

How many seconds did the fish spend on side A?

_____

On side B? _____

What percentage of the time did the fish spend on side A?

_____

On side B? _____

If your fish spent more than about 75% of the time on

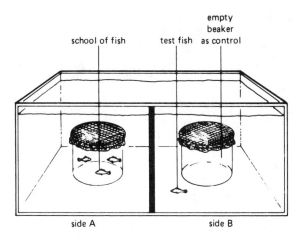

Figure 32-3. Schooling behavior. In the aquarium setup for testing with one school, a beaker with fish is placed on side A and an empty beaker on side B to serve as the control. The test fish is free to swim throughout the aquarium.

one side, it will be hard to draw valid conclusions from any experiment that you might try. You should probably proceed with one of the following alternatives:

a) If the fish did not actively swim about, or if it stayed on one side, place it on the opposite side of the tank and repeat the test.
b) Move the fish to another tank and repeat the test.
c) Obtain another fish and repeat the test in your tank.

Consult with the instructor if you can't demonstrate that your fish visits both sides of the tank. When your fish does visit both sides, go on to the experiments below.

TEST 1 (Figure 32-3)

■ Place several fish with markings, such as zebra danios, in a beaker. Cover the beaker with the screen, and immerse it slowly in the aquarium. Place it into position on side A.

■ Place an empty beaker on side B to serve as the control.

■ Place a single test fish of the same species in the tank.

■ Use a stopwatch to time the number of seconds spent by the test fish in each half of the tank during a 5-min period (300 sec). Record the results on your data sheet at the end of this topic.

■ Calculate the percentage of the time the test fish spent on side A and on side B.

Did the fish spend more time on side A or side B?

_____

What hypothesis was tested by this experiment?

_____

_____

■ Record your conclusion.

TEST 2 (Figure 32-3)

■ Place two fish in the beaker, and repeat the experiment using a different single fish of the same species.

■ Record the results.
■ Calculate the percentage of the test period that the fish spent on each side.

If you have time, repeat the test using different numbers of fish in the beaker, and using a different test fish each time.

■ Calculate the percentage of the test period that the test fish spent with the school and the percentage of time that it spent alone.

State the hypothesis being tested by varying the number of fish in the school:

_____

_____

Did the number of fish in the school affect the tendency of the single test fish to spend time with the school?

_____

TEST 3 (Figure 32-4)

■ Place three fish with markings, such as zebra danios, in a beaker on side A of the aquarium, and three fish of another species without markings, such as white clouds, in a beaker on side B. Be sure to put the *same number* of fish in each beaker.
■ Place a single test fish *with markings* in the center of the aquarium.
■ Use a stopwatch to time how many seconds in a 5-min period the test fish spends with its own species (section A), with the other species (section B), and alone (section C).
■ Calculate the percentage of time that the test fish spent in each section of the tank.

In which of the three sections did the fish spend the most time? _____

Is there a big difference in the percentage of time spent with the two species? _____

How would you state the hypothesis being tested?

_____

_____

Was the hypothesis supported? _____

Schooling Fish without Visual Markings

Visual markings may help fish to identify other members of the same species, but not all schooling fish have prominent markings. Test the schooling tendency of fish without prominent markings in the following experiments, and compare your results to those you obtained for the fish with markings.

TANK TEST (Figure 32-3)

Since you will be using a different test fish, repeat the tank test using a test fish without markings.

TEST 4 (Figure 32-3)

■ Place several fish without markings in a beaker on side A of the aquarium, an empty beaker on side B,

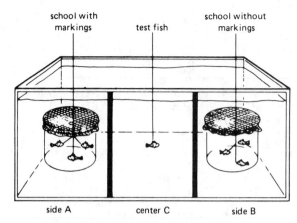

Figure 32-4. Schooling behavior. When two schools are used, the aquarium is divided into three parts. A school of one species of fish is placed on side A and a school of another species on side B. The free test fish can choose school A, school B, or neither school.

and a single test fish of the same species free in the aquarium.
■ Use a stopwatch to time the number of seconds spent in each half of the the aquarium during a 5-min period. Record the results.
■ Calculate the percentage of the time the test fish spent on side A and on side B.

On which side did the test fish spend more time—side A or side B? _____

What hypothesis was tested by this experiment?

_____

_____

■ Record you conclusion.

TEST 5 (Figure 32-3)

■ Place two fish in the beaker, and repeat the experiment using a different single fish of the same species. Record the results.
■ Calculate the percentage of the test period that the fish spent on each side.

If you have time, repeat the test using a different number of fish in the beaker and using a different single fish each time.

■ Calculate the percentage of time the fish spent with the school and alone for each test.

State the hypothesis being tested by varying the number of fish in the school.

_____

_____

Did the number of fish in the school affect the tendency of the single test fish to swim with the school?

_____

TEST 6 (Figure 32-4)

■ Place three fish with markings in a beaker on side A of the aquarium and three fish without markings in a beaker on side B. Be sure to put the *same number* of fish in each beaker.

■ Place a single test fish *without markings* in the center of the tank.

■ Use a stopwatch to time how many seconds in a 5-min period the test fish spends with its own species (section B), with the other species (section A), and alone (section C). Record your results.

■ Calculate the percentage of time that the test fish spent in each section of the tank.

In which of the three sections did the fish spend the most time? _____

Is there a big difference in the percentage of time spent with each of the two species? _____

How would you state the hypothesis being tested?

_____

_____

Was the test fish more attracted to visual markings or to members of its own species?

_____

    Return all fish to the proper tanks when you are finished.

THE OPTOMOTOR RESPONSE

In this experiment, the fish is presented with a pattern of moving stripes in the apparatus shown in Figure 32-5.

    A response to the moving stripes has been found in both schooling and nonschooling fish, and it may be present even before young fish have begun to school. Test for the presence of the optomotor response in both the marked and the unmarked fish.

■ Place a fish with markings in the beaker, and observe its behavior with no special stimulus. Record the results.

■ Attach a paper cylinder with vertical stripes to the drum of the kymograph, and observe the reaction of the fish to stationary vertical stripes. Record the results.

■ Start the drum rotating at about 0.5 revolutions per second, and observe the behavior of the fish for 3 min.

■ Record how the fish behaves.

Did the rotating stripes change the behavior of the fish?

_____

■ Change the paper cylinder to one with horizontal stripes, and observe the response of the fish to stationary horizontal stripes. Record the results.

■ Start the drum rotating at about 0.5 revolutions per second, and observe the behavior of the fish for 3 min. Record the results.

Did the rotating stripes change the behavior of the fish?

_____

    Be sure to return the fish to the aquarium when you are finished.

■ Place a fish without markings in the beaker, and repeat your observations on the fish's response to no stimulus, stationary and moving vertical stripes, and stationary and moving horizontal stripes.

■ Record the results, and return the fish to its tank.

Figure 32-5. Optomotor response. A striped paper cylinder is the visual stimulus. It is attached to the drum of a kymograph and rotated around the outside of the beaker containing the test fish.

Did the fish without markings show the optomotor response? _____

AGONISTIC BEHAVIOR IN SIAMESE FIGHTING FISH

These fish *(Betta splendens)* live in the freshwater tropical streams of Indochina and have been bred for exaggerated agonistic behavior. The male fish shows its intention to attack another male or to flee by visual displays. One of the male fish eventually will get the upper hand and bluff its competitor into leaving.

    When the fish are confined within an aquarium, however, the winner will chase and bite the losing fish.

YOU MUST BE READY TO REMOVE ONE OF THE FISH AS SOON AS THE WINNER IS CLEARLY APPARENT.

    The balance between the tendency of the fish to fight or flee is strongly dependent on whether it is in its own territory and whether it has just defeated another fish or has just been defeated itself. The most impressive displays are observed with closely matched fish.

    The components of the agonistic display are shown in Figure 32-6. The normal resting fish (a) is drab or only slightly colored and keeps the dorsal and ventral fins folded. When another male appears, the fish will probably challenge the intruder with a **broadside display** (b). Two fish may swim side by side for several minutes in this display, each trying to intimidate the other. Finally, one will get a slight edge, and the subordi-

(a) resting or submissive

(b) broadside display

(c) frontal attack

Figure 32-6. Agonistic displays in a Siamese fighting fish. The display in (a) is the least aggressive and is shown by the resting fish. Its coloring is dull or moderately bright. The broadside display in (b) is commonly seen between closely matched equals, brilliant in color. The fish in (c) is dominant and about to drive the submissive fish away with its brilliant coloring and fierce frontal attack.

nate fish will gradually give up the broadside display, and lose some of its brilliant color. The dominant fish will then probably attempt a **frontal attack** (c) and will pursue and thrust at the fins of the submissive fish.

The display of agonistic behavior will also be shown in response to artificial stimuli. The most effective is a mirror image of the fish itself. A fish-colored model in the shape of the fish or even in a different shape will usually also cause a response. Models of different colors are generally ignored. Artificial stimuli are most effective if the fish has recently defeated another fish and is in its own territory so that its motivation to display is high. The broadside display of the male is also used during the courtship ritual to attract the female to the bubble nest. The male maintains the display during mating, and the female must make herself as inconspicuous as possible to avoid being attacked.

Record your observations on the fighting fish on a data sheet at the end of this topic.

TEST 1

■ Place a male fighting fish (fish #1, "Red Raider" or whatever) in an aquarium, and observe its normal behavior. Allow time for the fish to adjust to the new environment.
■ Show the fish an image of himself in a mirror. Move the mirror along as the fish swims to imitate an intruder.
■ Observe the fish's behavior for at least 5 min.
■ Note and record the fish's behavior, especially his orientation, color, the position of the fins (dorsal, ventral, tail, pectoral), and the position of the gill covers (opercula).

Did the fish respond to its mirror image?

_____

Did it try to attack the image? _____

TEST 2

■ Choose one of the models provided, and move it slowly close to the fish. If your models are plastic, they can be held in the water near the fish.
■ If the fish moves away, follow it, but avoid moving the model very close to the fish or touching the fish with it.
■ Continue presenting the model until there is a response or until 5 min have passed. Record your observations by checking for each of the following reactions shown by the fish:

no response
swimming
swimming away
pectoral fin movement
raising of dorsal fin
lowering of ventral fin
expansion of tail
increased coloring
extension of gill covers
facing the model
biting the model

Which of the following general response patterns did the fish show?

no response
fleeing from the model
broadside display
frontal attack

_____

Was the response greater or less than the response to another fish?

■ Obtain the results of other class members using different models, and record them alongside your own results for comparison.

Did shape strongly influence the response of the fish to the models?

Did color strongly influence the response?

TEST 3

■ Place a second fish in the tank and observe the behavior of both.
■ Record their orientation with respect to each other, their color, the position of their fins, and the position of the gill covers.

If the fish were equally matched before the experiment, which one theoretically has an advantage now?

Why?

■ Continue your observations for 5 min or until one of the fish starts pursuing the other.

IMMEDIATELY REMOVE ONE OF THE FISH IN THIS CASE.

TEST 4

■ Replace the dominant fish with one provided by the instructor, which was submissive in a previous experiment.
■ Observe the two submissive fish for 5 min.

Did either of the submissive fish show agonistic behavior?

When you are finished with these experiments, return all the fish to their proper containers as directed by your instructor.

EXPLORING FURTHER

Alcock, J. *Animal Behavior: An Evolutionary Approach.* 3rd ed. Stamford, Conn.: Sinauer, 1983.
Barash, D. P. *Sociobiology and Behavior.* 2nd ed. New York: Elsevier, 1982.
Gould, J. L. *Ethology.* New York, Norton, 1982.
Kalmus, H. *101 Simple Experiments with Insects.* Garden City, N. Y.: Doubleday, 1960.
Lorenz, K. Z. *King Solomon's Ring.* London: Methuen, 1942.
Manning, A. *An Introduction to Animal Behavior.* New York: Addison-Wesley, 1979.

Journal Articles

Benzer, S. "Genetic dissection of behavior." *Scientific American*, December 1973 (#1285).
Crews, David. "The hormonal control of behavior in a lizard." *Scientific American*, August 1979 (#1435).
Eibl-Eibesfeldt, Irenäus. "The fighting behavior of animals." *Scientific American*, December 1961 (#470).
Erickson, Robert P. "On the neural bases of behavior." *American Scientist 72(3):233*, May–June 1984.
Fernald, Russell D. "Vision and behavior in an African cichlid fish." *American Scientist 72(1):58*, January–February 1984.
Gould, S. J. "The guano ring." *Natural History*, 12, January 1982.
Hallman, Jack P. "How an instinct is learned." *Scientific American*, December 1969 (#1165).
MacNichol, Edward F., and Joseph S. Levine. "Color vision in fishes." *Scientific American*, 140, February 1982.
Moore, Janice. "Parasites that change the behavior of their host." *Scientific American*, 108, May 1984.
Mykytowycz, Roman. "Territorial marking by rabbits." *Scientific American*, May 1968 (#1108).
Partridge, Brian L. "The structure and function of fish schools." *Scientific American*, 114, June 1982.
Ryker, Lee C. "Acoustic and chemical signals in the life cycle of a beetle." *Scientific American*, 112, June 1984.
Saunders, D. S. "The biological clock of insects." *Scientific American*, February 1976 (#1335).
Sheller, Richard H., and Richard Axel. "How genes control an innate behavior." *Scientific American*, 54, March 1984.
Tinbergen, N. "The curious behavior of the stickleback." *Scientific American*, December 1952 (#414).
Tinbergen, N. "On war and peace in animals and man." *Science 160:1411*, 1968.
Todd, John H. "The chemical language of fishes." *Scientific American*, May 1971 (#1222).
Webb, Paul F. "Form and function in fish swimming." *Scientific American*, 72, July 1984.
Whitehead, Hal. "Why whales leap." *Scientific American*, 84, March 1985.
Wilson, E. O. "Pheromones." *Scientific American*, May 1963 (#157).

Student Name _____ **Date** _____

BEHAVIOR DATA SHEET

_____
_____
_____
_____
_____
_____
_____
_____
_____
_____
_____
_____
_____
_____
_____
_____
_____
_____
_____
_____
_____
_____
_____
_____
_____
_____
_____
_____
_____
_____
_____
_____
_____
_____
_____
_____
_____
_____
_____
_____
_____
_____

BEHAVIOR DATA SHEET

Student Name _____ **Date** _____

BEHAVIOR DATA SHEET

BEHAVIOR DATA SHEET

Student Name _____ **Date** _____

BEHAVIOR DATA SHEET

_____
_____
_____
_____
_____
_____
_____
_____
_____
_____
_____
_____
_____
_____
_____
_____
_____
_____
_____
_____
_____
_____
_____
_____
_____
_____
_____
_____
_____
_____
_____
_____
_____
_____
_____
_____
_____
_____
_____
_____
_____
_____

BEHAVIOR DATA SHEET

_____
_____
_____
_____
_____
_____
_____
_____
_____
_____
_____
_____
_____
_____
_____
_____
_____
_____
_____
_____
_____
_____
_____
_____
_____
_____
_____
_____
_____
_____
_____
_____
_____
_____
_____
_____
_____
_____
_____
_____
_____
_____

Introduction to the Projects

The following projects require more than a single laboratory period. Your instructor will give you specific directions as to how the project will be carried out. Because you will be working more independently than usual, it is important that you understand the rationale behind the experiments and exactly how they are to be done before you begin work.

You and your partner are about to become researchers in plant physiology or ecology and will carry out some experiments in order to answer certain questions. Because you may be asked to design the experiments yourself, you should read over the discussion of the scientific method given below. Then, because the first step in any research is a review of the current knowledge, you should read over the sections in your textbook relevant to your project and refer to any other sources that you can find. You will then be ready to prepare a written description of the planned work. You should bring the written plan with you to the laboratory, or hand it in ahead of time. Your instructor will check it over before you actually start your experimental work.

During the project, be careful to *record all of the manipulations and observations at the time*. Do not rely on your memory alone, or you may end up in serious difficulty when you attempt to write up the results in the laboratory report. Label all records with your name and the date they were made, since your instructor may ask you to include the raw data in your report.

When the project is finished, write up the results in a written report according to the directions given in Appendix A.

THE SCIENTIFIC METHOD

In your study of the scientific method you learned that there are two basic ways that modern science progresses. When scientists use **inductive logic,** they gather observations on a phenomenon and then formulate a generalization or scientific law from these observations. The generalization represents new knowledge and will be used to make predictions until it is shown to be invalid by a new observation. The more observations that have been made, the more likely the generalization is to be valid.

The generalization can be used to generate a **hypothesis** according to the process of **deductive logic.** A hypothesis is a trial, unproven idea put forward as a possible explanation of observed events to provide a

basis for further study. It must make a testable prediction. The hypothesis itself is stated as the **major premise,** its application to a particular case is the **minor premise,** and the result of applying it to a particular case is the **conclusion.** Here is an example:

Major premise: All green plants contain chlorophyll.
Minor premise: This mint plant is green.
Conclusion: This mint plant contains chlorophyll.

Deduction does not generate new knowledge, but it proposes **experiments** that will support or disprove the major premise. In this example, if a single plant were found to be green but not to contain chlorophyll, the major premise would be discarded because it had been proved to be false. If, on the other hand, many mint plants were tested and were all found to contain chlorophyll, the major premise would be supported. The major premise would not be proved because it is not deductively valid to argue it is proved by one or more supporting observations. (There might be exceptions yet to be discovered.) When many supporting experiments have been done, the hypothesis is regarded as very probably true, and it will gain the status of a **theory** and may eventually become a **scientific law,** or "fact."

In summary, one observation that is inconsistent with the conclusion is sufficient to disprove the major premise. Many observations consistent with the conclusion will support but not prove the major premise.

When hypotheses are formulated, they often take the form:

If: A is true
Then: B is true

A is the generalization or hypothesis to be tested and B is the experimental observation to be made. According to the preceding discussion, if B is false, A must be false. If B is true, however, A may or may not be true. The example just given can be restated:

If: all green plants contain chlorophyll
Then: this green mint plant contains chlorophyll

An experiment would be done to test for the presence of chlorophyll. If it were present, the hypothesis would be supported but not proved, and if it were absent, the hypothesis would be disproved, according to deductive logic. In the latter case, the scientist would have to turn to a new hypothesis or develop a more sensitive method of testing for chlorophyll.

The experiment will often be set up so that there is an **experimental situation** and a **control situation,** which differ only by a single variable. In this case, we would test a tube with chlorophyll as a **positive control,** a tube without chlorophyll as a **negative** **control,** and a tube with material from the mint plant. Without controls we cannot be sure that the results we see are really due to the factor that we are testing, namely the presence of chlorophyll.

Plant Hormones

OBJECTIVES

When you have completed this topic, you should be able to:
1. Define hormone and describe how plant hormones tend to differ from animal hormones.
2. Explain the role of the plant hormone auxin in cell elongation, lateral bud development, ethylene production, root formation, and fruit formation.
3. Given a living plant or a diagram of a plant, show where each of the effects of auxin occurs.
4. Describe five criteria for establishing that a certain process in under the control of a plant hormone.
5. Given the laboratory facilities and equipment at your disposal, design and carry out an experiment to test the hypothesis that apical dominance is due to production of auxin by the apical meristem.
6. Write up your results in a formal laboratory report.
7. Describe several other experimental approaches that might be used to test this hypothesis.

KEY TOPICS

Scientific method, hypothesis, auxin, apical dominance.

INTRODUCTION

The observations for this experiment must be made over a period of at least 2 weeks. The experimental procedures and measurements themselves do not take much time.

Hormones are chemical messengers synthesized in one part of an organism that are transported to a different part of the organism's body. There they have an effect on its development or physiology. Because animals spend a large portion of their lives in a stable adult form without much growth or differentiation, many animal hormones are directed toward maintaining the status quo, or **homeostasis.** In most plants, on the other hand, growth and differentiation tend to continue throughout the life of the organism, so plant hormones tend to be directed toward controlling growth and differentiation in the developing tissues. In some plants, aging and senescence are also closely regulated by hormones. As in animals, certain hormones regulate the events leading up to the reproduction of a mature plant. In animals, hormones are produced in specific organs, the endocrine organs, and they usually act on specific organs called the target organs. Plants, on the other hand, do not have organs with the specific function of producing hormones. Their hormones are produced by parts of the plant that have other functions as well. The hormones may then act on several different organs of the plant.

IDENTIFICATION OF PLANT HORMONES

If a certain substance is a plant hormone, you must be able to show that:

1. The substance is produced naturally by the plant.
2. It exerts a physiological effect on another part of the plant in low concentrations.
3. It is normally transported between the two parts of the plant.

The generally accepted experimental criteria for establishing that a process is under hormonal control were first articulated by Jacobs in 1959. (See **Exploring Further**.) They can be summarized as follows:

1. **Parallel variation.** The substance must be present in the intact plant that shows the response or

process, and the degree of response must vary with the concentration of the substance.

2. **Excision.** Removal of the substance from the plant should result in a loss of the regulatory effect. This may be done by any of these procedures:

    a. Surgically removing the part of the plant producing the hormone
    b. Blocking the production of the hormone by poisoning the metabolic pathway
    c. Blocking the effect of the hormone by using competitive antagonists
    d. Developing a mutant strain that lacks the suspected hormone

3. **Substitution.** Replacement of the suspected hormone should reinstate the regulatory effect. For a new hormone whose structure may not be known, this can be done by using an extract from or homogenate of the tissue thought to produce the hormone. If such a substitution experiment is successful, the next step is to isolate and identify the chemicals in the preparation that are responsible for its biological activity.

4. **Specificity.** It should be shown that other naturally occurring substances do not have the effect shown by the substance isolated in step 3. Testing of other compounds might identify factors that contribute to the observed effect and will help clarify the exact role that the isolated substance plays in the regulatory process.

5. **Generality.** Once hormonal control of a process has been demonstrated in one species, it is desirable to test whether the substance tentatively identified as the controlling hormone will exert similar control on the same process in other species.

AUXIN

Auxins are a group of structurally related small molecules derived from the amino acid tryptophan. The most commonly studied auxin is indoleacetic acid. Auxin is a stimulatory hormone that causes plant cells to elongate if it is present in the right concentration. It acts partly by stimulating the activity of **cellulases,** enzymes that soften the material between the cell walls and allow the cells to expand. If there is a greater concentration of auxin on one side of a plant stem, that side will elongate faster, causing the plant to bend toward the *other* side. Sunlight causes auxin to accumulate on the shady side of a plant stem so that the plant bends *toward* the source of the sunlight and shows **positive phototropism.**

Auxin is stimulatory only when it is present in a certain concentration range and the concentrations of other hormones are appropriate. This range is different for different tissues and, if the concentration is above the stimulatory range, the auxin will act to *inhibit* elongation and growth. In the plant, auxin is produced by the tissue of the **apical meristem** at the tips of the branches of the shoot. It is transported from the meristematic tissues to the rest of the plant. Buds are stimulated by a lower range of auxin concentrations than are stems, so the concentrations of auxin that stimulate growth of the stem will tend to inhibit the development of adjacent buds. This is the basis of **apical dominance.** As long as the apical meristem is growing, it will produce auxin in sufficient concentration to inhibit the development of the lateral

buds next to it. If the meristem is removed, the auxin concentration reaching the buds will decrease, and the buds will start to develop and will now be much less sensitive to inhibition. Once a bud has broken dormancy and has started to grow into a new stem it will be stimulated by the same concentration of auxin that inhibited the bud. Apical dominance may be strong or weak in different species, as shown in text Figure 29-7.

Auxin is also involved to some extent in the response of roots to gravity. If a root happens to be in a horizontal position, high concentrations of auxin will accumulate on its lower side and inhibit those cells. As a result, the root will bend downward and grow towards the center of the earth. The root of a plant thus shows **positive geotropism.** Abscisic acid also accumulates on the lower side and contributes to geotropism by inhibition.

In addition to stimulating elongation, inhibiting lateral bud development, and controlling the response of plant stems to light and gravity, auxin is important in inducing the formation of lateral and adventitious roots, stimulating cell division in the cambium to form reaction wood in response to stress, stimulating cytoplasmic streaming, inducing development of the fleshy parts of some fruits, and promoting the development of female flower parts. Auxin stimulates production of another hormone, ethylene.

Study a diagram of a plant, or better yet, a living plant to review the sites of production and sites of action of auxin and the other plant hormones.

EXPERIMENTS ON APICAL DOMINANCE

Apply your understanding of the scientific method to the problem of apical dominance. Read over the following instructions before you begin to plan your project. You must then prepare a detailed written description of your experimental plan before coming to laboratory to start the experiment, and obtain the instructor's approval of the plan before starting the experiment.

Hypothesis

The hypothesis of this project is that the growth of lateral buds in bean plants is normally inhibited by auxin produced in the apical meristem.

Implications

Use your knowledge of the effects of hormones on plant development to make a list of testable or measurable phenomena you could study to help support or disprove the hypothesis.

1. _____

   _____

2. _____

   _____

3. _____

   _____

4. _____
   _____
5. _____
   _____

Which of these implications could be most easily tested experimentally? _____

If you wished to demonstrate **parallel variation,** what kinds of experimental problems would you have to overcome?

_____
_____
_____

Specificity might be difficult to demonstrate; in terms of what you know about the complexities of plant physiology, why might this criterion be hard to meet?

_____
_____

How would you demonstrate **generality?**

_____
_____

Why is it important to do so?

_____
_____

Materials and Methods

In this exercise you will do only **excision** and **substitution** experiments using the following materials and any others that may be available to you:

Young bean plants
Auxin in lanolin paste
Plain lanolin paste
Razor blades
Plant tags

For each of the experiments to be done, describe in your written plan the manipulations that you must do to the experimental plants, the proper controls that you must include for comparison, and the measurements that you will make.

Because you are studying the effect of the manipulation that you will perform on the development of the plant, all other factors should be kept constant.

List in your written plan all the factors that might affect the growth of your plants.

In addition, because you are going to compare experimental and control plants during the experiment, you will need to start out with plants that are as nearly identical as possible and certainly the same species, age, and size. The lateral buds on the plants must be dormant.

Why?

_____
_____
_____

Do not choose plants in which the dormancy of these buds has been broken. Carry out your treatments quickly, so that their dormancy will not be broken by the experimental procedure. Your plants should be about 10-14 days old and should look like the young plant shown in Figure P-1.

The anatomy of the apical meristem and lateral buds of a young bean plant is shown in Figure P-2. The apical shoot of the plant should be about 2-3 cm long, and the lateral buds must be dormant in order for the experimental procedure to be valid.

Once the experimental manipulations have been performed, follow the growth of the lateral buds for at least a 2-week period, taking measurements as often as necessary.

How often will you be able to measure your plants?

_____

Design a format for recording your data in the same way each time you take measurements. Include all measurements in your laboratory report.

BE SURE EACH ENTRY INCLUDES YOUR NAME AND THE DATE.

When you are finished with your experimental work, dispose of the plants according to the directions given by your instructor.

Figure P-1. A bean seedling. The lateral buds on either side of the shoot must be dormant at the beginning of the experiment. The shoot must be long enough so that lanolin paste can be applied to it after excision of the apical bud, without having the paste slide down directly onto the lateral buds as well. (Photo: C. Eberhard).

Figure P-2. Apical shoot. The shoot of a 12-day-old bean plant will show apical dominance of the lateral buds by the apical meristem located within the apical bud.

Results

The number of plants in your individual experiment is too small to yield statistically valid results. When a large number of such results are combined, however, the results may become statistically meaningful. Read the information on statistics given in Appendix B so that you will be able to understand the analysis of the class data. Your instructor may ask you to calculate the standard deviation for the class results. After the analysis, answer these questions:

Are the class's results statistically significant?

_____

What does the statistical analysis tell us about the experiment?

_____

_____

_____

_____

Discussion and Conclusions

Is the hypothesis supported? _____

Is the hypothesis proved? _____

Is there an alternative hypothesis that could explain the results?

_____

_____

What experiment could you do to test the alternative hypothesis?

_____

_____

If an externally applied hormone can be shown to affect a given phenomenon, does this necessarily mean that the hormone controls the process in the intact plant?

_____

What else would you want to know in support of the conclusion?

_____

_____

_____

Consider these points in formulating your discussion:

1. The apical meristem may draw nutrients away from the lateral buds.
2. Cytokinin from the roots may be preferentially transported to the apical meristem.
3. The apical meristem may receive more light than do the lateral buds.

Write up this experiment according to the instructions given in Appendix A, including the class analysis and an explanation of what the analysis means. Hand in your report to your instructor.

EXPLORING FURTHER

Bidwell, R. G. S. *Plant Physiology.* 2nd ed. New York; Macmillan, 1979.

Galston, Arthur W., and Peter J. Davies, *Control Mechanisms in Plant Development.* Englewood Cliffs, N.J.: Prentice-Hall, 1970.

Galston, Arthur W., Peter J. Davies, and Ruth L. Satter. *The Life of the Green Plant.* 3rd ed. Englewood Cliffs, N. J.: Prentice-Hall, 1980.

Newcomb, E. H., G. C. Gerloff, and W. F. Whittingham. *Plants in Perspective.* San Francisco: W. H. Freeman, 1965.

Raven, P. H., R. F. Evert, and H. Curtis. *Biology of Plants.* 3rd ed. New York, Worth, 1981.

Ray, P., T. A. Steeves, and S. A. Fultz. *Botany.* Philadelphia: Saunders College Publishing, 1983.

Salisbury, Frank B., and Cleon W. Ross. *Plant Physiology.* 2nd ed. New York: Harper and Row, 1978.

Wareling, P. F., and I. D. J. Phillips. *Control of Growth and Differentiation in Plants.* 2nd ed. Elmsford, N. Y.: Pergamon Press, 1978.

Journal Articles

Flagg, R. O. "Plant growth regulators." *Carolina Tips 26(3, 9),* 1963 and *27(9, 10).* Burlington, S. C.: Carolina Biological Laboratory, 1964 (reprint 1965).

Jacobs, W. P. "What substance normally controls a given biological process?" *Devel. Biol. 1:* 6, 1959.

Plant Nutrition

When you have completed this topic, you should be able to:
1.   List the seven elements that are macronutrients needed by all plants.
2.   Give at least one example of how each macronutrient is used.
3.   Give some examples of micronutrients and describe why each is needed.
4.   Describe how a plant could show a deficiency of a nutrient known to be present in its soil.
5.   Describe two ways in which a plant might obtain a nutrient other than from its soil or water supply.
6.   Give two ways in which a plant can compensate for a limited supply of a nutrient; explain how such compensation would affect nutritional experiments.
7.   Identify the deficient nutrient for a seedling by comparing its appearance with that of seedlings grown under conditions of known nutrient deficiencies.

KEY TOPICS

Macronutrients, micronutrients, soil solution, absorption.

INTRODUCTION

The laboratory work for this project continues for 3 to 4 weeks. Once the experiment has been set up, brief measurements (15 min) must be made every few days.

Plants obtain energy reserves and the bulk of their structural material from the carbon dioxide that they take in from the air. In order to carry out the metabolic processes necessary to convert CO_2 to carbohydrates and cellulose and to simply maintain the components of their cytoplasm, however, they need many other substances in lesser amounts.

Macronutrients: Nitrogen (N) and phosphorus (P) are elements needed for synthesis of amino acids and nucleotides. Potassium (K) is the main cation (ion with a + charge) in plant tissue. These elements are needed in the greatest amount. Sulfur (S) is needed in lesser amounts for amino acids. Calcium (Ca) is required for many enzyme reactions (as are iron, manganese, and magnesium). Magnesium (Mg) forms part of the structure of the chlorophyll molecule.

Micronutrients: Many elements are needed in tiny amounts by all plants and others are especially needed by certain plants for specialized functions. For example, when plants are associated with nitrogen-fixing bacteria, molybdenum is required because it is necessary for that reaction. This element is also needed by plants for their enzyme nitrate reductase when nitrate is the source of nitrogen. Iron (Fe) is required by many enzymes, including those of the electron transport chain. Cobalt, a component of vitamin B_{12}, is also needed for nitrogen fixation. Zinc is necessary for the synthesis of auxins. Silicon, boron, copper, sodium, chlorine, and selenium are all important to at least some plants but are needed in only tiny amounts.

Plants that are deficient in a mineral will grow poorly and also show signs of deficiency characteristic of that mineral. In fact, if a plant is greatly deficient in one particular mineral, it is possible to identify the responsible mineral from the appearance of the plant. An experienced person can describe the deficiencies found in a certain sample of soil by studying the appearance of the plants growing in it.

The characteristic effects that certain mineral deficiencies have on growing plants are shown in Table P-1. In nature, it is possible for the plant to show deficiency

TABLE P-1. SYMPTOMS OF MINERAL DEFICIENCIES IN PLANTS

Mineral that is deficient:	Symptoms that result:
Nitrogen	Leaves change from a green-yellow at the top to yellow to brown, dead leaves at the bottom. In many species a red or purpling occurs along the veins. Plant shows stunting.
Potassium	Limited growth, weak stems, and a yellow mottling of the leaves; ultimately necrotic areas on leaf tips and edges; a general overall yellowing appearance of the leaves.
Phosphorus	Plant stunted; leaves small and dark green; occasionally production of anthocyanins causes a red or purple color. Dead areas develop on leaves, petioles, and (in older plants) fruits, causing some dropping. Roots are poorly developed.
Sulfur	Yellowing of the younger leaves in the early stages; ultimately an overall pale green may dominate (chlorosis). Roots are poorly developed.
Calcium	First symptom usually deformation of younger leaves, and then a disintegration of terminal growing areas, due to the death of the meristem tissue.
Magnesium	Lower leaves show symptoms first, mottled yellowing (chlorosis) from the tip and eventually falling. Veins remain green longer than the rest of the leaf.
Micronutrients	*Iron:* Young leaves light green or almost white (chlorosis), while older leaves are green. Unlike most other elements, iron cannot be withdrawn from the older leaves, so they retain a normal appearance. The yellowing of the younger leaves is most obvious between the veins (interveinal chlorosis). *Boron:* abnormally dark green leaves; abnormal growth with malformations; root tip growth slows. *Chlorine:* retarded photosynthesis causes very small leaves that become wilted, chlorotic, or necrotic; growth slows. *Manganese:* Leaves become spotted with dead areas and fall. *Copper:* Tips of young leaves are dark green and wither; plant may wilt even when it is watered. *Zinc:* Yellowing of lower leaves at tips and margins; leaves small and deformed; stems stunted. *Molybdenum:* Required for nitrogen metabolism, so symptoms resemble those of nitrogen deficiency.

symptoms even though the nutrient is actually present in the soil around the plant. The nutrient may be in a form held tightly to the soil particles or insoluble at the soil pH. Even if it enters the plant, it may not be in a form that can be transported to the site where it is needed. Finally, it may be available in the needed location, but the combination of other nutrients may not be adequate for the nutrient to serve its necessary function. In this laboratory exercise, you will provide the plants with the nutrients in a readily available form and do not need to consider problems of availability, uptake, or transport.

In some cases a plant will actually be deficient for a certain nutrient but will compensate so that the effect of the deficiency is minimal. If, for example, calcium is required for a certain reaction but is present only in small amounts, magnesium or manganese, also divalent cations, will be able to substitute. Sometimes minerals can be removed from an older part of a plant and relocated to the new, growing part where they are more urgently needed. This type of recycling can prolong the active life of a plant growing under poor conditions. Compensation will complicate nutritional studies because the differences between a healthy plant and one with a deficiency will tend to be masked. Since most nutrients are needed for many processes, however, a deficiency will usually at least result in a slower growth rate, even if no overt deficiency symptoms appear in the experiment.

EFFECT OF NUTRITIONAL DEFICIENCIES

Experiment

In this exercise you will work with a partner and test the effect of two different deficiencies on young seedlings. You will measure the growth rate and observe the appearance of the experimental seedlings and compare your observations with similar ones on seedlings deficient for an unknown nutrient. The control seedlings will be given all the necessary nutrients. All of the seedlings will be grown under identical conditions of light, temperature, and moisture.

Procedure

Obtain 12 seedlings that have been grown in washed sand. Obtain 4 growth jars and label them properly with the labels provided:

A = experimental solution deficient in _____

B = experimental solution deficient in _____

C = experimental solution with unknown deficiency

D = control solution with no deficiency

The components of the experimental solutions are given in Table P-2 at the end of this project.

Follow these instructions exactly in filling your bottles:

1. Add 200 mL of distilled water to each bottle.
2. Locate the column in the table for the first mineral deficiency that you have been assigned and mark it A.
3. Add each of the ingredients called for in turn, *MIXING THOROUGHLY AFTER EACH ADDITION.*
4. Fill bottle A with distilled water.
5. Locate the column in the table for the second mineral deficiency that you have been assigned and mark it B.
6. Add the ingredients called for as before and fill bottle B with distilled water.
7. Add 15 mL of an unknown solution to bottle C and fill it with distilled water. Record the unknown number in your procedure.
8. Add the components called for under "complete" in the table to bottle D and fill it with distilled water.

Measure the pH of one of your solutions by adding a drop of it to a piece of pH paper:

pH = _____

Iron is insoluble at neutral or basic pH values. Why is the iron provided in the form of FeNaEDTA?

_____

What kind of compound is EDTA? _____

Obtain four aluminum lids for your bottles, punch four holes in each, and cover your bottles as shown in Figure P-3. One hole is for adding distilled water to your plants and the other three are for the plants themselves. Label three holes in each lid 1, 2, and 3, so you will be able to identify the individual plants.

When your bottles are ready, obtain twelve 10-day-old corn or sunflower seedlings that have been grown in washed sand and a few pieces of cotton. The plants should be about 8 cm long. Rinse the roots of the plants carefully in distilled water to remove the sand. Wrap a piece of cotton around the stem of each plant and insert three plants into the lid of each bottle. Arrange the bottles neatly in the greenhouse space assigned to your class. All bottles must be labeled with your name and the date.

Results

When the plants are in place in the greenhouse, measure the height of each plant and record the data in Table P-3 at the end of this project. Repeat the measurements once or twice each week for four weeks and note the appearance of the plants in the table. Notice the appearance of the experimental seedlings of the other students as well.

At the end of the experiment summarize your results and obtain the results for the other deficiencies that you did not test yourself. Summarize the data in Table P-4 at the end of this project.

Figure P-3. Nutritional testing. Seedlings are grown in a bottle to test for nutritional requirements. The bottle must be kept completely filled by adding distilled water to replace water lost.

Conclusions

a. Which single mineral deficiency had the greatest effect on the seedlings? _____

b. Did the seedlings in plain distilled water show any growth at all? _____

c. If there was growth in these seedlings, how could you explain it? _____

_____

_____

_____

d. If your class studied both corn seedlings and sunflower seedlings, which type was more sensitive to iron deficiency? _____

e. Were there other differences in corn and sunflower seedling responses to different deficiencies?

_____

_____

_____

_____

Compare the appearance and growth rate of the seedlings in the solution with an unknown deficiency (bottle C) to those of the other seedlings studied by the class.

f. Was the growth of these seedlings similar to that of the control (no deficiency) or did the unknown solution appear to be deficient in one or more minerals?

_____

_____

When the experiment is over, dispose of the plant remains properly and wash the bottles very carefully in hot soapy water. Rinse them six times in tap water and three times in distilled water so that all traces of the mineral solutions have been removed.

EXPLORING FURTHER

Bowling, D. J. F. *Uptake of Ions by Plant Roots*. London: Chapman and Hall, 1976.

Epstein, E. *Mineral Nutrition of Plants: Principles and Perspectives*. New York: John Wiley and Sons, 1972.

Galston, Arthur W., and Peter J. Davies. *Control Mechanisms in Plant Development*. Englewood Cliffs, N. J.: Prentice-Hall, 1970.

Galston, Arthur W., Peter J. Davies, and Ruth L. Satter. *The Life of the Green Plant*. 3rd ed. Englewood Cliffs, N.J.: Prentice-Hall, 1980.

Kaufman, Peter B., John Labovitch, and Anne Anderson. *Laboratory Experiments in Plant Physiology*. New York: Macmillan, 1975.

Journal Articles

Jordan, Carl F. "Amazon rain forests." *American Scientist* 70(4): 394, 1982.

Olsen, Ralph A., Ralph B. Clark, and Jesse H. Bennett. "The enhancement of soil fertility by plant roots." *American Scientist 69:* 378, 1981.

Student Name _____ Date _____

TABLE P–2. PREPARATION OF EXPERIMENTAL SOLUTIONS*

Stock Solution	No minerals = COMPLETE	Solutions Deficient In:								All minerals = DISTILLED WATER
		Ca	S	Mg	K	N	P	Fe	Micro-nutrients	
		Add (mL)	Add (mL)	Add (mL)	Add (mL)	Add (mL)	Add (mL)	Add (mL)	Add (mL)	No additions
0.5 M $CaNO_3$	5	0	5	5	5	0	5	5	5	0
0.5 M KNO_3	5	5	5	5	0	0	5	5	5	0
0.5 M $MgSO_4$	2	2	0	0	2	2	2	2	2	0
0.5 M KH_2PO_4	1	1	1	1	0	1	0	1	1	0
FeNa EDTA	1	1	1	1	1	1	1	0	1	0
Microelements	1	1	1	1	1	1	1	1	0	0
0.5 M $NaNO_3$	0	5	0	0	5	0	0	0	0	0
0.5 M $MgCl_2$	0	0	2	0	0	0	0	0	0	0
0.5 M Na_2SO_4	0	0	0	2	0	0	0	0	0	0
0.5 M NaH_2PO_4	0	0	0	0	1	0	0	0	0	0
0.5 M $CaCl_2$	0	0	0	0	0	5	0	0	0	0
0.5 M KCl	0	0	0	0	0	5	1	0	0	0
	15	15	15	15	15	15	15	14	14	0

*Reprinted with permission of Macmillan Publishing Co., Inc. from *Laboratory Experiments in Plant Physiology* by Peter B. Kaufman, John Labovitch and Anne Anderson. Copyright © 1975 by Peter B. Kaufman, John Labovitch and Anne Anderson.

TABLE P–3. EXPERIMENTAL DATA ON MINERAL-DEFICIENT PLANTS.

(Experiment started on (date): _____)

Plant	Deficiency	Date: _____ Height	Appearance	Date: _____ Height	Appearance	Date: _____ Height	Appearance
A-1							
A-2							
A-3							
B-1							
B-2							
B-3							
C-1	Unknown #: ____						
C-2	Unknown #: ____						
C-3	Unknown #: ____						
D-1	Complete						
D-2	Complete						
D-3	Complete						

Student Name _____ Date _____

TABLE P–3. (contd.)

Plant	Date: _____ Height	Appearance	Date: _____ Height	Appearance	Date: _____ Height	Appearance	Date: _____ Height	Appearance
A-1								
A-2								
A-3								
B-1								
B-2								
B-3								
C-1								
C-2								
C-3								
D-1								
D-2								
D-3								

Student Name _____   Date _____

344   PROJECT B ■ PLANT NUTRITION

TABLE P–4.   SUMMARY OF EFFECTS OF NUTRITIONAL DEFICIENCIES

Plants	Deficiency	Corn Seedlings		Sunflower Seedlings	
		Total Growth (cm)	*Final Appearance*	*Total Growth (cm)*	*Final Appearance*
Controls	none				
Expt.	Ca				
Expt.	S				
Expt.	Mg				
Expt.	K				
Expt.	N				
Expt.	P				
Expt.	Fe				
Expt.	micronutrients				
Expt.	all minerals				
Unknown #					

Unknown is probably deficient: _____ /probably not deficient: _____

Unknown might be deficient in: _____

Unknown is probably not deficient in: _____

The Pond Ecosystem

OBJECTIVES

When you have completed this topic, you should be able to:
1. Define ecosystem, community, and succession.
2. Explain the advantages of a microecosystem (microcosm) over an outdoor ecosystem.
3. Give examples of the following that might be found in a pond: abiotic substance, producer organism, macroconsumer organism, saprobe, decomposer, detritus, scavenger, primary carnivore, secondary (top) carnivore.
4. Define species, species diversity, and climax community.
5. Describe a laboratory experiment designed to compare succession in two pond microcosms.
6. Analyze the results of such an experiment and present them in a formal laboratory report.

KEY TOPICS

Binomial nomenclature, ecosystems, populations, communities, competition, succession.

INTRODUCTION

THE LABORATORY WORK FOR THIS PROJECT EXTENDS OVER A PERIOD OF AT LEAST 3 WEEKS. ONE LABORATORY PERIOD IS REQUIRED TO SET UP THE EXPERIMENT, AND THE TIME SPENT IN FOLLOWING IT IS OPEN-ENDED (10-20 HR).

The Microecosystem

An **ecosystem** includes the organisms in a certain area and their interactions with the physical environment with which they exchange energy and materials. The group of organisms living in an ecosystem is called a **community.** The energy flowing through the ecosystem will result in a diversity of species in different trophic levels and in a cycling of materials through the system. The **microcosms,** or microecosystems, that we will establish in the laboratory fit the definition of ecosystems. However, the microcosms also have properties unlike those of most natural ecosystems, which must be taken into account.

Today many ecologists are turning to laboratory and field microecosystems or microcosms, which have discrete boundaries and can be manipulated and replicated at will, because outdoor ecosystems are complex, hard to delineate, and often difficult to study by the traditional means of "experiment and control." Whereas you cannot remove the sediments from a pond to see what effects this action would have, you can set up a microcosm without sediment and observe the results. Another advantage of a microcosm is that the time scale of events is shortened. Normally, **succession,** which is the more or less orderly pattern of changing communities over time, is very slow. This is particularly true of primary succession in which organisms first colonize a nonliving habitat. In the microcosm, however, secondary succession to a stable system takes place in a few weeks. Microcosms also generally have fewer species than their parent ecosystem as well as simpler communities.

In what ways are microcosms unlike the environments that they are supposed to mimic? Size and isolation are two obvious differences. Organisms in the microcosms tend to diverge from those in their parent communities and each other, but this problem can be eliminated to an extent by cross-seeding the jars: We mix the water in each jar with water from other jars after they have stabilized for a few days.

The Pond

Let us first consider the natural pond ecosystem. (See text Figure 50-2). Not only is the pond a place where organisms live, but organisms make the pond what it is. Despite the complexities of this system, we can reduce it to several basic units.

ABIOTIC SUBSTANCES

These are simply **organic** and **inorganic compounds** such as H_2O, CO_2, O_2, calcium, nitrogen and phosphorus salts, and so on. A small portion of these vital nutrients is in solution and immediately available to organisms, but a much larger portion is held in reserve in particulate matter (especially in the bottom sediments) as well as in the organisms themselves. The rate of nutrient release, the solar input, temperature, and other climatic factors are the most important processes that regulate the rate of function of the entire ecosystem on a day-to-day basis.

PRODUCERS

Generally speaking, there are two main types of producers in a pond: rooted or large floating **plants** and minute floating plants, called **phytoplankton.** Phytoplankton are usually much more important than rooted vegetation in the production of food for the ecosystem. Producers occur mostly in the green belt stratum.

CONSUMERS

Unicellular protozoans and zooplankton are the **microconsumers.** They feed on bacteria and planktonic organisms smaller than themselves. The **primary macroconsumers** are herbivores that feed directly on living plants or plant remains and are of two types. Zooplankton are the small animal plankton, and benthic (profundal) organisms are the bottom-dwelling forms. The **secondary consumers** are carnivores such as predacious insects and game fish, which feed on the primary consumers. **Tertiary consumers,** such as large fish, feed in turn on the secondary consumers.

DECOMPOSERS

Decomposers perform the vital function of recycling nutrients in the environment. The **saprobes** are the aquatic bacteria, flagellates, and fungi that cannot make or ingest food and so absorb it through their cell membranes. They are distributed throughout the pond but are especially abundant at the mud-water interface in the brown belt stratum along the bottom, where the bodies of plants and animals accumulate. Larger detritus feeders that ingest dead or decaying material are called **scavengers.** All these organisms are saprotrophic because they feed on dead remains. Scavengers can be considered to be a special type of consumer that is also a decomposer.

It is important to remember that although the pond may seem to be a self-contained unit, its productivity and stability over a period of years is very much determined by the input of solar energy and especially by the rate of inflow of water and materials from the watershed. The watershed is the whole drainage basin, that is, all the land that contributes runoff to the pond.

Succession

Succession, the more or less orderly process of community change, involves replacement, in the course of time, of the dominant species within a given area by other species. The ecological succession that you will be observing in your microcosms is a temporal succession. The microcosms will develop a series of different communities as the physical environment becomes modified by the community. Therefore, succession is community-controlled even though the physical environment determines the pattern, the rate of change, and often sets the limits as to how far development will go. This is very true of your microcosms because they are limited by the size of the container, the amount of incoming solar radiation, and so on. As succession proceeds, you should notice a change in species composition and an increase in species diversity. The diversity of species will increase because rare species that were unnoticed at first may increase in abundance so that they are eventually included. The successional pattern will culminate in a **climax community,** whatever that may be for a particular ecosystem.

Aquatic microecosystems derived from ponds will maintain themselves in a climax state indefinitely with only light input. They will usually reach this level in less than 100 days.

■ Be sure to examine the microcosms that have been growing for 1 or 2 years if they are on display in the laboratory.

PLANNING YOUR EXPERIMENT

Lab Groups

Work in groups of four. Each group will have two microcosm jars—one to be used for an experimental treatment, the other for a control. Two students will be in charge of each jar. There is a lot of work involved in this project, but a smoothly functioning team can handle it with a reasonable expenditure of time and effort. Because you will need to exchange data among yourselves, you should choose your group with two things in mind:

1. You should be able to come to lab at the same time to set up your experiment and to take your subsequent observations. This way, you will all be referring to one kind of organism by the same name!
2. You should be people who see each other frequently (have classes together, live in the same dormitories, and so on) if possible. Then you will be able to get hold of each other easily to exchange data.

Materials

The water you will use comes from a nearby pond. Three types of microcosms have been set up, all containing about 3 liters of water:

1. Microcosm—no sediment. There will be little exchange of nutrients, no sediment biota, and no species refuge.
2. Microcosm—sand. No exchange of nutrients, no sediment biota, but a refuge for other species.

3. Microcosm—sediment. The "natural look." There will be nutrient exchange, a refuge for species, and a good healthy sediment biota.

You may wish to use additional chemicals, lights, aerators, heaters, and the like. If you plan in advance what you will need and notify the staff, they will let you know whether it can be obtained. You may wish to bring additional materials of your own on the day that you set up the experiment.

Experimental Design

Prepare a detailed written description of your experimental plan before coming to laboratory to start the experiment, and obtain the instructor's approval of your plan before starting the experiment. This plan should include:

1. The nature of the experimental and control microcosms.
2. The amounts of components and concentrations of added materials or chemicals.
3. A schedule for gathering data.
4. Criteria for deciding whether or not the experimental treatment had an effect.

As a group, you should discuss and decide on a semioriginal experimental design. Here are some suggestions to mull over:

Have a microcosm with sediment as your control and one with no sediment as the experimental model. Then compare and contrast trends.

Expose one microcosm to constant light and one to the natural diurnal pattern. Again, compare and contrast trends.

Enrich one microcosm with glucose as an immediately available carbon source. Use 3 g of glucose for 3 L of water. Please be aware that this treatment creates quite a stench in the experimental jar!

Be sure that both your microcosms are receiving the *same light exposure* (both in the south window, etc.) unless you are deliberately using different exposures. Also, cross-seed your jars before you begin so that they have the same organisms at the beginning of the experiment.

STARTING YOUR EXPERIMENT

■ Choose two microcosm jars.

■ Label each microcosm with your names, the treatment, the date, and a number.

■ Record the qualitative aspects of your microcosms. What organisms can you see with the naked eye? Is there anything living in the sediment? Are there snails present? Whenever you record data, label it with your name and the date on which the observations were made. Do not rely on your memory alone, or you may end up in a state of great confusion when you attempt to write up the results. If possible, use a notebook for your data.

■ Remove a 5-mL sample from the center of your microcosm using the pipets and bulbs provided. If you are not going to examine the sample immediately, transfer it to a small sample bottle and add one drop of acid Lugol's solution to preserve the sample. Cork the sample tightly, and label it completely (name, date, microcosm, number).

■ Examine your sample in the microscope by making a wet mount of one drop or by placing a drop in a depression slide and adding a cover slip. The depression slide will allow wiggly animals more freedom of movement but it will also be more difficult to keep them in focus as they move vertically in the field.

■ While viewing the sample under low power, move the slide around to locate as many different kinds of organisms as you can. Switch to high power to search for smaller organisms. If the motile organisms are swimming too fast, add a drop of Protoslo, which will slow them down.

The search you just finished was designed to familiarize you with the different organisms. Obviously classification of the organisms is the most difficult part of this lab. Using the posters and books in the lab, try to identify the organisms that you examine. But *do not become overly concerned* with scientific identification of the organisms. It is *more* important to be able to distinguish one kind from another and to be able to communicate with other members of your group so that all of you are using the same name for the same thing.

■ When you find a new organism:

1. Draw it in your data chart, which should also have space to record the date, the kind of organism, the number in each of five fields, and the total number.
2. Place it into a taxonomic group, for example, bacterium, cyanophyte (blue-green), diatom, protozoan, multicellular animal, or multicellular plant.
3. Try to find its picture in one of the posters or books in the lab, and call it by its accepted name. For bacteria, classification as rod-, sphere-, or spiral-shaped will suffice.
4. If you cannot locate a picture that looks like the organism in one of the sources provided, give it your own name, and make sure the others in your group have a good look at it in your microscope so that all of you will be calling it the same thing. At the same time, try to distinguish and name as many different kinds of organisms as possible.

■ Now that you have identified the organisms in your sample, you will try to count them.

The following procedure is to provide a random count that gives an accurate representation of the relative abundances of organisms in the sample. You should avoid the "cheating" that would result from deliberately seeking out the most interesting or abundant organisms. Always record exactly what you see.

■ Looking at the microscope from one side, center the cover slip of your slide on the microscope stage. View the slide under low power. Count the number of each kind of organism in the field, and record it in the data table. If there are too many of some kinds or organisms to count, estimate the order of magnitude (10^2, 10^3, and so on) of individuals in each field.

■ Switch to high power to count bacteria, and be sure to make adjustments for the change in field size at the higher magnification when you record the number present.

■ Move the slide in turn to the four corners of the cover slip (again watching from the side, *not* through the microscope), and record the numbers of each type of organism present in each field.

■ In the right-hand column of the data sheet, record the total number of each type of organism observed.

■ Examine a larger sample of water in a watch glass under the dissecting microscope to identify and observe zooplankton present. You may be able to see *Daphnia* (water flea) with young in their brood pouch as well as many other interesting organisms. Carefully return this sample to your microcosm.

■ Do a chlorophyll analysis to give you some idea of the overall size of the producer trophic level. (See Figure P-4.)

1. **Sampling.** Dip a 100-mL beaker into the middle of your microcosm to get a 100-mL sample of phytoplankton. Estimate what proportion of your water is occupied by green masses of algae floating or attached to the side of the jar, and then add to your 100-mL sample of water a mass of algae to take up the same proportion of space in the beaker. (For example, if your microcosm has a clump of algae that occupies 10% of the jar, you will take out a piece of the clump that will occupy 10% of the beaker.)

2. **Filtration.** Flute a piece of Whatman filter paper, place it in a funnel, and place the stem of the funnel into an Erlenmeyer flask. Pour the contents of your beaker into the filter paper; than wait till all the liquid has gone through. Return the liquid in the flask to the microcosm.

1. Take representative sample.

2. Filter.

3. Grind in mortar with acetone.

4. Measure absorption of extract.

Figure P-4. Chlorophyll analysis. The concentration of chlorophyll will be proportional to the difference between the absorbance at 663 nm and 750 nm.

3. **Pigment extraction.** The algae are now clinging to the filter paper. Place the paper in the mortar and add 5 mL of acetone. Gently grind with the pestle, hard enough to break the algal cells but not hard enough to shred the paper. Remove the filter paper and let any paper fibers settle. Pour off the acetone, containing the algal pigments, into a spectrophotometer cuvette.

4. **Chlorophyll measurement.** Fill a second cuvette with acetone for your blank.

BE CAREFUL NOT TO SPILL ACETONE ONTO THE SPECTROPHOTOMETER.

Following the directions in Topic 6 for operating the spectrophotometer, take readings of both tubes at 663 nm (the absorption maximum of chlorophyll *a* in acetone solution) and at 750 nm (where chlorophyll *a* absorption is negligible). The second reading will give you some idea of the contamination of your sample by pigments other than chlorophyll and by light-scattering debris.

FOLLOWING YOUR EXPERIMENT

Sample you microcosms every 2-3 days for 3-5 weeks, making sure to keep accurate records of the distribution of large and small organisms.

Repeat the chlorophyll analysis a total of three to four times during the course of your experiment. If you expect the producers to be experiencing major population changes because of your particular experimental treatment, you should do it more often.

At the end of the experiment, follow your instructor's directions for disposing of the microcosms (some may be kept for a longer period). Clean up any equipment that you have used.

ANALYZING YOUR EXPERIMENT

Now that you have all these data, what are you going to do with them?

1. Summarize your data in tables and graphs, when possible. Graph the abundance of different kinds versus time following the example shown in Figure P-5. To simplify your data summary, you may want to lump organisms of one type (ciliated protozoan, diatom, green alga, rod-shaped bacteria, and so on) together.

2. Calculate a simple diversity index:

$$D = \frac{\text{total number of kinds}}{\log_{10} \text{ of total number of individuals}}$$

3. Classify the organisms present in your habitat as rare (10 or fewer individuals), common (11-50), or abundant (more than 50).

4. Write a laboratory report on this experiment according to the standard form given in Appendix A of this manual. Try to answer the following questions in the course of your discussion:

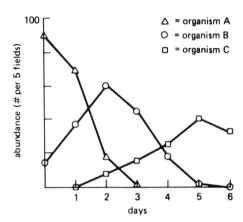

Figure P-5. Changing abundances.

a. Compare and contrast your microcosm with the pond this water came from, or ponds in general (food chains, size, diversity, and so on). What are the properties peculiar to the microcosm?
b. Can you draw any conclusions from your data about ponds or ecosystems in general? Did you learn anything about aquatic ecosystems or is the microcosm simply an anomaly?
c. How could you conduct the same experiment in the field? (The answer "it is not possible" will not be accepted.)

EXPLORING FURTHER

Abramoff, P., and R. G. Thomson. "The microscope." in *Laboratory Outlines in Biology II.* San Francisco: W. H. Freeman, 1972. (Freeman laboratory separate #846.)

Bold, Harold C., and Michael J. Wynne. *Introduction to the Algae: Structure and Reproduction.* 2nd ed. Englewood Cliffs, N. J.: Prentice-Hall, 1985.

Coker, R. E. *Streams, Lakes and Ponds.* New York: Harper and Row, 1968.

Jahn, T., and F. Jahn. *How to Know the Protozoa.* 2nd ed. Dubuque, Iowa: W. C. Brown, 1979.

Klots, E. B. *The New Field Book of Freshwater Life.* New York: Putnam, 1966.

Krebs, C. J. *Ecology: The Experimental Analysis of Distribution and Abundance.* 2nd ed. New York: Harper and Row, 1978.

Odum, E. P. *Basic Ecology.* Philadelphia: Saunders College Publishing, 1983.

Prescott, G. W. *How to Know the Freshwater Algae.* 3rd ed. Dubuque, Iowa: W. C. Brown, 1978.

Reid, George K. *Pond Life: A Guide to Common Plants and Animals of North American Ponds and Lakes.* New York: Golden Press, 1967.

Southwood, T. R. E. *Ecological Methods.* 2nd ed. London: Chapman and Hall, Metheun, Inc., 1978.

Turk, J. *Introduction to Environmental Studies.* 2nd ed. Philadelphia: Saunders College Publishing, 1985.

Whittaker, R. H. *Communities and Ecosystems.* 2nd ed. New York: Macmillan, 1975.

Journal Articles

Bormann, F. H., and G. E. Likens. "The nutrient cycles of an ecosystem." *Scientific American,* October, 1970 (#1202).

Clark, John R. "Thermal pollution and aquatic life." *Scientific American,* March 1969 (#1135).

Forbes, S. A. "The lake as microcosm." *Bulletin of the Illinois Natural History Survey 15:* 537, 1887.

Gosz, J. R., R. T. Holmes, G. E. Likens, and F. H. Bormann. "The flow of energy in a forest ecosystem." *Scientific American,* March 1978 (#1384).

Janick, J., C. H. Noller, and C. L. Rhykerd. "The cycles of plant and animal nutrition." *Scientific American,* September 1976 (no offprint).

Likens, Gene E., Richard F. Wright, James N. Galloway, and Thomas J. Butler. "Acid rain." *Scientific American,* October 1979 (#941).

Woodwell, George M. "Toxic substances and ecological cycles." *Scientific American,* March 1967 (#1066).

Writing a Lab Report

FORMAT

A formal lab report should follow the general format used for a research report published in a scientific journal. Although different journals require different formats, all papers have a roughly similar outline. They reflect the basic scientific method of asking a question, formulating hypotheses, conducting experiments to test the hypotheses, and interpreting the results. You may want to go to the library to look at articles in journals such as *Bioscience, Proceedings of the National Academy of Sciences,* or *Limnology* to get an idea of how to write a scientific paper. (*Scientific American* is *not* considered a scientific journal because its purpose is not communication between research scientists engaged in related work.)

Although not all journals require authors to divide their papers into clearly labeled sections, this practice will help you develop good habits in reporting your findings. Therefore, you are asked to label clearly each section in your paper except for the title.

Title

The title should consist of a few well-chosen words indicating the subject of the report. "Well-chosen" means that the title reflects the scope of your report accurately: do not call your paper "Effects of Chemicals on Animals" if you really studied how feeding dietary supplements of vitamins A and D affected the appearance of the fur of three white rats.

Abstract

The abstract is a short paragraph of 150 words or less that summarizes your experiment, including pertinent information about your experimental subjects, materials and methods, results, and conclusions. This is the part of the paper scientists read to decide whether they are interested in looking at the rest of the paper. Thus the information the abstract contains should help people decide whether your research sheds any useful light on what they are studying.

Introduction

The introduction gives the background of the experiment. It should include an explanation of the background of the general problem or area being investigated, telling why this problem is of interest and outlining what information is already known about the problem.

The problem does not necessarily have to be relevant to the health and welfare of human beings or of immediate economic importance to be of interest. Students often attempt to force a human perspective on a problem that is of interest because it is related to broad underlying principles of the structure or functioning of living things. In building up this part of your report you may want to consult outside references or, at the very least, reread the relevant parts of your text. But be sure to keep track of where you get this information and list all references used, including your textbook and laboratory guide, in a reference list at the end of the paper.

The introduction should also present the question you are trying to answer or the hypothesis you are testing. You should include what outcome you expect, and how it would help support or refute your hypothesis or answer your question. Be sure to distinguish between the hypothesis itself and the experiment you will do to test the hypothesis.

Materials and Methods

This section should include a concise description of the materials, procedures, and equipment used. It should clearly describe the experimental situation, the control situation(s) and the type of observations you made. There should be enough detail so that someone else could repeat your work. Therefore, brand names of equipment, concentrations and amounts of solutions, species, size or age, sex, and other information about the experimental subjects should be included. If you follow directions from a book or paper, just say so. You need not repeat them in your paper. If, however, you change the procedure, you should explain why you did so and exactly what you did differently.

Do not include the rationale for your work in this section. Also, be sure to report your procedure as a past event rather than writing this section as a set of directions to your reader. You do not need to report attempts at the experiment with techniques that failed unless these techniques are very likely to be tried by other people in the future.

Results

Present your findings in a logical, not chronological, order. Give the results that you found, not what you think you should have found. The organism is always right! You may have to do some thinking, however, to find out why the results came out as they did. Do not explain your results in this section. Many papers are valuable for their correct results, although the interpretation of the results may be completely wrong and may later be modified in light of further information.

Results can often be reported more effectively in the form of one or more tables or graphs or drawings. These should have clear labels and captions. Be sure to indicate whether the data reported are single readings or averages. Statistical analyses of your data should also be included here if appropriate. In addition, a written description should summarize the results illustrated in the graph or figures. This should point out trends or inconsistencies but should not include explanations or opinions.

Discussion

Here you should give your interpretations of the data and relate them to the questions you posed in the introduction. Be careful to avoid making this section just a repetition of the introduction. If you have any data to explain away, do it here or make a new hypothesis as to why the results came out in a way you did not expect. Did the results answer your question? Did they support or disprove your hypothesis? Draw some conclusions, supporting them with your data. What is the significance of your results in the general area you studied? What are the main principles demonstrated by your results?

What further experiments should be performed to clear up discrepancies or ambiguities in your results? How might your work best be continued or extended?

Conclusion

This should be a separate section only if you have a lot of conclusions. Otherwise you should simply round off your discussion section with the conclusions that you can draw from your experiments.

References

You must refer to all the sources of information that you used in your paper. Failure to do so is a serious offense, **plagiarism,** and will result in rejection of your laboratory report or worse. All of the sources in the reference list must be cited in the paper and vice versa. Usually your sources will be books or articles in the scientific literature, but you must also cite any persons from whom you obtained information directly as "personal communication."

There are several possible systems for organizing your references. You may choose to list the references in the order in which you cite them in the text. In this case you place a number in your paper after a comment from the reference: for example, "The Loch Ness monster is a big worm (1)," and then list the reference from which you obtained this information as number 1 in your refer-

ence list. Alternatively, you may alphabetize your list of references and then number the list when you have finished preparing your report. In that case you can use either the number or the author's last name(s) to refer to the source.

Whichever system you use, you may sometimes want to cite the author and date of the source in your text. This has the advantage of letting your reader know something about the authority and how recent your information is without flipping to the end of the report all the time. For example, you could say, "The Loch Ness monster is a giant worm (Smith, 1970)," or "Smith (1970) has found that the Loch Ness monster is a huge worm," or "In 1970, Smith found that the Loch Ness monster is a large worm." With three or more authors, name them all the first time that you cite them and then use "Smith et al." subsequently (et al. means "and others"). You do not need to repeat the date each time unless you have more than one reference from the same author.

SUGGESTED FORMAT FOR REFERENCE LIST ENTRIES

Here are examples of three types of entries that you might make in your reference list. You may also use the format used by a prominent scientific journal or one suggested by your instructor. Once you have decided on the format, use it consistently for all of your references.

A book reference might read as follows:
Vince, Prae D. *Photoperiodism in Plants.* New York: McGraw-Hill, 104, 194, 1975.

A reference to a journal article:
Raymond, J. A., and A. L. DeVries. "Adsorption inhibition as a mechanism of freezing resistance in polar fishes." *Proc. Nat. Acad. Sci., U.S.A.* 74: 2589-2593, 1977.

A reference to an article that appeared in a book:
Rehn, S. "Chemical defenses of ant acacias." In J. Pearson, ed., *Phytochemistry.* New York: Academic Press, 1973.

A reference to discussion with or letter from an individual:
Villee, C. A. personal communication.

WRITING TIPS

Your report will be easier to read and understand if you follow these tips and try to conform to the accepted style of scientific writing that is required for scientific papers. Conformity can be a good thing if it increases communication!

1. Write in the past tense, not present or future: "Two rats were anesthetized and . . ."
2. Use metric units (gram, meter, liter, second) and the Celsius temperature scale.
3. Use correct abbreviations *without* periods:

10 milliliters	= 10 mL
12 liters	= 12L
3 micrograms	= 3 μg
7 grams	= 7 g
24 kilograms	= 24 kg
663 nanometers	= 663 nm
8 micrometers	= 8 μm
21 centimeters	= 21 cm
9 meters	= 9 m
52 kilometers	= 52 km
37 degrees Celsius	= 37° (37°C)

4. If you start a sentence with a number, write out the number: "Twelve grams of minced toad brain were . . ."

5. For solutions, use molarity (moles per liter) rather than normality:

$$5 \text{ molar} = 5 \text{ M}$$
$$.005 \text{ molar} = 5 \times 10^{-3} \text{ M or } 5 \text{ mM}$$
$$.000005 \text{ molar} = 5 \times 10^{-6} \text{ M or } 5 \text{ } \mu\text{M}$$

If the solution is given as a percent solution, indicate whether it was made up on the basis of weight or volume:

5 g glycerol + 95 g H_2O = 5% glycerol (w/w)
5 mL glycerol + 95 mL H_2O = 5% glycerol (v/v)
5 g glycerol brought up to 100 mL with H_2O
= 5% glycerol (w/v)

6. Refer to animals and plants by their scientific names. (This is not necessary when referring to humans and common laboratory animals.) Always underline or italicize the genus and species names of organisms, for example, *Stentor coeruleus*. Be as specific as you can in naming the organism, but when the name is not known completely (as in your Pond Ecosystem report), write *sp.* after the generic name, for example, *Oscillatoria sp.*

7. Your report should be written in grammatically correct English; it should be concise and logically sound. Avoid boring the reader with copious verbiage and *excessively* formal writing. It is perfectly all right to sound excited about your work if you have worked carefully and have interesting results to report.

When in doubt, ask your instructor or try to find an example in a recent journal.

Biological Experiments and Statistics

INTRODUCTION

Many scientific experiments lead to observations that take the form of numerical data. An experiment is designed to make a limited number of observations from which the scientist would like to generalize to the whole of the population that is under study. (A population is a collection of organisms or phenomena that have something in common.)

The most direct way of showing how to deal with a large body of data is to use an example to illustrate the steps in analyzing and interpreting the results. We will use a familiar case: the results of a biology exam given to 100 biology students. Suppose the biology exam consisted of 40 questions. The scores of all the students constitute the **raw data.**

If the course is graded on a "curve," the instructor and students are eager to see the plot of the **frequency distribution.** This is a graph in which the number of students receiving each score (the frequency) is plotted against the individual scores (40, 39, 38, and so on). The basis of making the graph is a table of score frequencies as is shown in Table B-1.

The table shows that 13 students received a score of 38, 4 received a score of 30, and so forth. The high score was 40 and the low score was 24, so the **range** of the scores was 24-40.

ARITHMETIC MEAN

The **arithmetic mean** is the average of all scores: all scores are added together, and the total is divided by the number of scores. If the data are in the form of Table B-1, you know that 6 students received a grade of 40. You should thus multiply 40×6, 13×39 to give $f(x)$, and so on, and then add up all the products. The final total is divided by the number of students, which was 100. The results are given in Table B-1.

Mean $= \bar{x} = \Sigma x/N$, or $= \Sigma fx/N$,

where
$\bar{x}$ is the average or mean;
Σfx is the sum of all fx;
N is the number of scores.

What is the arithmetic mean for this test? _____

354

TABLE B-1. FREQUENCY DISTRIBUTION AND fx

Score (x)	Frequency (f)	fx
40	6	240
39	13	507
38	13	494
37	13	481
36	9	324
35	15	525
34	8	272
33	8	264
32	3	96
31	4	124
30	4	120
29	1	29
28	1	28
27	1	27
26	0	0
25	0	0
24	1	24
		Total: 3555

STANDARD DEVIATION AND VARIANCE

Variance is a measure of how far the scores tended to stray away from the average score of 35.6. One class might all score in the 30s with a mean of 35.6, and another class might include many 40s and some scores in the 20s and still have a mean of 35.6. The first class would have a lower variance than the second.

The formula for variance is:

$$\text{variance} = s^2 = \frac{\Sigma f(x - \overline{x})^2}{N - 1}$$

where

s is the standard deviation;
f is the frequency of a score x;
$\overline{x}$ is the mean of all scores;
N is the number of scores.

The difference between each score and the mean was determined, squared, and multiplied by the frequency of that score. All the products were added up, and the total was divided by the number of scores minus 1. In our example,

$$s^2 = 1068.5/99 = 10.8$$

The **standard deviation** is the square root of the variance. Thus in our example:

$$s = \sqrt{10.8} = 3.3$$

Any scores within 1 standard deviation of the mean (3.3 points, in this example) are said to be within 1 **standard deviation unit** of the mean. When there are many data points, as in our example, the mean should be expressed as mean ± standard deviation (for example, 35.6 ± 3.3). This form of presenting experimental data in a report tells the reader how much variance there was in the data gathered, and, therefore, how accurate the mean value really is. The smaller the standard deviation, the smaller the variance in the sample, and the more confident we are that the reported result is close to the true value of the mean and standard deviation for the population from which our sample was drawn.

When the class data for the plant hormone experiment (Project A) are analyzed, the results will be expressed by calculating the mean and standard deviation for each group of data. There will be a mean ± standard deviation for the lengths of the axillary buds on the control plants, another for the buds on the plants treated with lanolin, and so forth.

If the frequency distribution is a normal distribution, it will form a graph that is symmetrical about the mean and approximates a bell-shaped curve. The standard deviation then takes on additional meaning. In that case, about 68% of the values, that is, the bulk of the data, will fall within 1 standard deviation unit on either side of the mean. Furthermore, 95% of the data will fall within 2 standard deviation units, and 99% will fall within 3 units of the mean. In the case of the test scores, we would expect 99% of all students taking the test to score within 9.9 points (3s) of the mean, or above 25.7. The standard deviation can be used in this way only if the sample was drawn from a "bell-shaped" population. (Persons who didn't study for the test or who had taken an advanced course in the subject would tend to invalidate the test results.)

SIGNIFICANT FIGURES

The **significant figures** in a number are those that convey information. It is important that your reported data reflect the accuracy of your measurements and calculations, no more and no less. The number of significant figures is the number of digits except for those zeroes used to indicate the decimal point position. By convention, all digits to the left of an indicated decimal point (including zeroes) are significant.

Here are some examples:

number	sig figs	
27	2	
270	2	no decimal indicated
270.	3	
0.27	2	
0.2700	4	2 zeroes added solely
0.027	2	to indicate sig figs

In measurements, you should report your results to the smallest unit of which you are absolutely sure, plus one significant figure that is an estimate. For example, if you are measuring length with a ruler marked in millimeter increments, measure the millimeters, estimate the tenths of millimeters and report your data in tenths as 27.1 mm or 2.7 mm.

In reporting the mean of data, the number of figures to be presented is determined by the **standard deviation of the mean.** By convention, the standard deviation of the mean is reported to two significant figures (or one for small samples). The overall mean is reported to the same *number of decimal points* as the standard deviation of the mean:

standard deviation of the mean = standard deviation of the data points /$\sqrt{N}$

where N is the number of data points.

For the data points in Table B-1:

mean = 35.55
standard deviation = 3.3
standard deviation of the mean to two significant figures will be 3.3/$\sqrt{100}$. = 3.3$\sqrt{10}$. = 0.33

The overall mean may thus be reported to two decimal places, i.e. hundredths:

mean = 35.55 ± 0.33*

The type of deviation must always be specified, as by the footnote (*). Note that when data are presented according to the convention, the last digit of the mean is in fact not significant, since it is completely uncertain.

SIGNIFICANT DIFFERENCE

When we examine the results of an experiment, we would like to find out whether the results are "significant" or not. There are two ways of looking at significance.

1. We predict the results that we would obtain according to a certain hypothesis. Then we see how far away from the expected our results actually were. This approach is the one you will use in testing the results from your genetics experiment to see whether they could have varied from expected due to random chance or are so far from expected that your hypothesis is doubtful (Chi square test).

*standard deviation of the mean

2. We compare an experimental group with a control group using the **null hypothesis**: The two groups will be the same unless the experimental treatment had an effect. The more the results from the two groups differ, the less likely it is that the null hypothesis is correct.

In Project A, we would like to decide whether the axillary buds in the plant group treated by removing the apical buds grew longer than the buds in the untreated group. This can be done by using the student's t test or the Wilcoxon test to determine whether there is a significant difference between the results for the two groups.

All the plants originally came from the same population. If samples had been drawn from this population before the experiment, they might have had different means, but the difference would be due to chance alone. Such a difference would not be significant. After one group of plants has been treated in the experiment, the means may differ significantly as a result of the experimental treatment. We would like to know whether the difference is due to just random chance or to the experimental treatment. The statistical test will show whether the difference in the means could be due to random chance, and is therefore not significant, or is not due to random chance but rather to the experimental treatment, and is significant.

Statistical significance is usually expressed as a decimal. A significance level of 0.05 or 5% means that we could expect to find a significant difference only about 1 out of 20 times the experiment is conducted, if there is really *no* difference between the populations. The exact significance level at which populations are assumed to be really different is fuzzy and depends on the size and type of study being conducted. As a rough guideline, however, a significance level of 0.05 is usually accepted as sufficient to assume that the two groups are likely to be from different populations. A level of 0.01 or 1% is considered highly significant.

THE CHI-SQUARE TEST

The chi-square statistic is a mathematical comparison of the data obtained with the data expected according to the rules of probability. A chi-square (χ^2) value represents the degree to which the data fit the hypothesis on which the experiment was based. If chi-square is small, the data fit the hypothesis well; a large chi-square value represents a large deviation and throws doubt on the hypothesis. The actual formula for chi-square need not concern us here. In all problems where we wish to compare the frequencies in an observed sample with an expected frequency distribution we calculate a value known as x^2, which for our purposes may be regarded as a good approximation to χ^2 for large sample sizes.

The formula for x^2 is:

$$x^2 = \sum_{i=1}^{c} \frac{(o_i - e_i)^2}{e_i}$$

where

e_i is the number expected in each class;
o_i is the number observed in each class;
c is the number of classes; and
$\sum_{i=1}^{c}$ means that the expression's value is summed for each class from 1 to c.
To calculate x^2 for a genetics experiment:

1. For each class of offspring, subtract the number expected in the class (e) from the number observed in the class (o) to find ($o - e$).
2. Square this difference ($o - e$)^2.
3. Divide the result by the number expected in the class (e).
4. Repeat for all classes of offspring.
5. Add up (Σ) all the results; the sum is x^2.

Let us apply this to a concrete example.

Problem: A genetics student crosses two fruit flies and obtains 150 offspring. He or she sorts the offspring according to sex and finds 85 females and 65 males. Is this close enough to the expected 75 of each sex so that the observed sex distribution can be regarded as due to chance? (An alternative hypothesis might be that males die as embryos more often than females.)

Solution: The experimenter obtained 150 offspring of which 85 were female and 65 male where you would have expected 75 of each sex. To calculate the x^2 value for these results we can conveniently make a table like Table B-2. The observed and expected numbers of each sex of offspring are entered in the two left columns of the table. Now we subtract the expected from the observed offspring in each class to get the deviation for each class ($o - e$). In the next column we square each deviation. Finally we divide the squared deviation for each class by the expected number in each class and add up all the results to obtain x^2, which in this case is 2.6 ($\Sigma = x^2 = 2.6$).

To determine whether this x^2 value, which we treat as chi-square, is significant, we look at a table of chi-square values (Table B-3). You will see that there is one item in the table that we have not yet mentioned and that we need before we can read off the probability: **degrees of freedom.** The degrees of freedom in a system are usually defined as the number of classes minus one. In this case, with two classes of offspring (male and female), there is only 1 degree of freedom. One way to look at degrees of freedom is to see that it represents the number of choices you can make in assigning an individual to a class. In this case, you have only one decision to make. If you decide that a particular fruit fly is not male, it must be female. If degrees of freedom are thought of as a number of decisions to be made, you can make one less decision than the number of classes, because after that number of decisions, the last class has been determined automatically. In our fruit fly problem we have an x^2 value of 2.6 and 1 degree of freedom. From the table we see that this value falls between 1.6 in the 0.2 (20%) column and 2.7 in the 0.10 column (10%). This means that we would obtain a chi-square value of 2.6 slightly more than 10% of the time if we performed numerous crosses and counted the sex of the offspring. We say that the chi-square value is **not significant.** The hypothesis that half the offspring of a fruit fly are male and half are female need not be questioned. If we obtained a chi-square value which fell in the 5% or 1% columns, we would suspect that another hypothesis would explain our results better than the one we used. A value in the 5% column would be **significant,** and a value in the 1% column would be **highly significant.**

Here is another example of the application of the chi-square statistic to a genetics problem:

Problem: A polled (hornless) bull with a straight coat (both of which are traits determined by dominant

TABLE B-2. GENETICS EXPERIMENT

Class	Observed (o)	Expected (e)	Deviation (o − e)	(o − e)²	$\dfrac{(o - e)^2}{e}$
Females	85	75	10	100	100/75
Males	65	75	−10	100	100/75

TABLE B-3. CHI-SQUARE VALUES

Degrees of Freedom (n)	Probability Values (P) Deviation from Hypothesis Not Significant								Deviation Significant	Deviation Highly Significant
	0.95	0.90	0.80	0.70	0.50	0.30	0.20	0.10	0.05	0.01
1	0.004	0.016	0.06	0.15	0.46	1.1	1.6	2.7	3.8	6.6
2	0.1	0.2	0.4	0.7	1.4	2.4	3.2	4.6	6.0	9.2
3	0.4	0.6	1.0	1.4	2.4	3.7	4.6	6.3	7.8	11.3
	Chi-square value consistent with hypothesis								Not consistent	

(Modified from Table IV in R. A. Fisher and F. Yates, *Statistical Tables for Biological, Agricultural, and Medical Research* (6th ed., 1974). Published by Longman Group Ltd., London. Previously published by Oliver and Boyd, Ltd., Edinburgh. Reprinted by permission of the authors and publishers.)

characteristics) is mated with 48 cows that show the recessive alleles of horns and curly coat. The following offspring are produced:

17 polled straight
15 horned curly
8 polled curly } recombinants?
8 horned straight

The third and fourth phenotypes might represent recombinants.

Do these results provide convincing evidence of linkage between the two loci involved?

Solution: This problem presents us with the following two alternative hypotheses, of which only the second can be tested statistically.

1. The loci are linked and $\frac{16}{48}$ = 33% of the offspring are recombinants. This hypothesis can be tested directly only by carrying out additional breeding experiments.
2. The loci are unlinked, in which case we would expect equal numbers of the four classes of offspring. We can test this hypothesis statistically.

If we can eliminate one of these alternate hypotheses, we shall have provided strong evidence for the other. Since the only hypothesis we can test at the moment is hypothesis 2, we test it. If it must be rejected, we are left with only one alternative, that the first hypothesis is correct. To test hypothesis 2, we assume that 12 offspring were expected in each of the four classes and calculate a value of x^2 equal to 5.49. In this example there are 3 degrees of freedom. From the chi-square table, we find that we would obtain a x^2 value of 5.49 in a system with 3 degrees of freedom between 10% and 20% of the time. We have said that by convention scientists have agreed that observed results cast doubt on a hypothesis if they differ from the results predicted by the hypothesis to such

an extent that the deviation observed would occur by chance less than 5% of the time. In this case, the observed deviation would occur by chance more than 10% of the time so we cannot reject hypothesis 2. In this particular case, this means that even if the loci are unlinked, the random fusion of the gametes at fertilization has resulted in offspring whose numbers differ from the 1:1:1:1 ratio of offspring expected for unlinked loci. But the chi-square test tells us that this deviation is not statistically significant. Because in science we can disprove, but never prove, a hypothesis, the answer to the problem is that these results do not provide convincing evidence of linkage between the loci. Only a larger sample size (that is, more calves) would provide the data that would permit us to make the determination whether the loci are linked or not.

Sample size has an important effect on the observed and expected results of an experiment. Intuitively, the larger the sample size taken, the closer you would come to the expected ratio. On the other hand, when sample sizes are small, you would not be surprised that results appear to deviate considerably (but *not significantly!*) from the expected.

There are two limitations on using the chi-square statistic to test closeness of fit between observed and expected results:

1. The chi-square method can be applied only to actual frequencies, not to percentages.
2. Chi-square is not reliable if applied to distributions in which the expected value is less than 5 for any class.

STUDENT'S *t* TEST

This test assumes that the populations under study each fit a normal distribution (bell-shaped curve), that the two populations have common variance, and that the samples within the group and between groups are independent of each other. It may be used to analyze the results from Project A.

The values of t for a significance level of 0.05 are given in Table B-4.

The degrees of freedom, N, is the sum of the degrees of freedom for each class. The degrees of freedom for a class is the number of plants in the class minus 1. If an experiment included 50 experimental and 49 control plants, N would equal $(50 - 1) + (49 - 1) = 97$. The value closest to this in the table would be 100. If your instructor provides you with the value of t for each experiment, you can interpret the results by following these steps:

1. Calculate the degrees of freedom for the experiment from the number of plants involved.
2. Note the value of t that you find in the table for that value of N at the 0.05 significance level.
3. Compare the value of t calculated from the experimental results with the value of t in the table.

TABLE B-4. VALUES FOR t AT A SIGNIFICANCE LEVEL OF 0.05 (one-tailed test)*

Degrees of Freedom	Value of t (0.05 Significance Level)
1	6.314
2	2.920
3	2.353
4	2.132
5	2.015
6	1.943
7	1.895
8	1.860
9	1.833
10	1.812
15	1.753
20	1.725
25	1.708
30	1.697
40	1.684
60	1.671
120	1.658
∞	1.645

*In student's t test, the calculated value of t is compared with that in the table. If it is higher than the value in the table, the groups being compared are probably different.

(Modified from Table III in R. A. Fisher and F. Yates, *Statistical Tables for Biological, Agricultural, and Medical Research* (6th ed., 1974). Published by Longman Group Ltd., London. Previously published by Oliver and Boyd, Ltd., Edinburgh. Reprinted by permission of the authors and publishers.)

If the magnitude of the observed t is *less* than the value in the table, there is *no significant difference* between the groups. We conclude that the experimental treatment of the plants had no effect. If the magnitude of the observed t is *greater* than the value in the table, there is a *significant difference* between the groups. We conclude that the experimental treatment did have an effect.

If you, rather than the instructor, are going to calculate the value of t, use the following formula which applies to cases where the two groups being compared are equal in size so that $N_1 = N_2 = N$:

$$t = \frac{(\overline{x}_1 - \overline{x}_2)\sqrt{N}}{\sqrt{(s_1)^2 + (s_2)^2}}$$

where
N = number of plants in *EACH* group;
$\overline{x}_1$ = mean of one group of plants;
$\overline{x}_2$ = mean of the second group;
s_1 = standard deviation of the first group;
s_2 = standard deviation of the second group.

Once you have the value for the magnitude of t, follow the steps given above to analyze the results of your experiment.

TABLE B-5. EXCISION EXPERIMENT

Bud Length in Excised Plants (mm)	Bud Length in Control Plants (mm)
1.0	0.8
2.5	0.9
3.6	1.1
4.2	1.4
7.1	1.5
9.2	1.9

TABLE B-6. RANKED DATA

Rank	Length (mm)	C = Control Group
1	0.8	C
2	0.9	C
3	1.0	
4	1.1	C
5	1.4	C
6	1.5	C
7	1.9	C
8	2.5	
9	3.6	
10	4.2	
11	7.1	
12	9.2	

THE WILCOXON TEST

If your class data for Project A consisted of only a few values, or if the results did not fit a bell-shaped curve, you should use another test, the Wilcoxon (or Mann-Whitney) test, which does not depend on the frequency distribution. This test uses a ranking system to compare data from two samples.

Suppose that an excision experiment were carried out with 12 plants, 6 excised and 6 control with the results shown in Table B-5. The first step in applying the test is to arrange the data from each group in increasing order of magnitude (Table B-6).

Next, all the data are ranked, keeping track of the data from one of the groups (the control plants) (Table B-6). The rank numbers of the control and excised groups are then added:

control ranks = 1 + 2 + 4 + 5 + 6 + 7 = 25
excised ranks = 3 + 8 + 9 + 10 + 11 + 12 = 53

The lower value, in this case 25 (sum of the control group ranks), is designated the Wilcoxon statistic, W. The value calculated for W is compared with the critical values given in Table B-7. If the calculated value is equal to or less than the critical value, there is probably a significant difference between the two groups with a significance level of 0.05.

In this example, read down the column of N_1 values (for the group with the smaller mean) to $N_1 = 6$. Then read across the rows of N_2, the second group, to $N_2 = 6$. The critical value of W is 28. Our value of $W = 25$ is less than 28, so the two groups of plants are probably different within our significance level of 0.05.

If W had been 29 or greater, we would have concluded that there was no significant difference between them.

If N is greater than 25, calculate W', which can be compared to normal distribution tables:

$$W' = \frac{W - [N_1(N_1 + N_2 + 1)/2]}{\sqrt{N_1 N_2 (N_1 + N_2 + 1)/12}}$$

TABLE B-7. CRITICAL VALUES OF W*

N_1 \ N_2	1	2	3	4	5	6	7	8	9	10	11	12	13	14	15	16	17	18	19	20	21	22	23	24	25
1	—	—	—	—	—	—	—	—	—	—	—	—	—	—	—	—	—	—	1	1	1	1	1	1	1
2	—	—	—	—	3	3	3	4	4	4	4	5	5	6	6	6	6	7	7	7	8	8	8	9	9
3	—	—	6	6	7	8	8	9	10	10	11	11	12	13	13	14	15	15	16	17	17	18	19	19	20
4	—	—	—	11	12	13	14	15	16	17	18	19	20	21	22	24	25	26	27	28	29	30	31	32	33
5	—	—	—	—	19	20	21	23	24	26	27	28	30	31	33	34	35	37	38	40	41	43	44	45	47
6	—	—	—	—	—	28	29	31	33	35	37	38	40	42	44	46	47	49	51	53	55	57	58	60	62
7	—	—	—	—	—	—	39	41	43	45	47	49	52	54	56	58	61	63	65	67	69	72	74	76	78
8	—	—	—	—	—	—	—	51	54	56	59	62	64	67	69	72	75	77	80	83	85	88	90	93	96
9	—	—	—	—	—	—	—	—	66	69	72	75	78	81	84	87	90	93	96	99	102	105	108	111	114
10	—	—	—	—	—	—	—	—	—	82	86	89	92	96	99	103	106	110	113	117	120	123	127	130	134
11	—	—	—	—	—	—	—	—	—	—	100	104	108	112	116	120	123	127	131	135	139	143	147	151	155
12	—	—	—	—	—	—	—	—	—	—	—	120	125	129	133	138	142	146	150	155	159	163	168	172	176
13	—	—	—	—	—	—	—	—	—	—	—	—	142	147	152	156	161	166	171	175	180	185	189	194	199
14	—	—	—	—	—	—	—	—	—	—	—	—	—	166	171	176	182	187	192	197	202	207	212	218	223
15	—	—	—	—	—	—	—	—	—	—	—	—	—	—	192	197	203	208	214	220	225	231	236	242	248
16	—	—	—	—	—	—	—	—	—	—	—	—	—	—	—	219	225	231	237	243	249	255	261	267	273
17	—	—	—	—	—	—	—	—	—	—	—	—	—	—	—	—	249	255	262	268	274	281	287	294	300
18	—	—	—	—	—	—	—	—	—	—	—	—	—	—	—	—	—	280	287	294	301	307	314	321	328
19	—	—	—	—	—	—	—	—	—	—	—	—	—	—	—	—	—	—	313	320	328	335	342	350	357
20	—	—	—	—	—	—	—	—	—	—	—	—	—	—	—	—	—	—	—	348	356	364	371	379	387
21	—	—	—	—	—	—	—	—	—	—	—	—	—	—	—	—	—	—	—	—	385	393	401	410	418
22	—	—	—	—	—	—	—	—	—	—	—	—	—	—	—	—	—	—	—	—	—	424	432	441	450
23	—	—	—	—	—	—	—	—	—	—	—	—	—	—	—	—	—	—	—	—	—	—	465	474	483
24	—	—	—	—	—	—	—	—	—	—	—	—	—	—	—	—	—	—	—	—	—	—	—	507	517
25	—	—	—	—	—	—	—	—	—	—	—	—	—	—	—	—	—	—	—	—	—	—	—	—	552

*If the calculated value of W is equal to or less than the value shown in the table, the two groups are statistically different at a significance level of 0.05. The values of N_1 are the numbers of entries in the first group and the values of N_2 are the numbers in the second group.

(Adapted from Table 1 in L. R. Verdooren, "Extended tables of critical values for Wilcoxon's test statistic," *Biometrika* **50:** 177, 1963. Used with the permission of the Biometrika Trust.)

Laboratory Equipment

Erlenmeyer flask

test tube

spectrophotometer
tube or cuvette

beaker

ringstand

clamp

funnel

ring

funnel and ringstand

striker

gas line

Bunsen burner

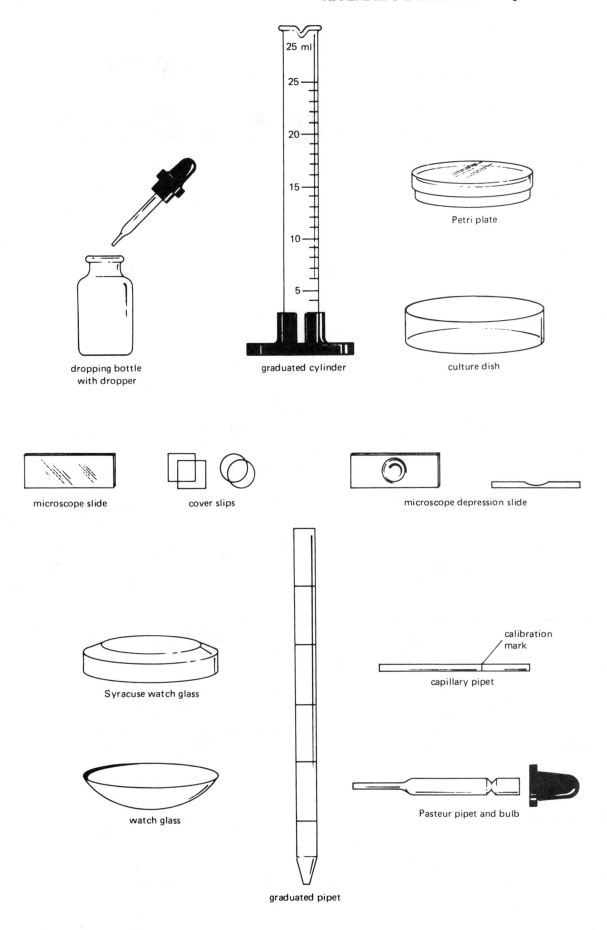

25 ml

dropping bottle
with dropper

graduated cylinder

Petri plate

culture dish

microscope slide

cover slips

microscope depression slide

Syracuse watch glass

calibration
mark

capillary pipet

watch glass

Pasteur pipet and bulb

graduated pipet

APPENDIX D
The Metric System

INTRODUCTION

These are the basic units of the metric system (abbreviations are in parentheses):

GRAM	METER	LITER
(g)*	(m)	(L)
mass or weight	length	volume

All other units are powers of 10 smaller or larger than the basic unit. The same prefixes are used to name these units regardless of the basic unit:

larger units   larger units

kilo- (k)	$10^3 \times$ basic unit
BASIC UNIT	
centi- (c)	$10^{-2} \times$ basic unit
milli- (m)	$10^{-3} \times$ basic unit
micro- (μ)	$10^{-6} \times$ basic unit
nano- (n)	$10^{-9} \times$ basic unit
pico- (p)	$10^{-12} \times$ basic unit

smaller units   smaller units

CONVERSION

Within one type of measurement, such as weight, it is possible to convert between larger and smaller units by simply moving the decimal:

Example: Convert 4729 grams (g) to kilograms (kg).

Solution: Working within weight we change into a *larger* unit so our value will be *smaller*. We will *divide* to obtain a smaller value. We will use the *factor 10³* because there are 10^3 meters/1 kilometer

$$4{,}729 \text{ g} \div 10^3 = 4\,7\,2\,9. = 4.729 \text{ kg}.$$

Ease of conversion between units is a big advantage of the metric system. Anyone who can change dollars to cents can do it!

INTERCONVERSION

The metric system is set up so that certain units are identical *with respect to the standard reference, water:*

---

*By convention, metric abbreviations never have periods or use "s" for plural: 1 gram (1 g) and 187 grams (187 g).

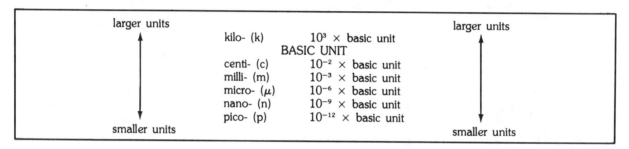

1 g	=	**1 cm³**	=	**1 mL**
H₂O		H₂O		H₂O

So, 27 mL of H_2O will occupy a cube 3 cm on each edge, 27 cm³, and weight 27 g. For other substances, the density (g/mL) must be known to interconvert units.

Example: Your queen-sized water bed measures 2.1 meters (m) × 1.5 m × .25 m. How much does it weigh in kg?

Solution: The volume of the bed needs to be expressed in cm³ before converting to weight:

$$210 \text{ cm} \times 150 \text{ cm} \times 25 \text{ cm} = 7.9 \times 10^5 \text{ cm}^3$$

Then 7.9×10^5 cm³ is equivalent directly to 7.9×10^5 g

$$7.9 \times 10^5 \text{ g} = 7\,9\,0\,0\,0\,0. \text{ g} = 790 \text{ kg}$$

Interconversion is a powerful tool that allows you to make "back of the envelope" calculations amazingly quickly.

LENGTH

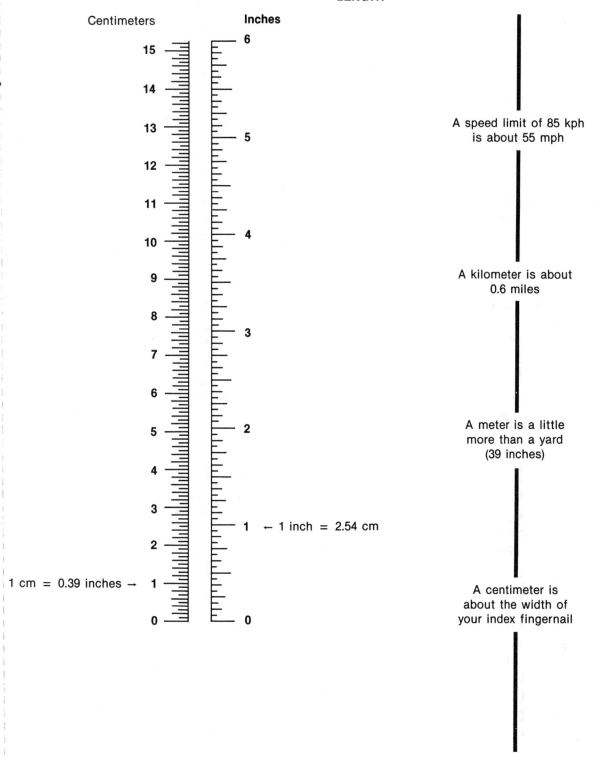

Centimeters

Inches

A speed limit of 85 kph
is about 55 mph

A kilometer is about
0.6 miles

A meter is a little
more than a yard
(39 inches)

← 1 inch = 2.54 cm

1 cm = 0.39 inches →

A centimeter is
about the width of
your index fingernail

Length Conversion		
1 in. = 2.5 cm		1 mm = .04 in.
1 ft = 30 cm		1 cm = .4 in.
1 yd = .9 m		1 m = 40 in.
1 mi = 1.6 km		1 m = 1.1 yd
		1 km = .6 mi

WEIGHT

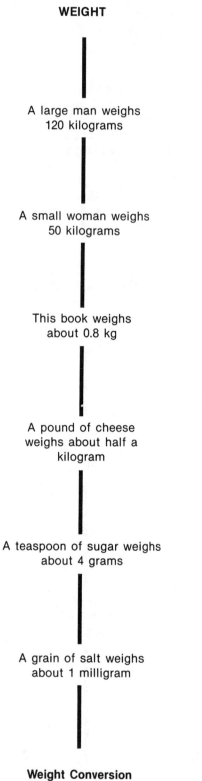

A large man weighs
120 kilograms

A small woman weighs
50 kilograms

This book weighs
about 0.8 kg

A pound of cheese
weighs about half a
kilogram

A teaspoon of sugar weighs
about 4 grams

A grain of salt weighs
about 1 milligram

VOLUME

A large gas tank
holds about 100 liters

One liter is a
standard "quart"
bottle of
soda, milk or wine

A cup of coffee is
about 150 mL

5 milliliters is a
standard teaspoon of
medicine

1 microliter is about 1/50
of a drop

Weight Conversion

1 oz. = 28 g	1 g = .035 oz.
1 lb = .45 kg	1 kg = 2.2 lb

Volume Conversion

1 tsp. = 5 mL	1 mL = .03 fl. oz.
1 tbsp. = 15 mL	1 L = 2.1 pt.
1 fl. oz. = 30 mL	1 L = 1.06 qt.
1 cup = .24 L	1 L = .26 gal.
1 pt. = .47 L	
1 qt. = .95 L	
1 gal. = 3.8 L	

TEMPERATURE

Fahrenheit
°F

Centigrade
°C

230 — 110
220
210 — 100 ← Boiling point of water
200
190 — 90
180
170 — 80 ← Hot coffee
160 — 70
150
140 — 60
130 ← Water too hot to touch
120 — 50
110
100 — 40 ← Human body temperature
90 — 30
80
70 — 20 ← Comfortable room temperature
61°F = 16°C 60
50 — 10
40
30 — 0 ← Freezing point of water
20
10 — −10
0
−10 — −20
−20 — −30
−30
−40°F = −40°C −40 — −40

Temperature Conversion

$$°C = \frac{(°F - 32) \times 5}{9}$$

$$°F = \frac{°C \times 9}{5} + 32$$

$$1°C = 1.8°F$$

World of Biology
3rd Edition
by Davis and Solomon

This laboratory manual also accompanies *World of Biology* 3rd edition. Text chapters corresponding to the appropriate laboratory topics are indicated as follows. A detailed correlation of experiments is to be found in the Instructor's Manual that accompanies this laboratory manual.

World of Biology 3rd ed. by Davis & Solomon	*General Biology Laboratory Manual* by Eberhard
CHAPTER 2: The Chemistry of Life: Atoms and Molecules	**TOPIC(S): 1.** Biologically Important Molecules
CHAPTER 3: The Chemistry of Life: Organic Compounds	**TOPIC(S): 1.** Biologically Important Molecules
CHAPTER 4: Cell Structure and Function	**TOPIC(S): 2.** The Life of Cells: The Microscope **3.** The Life of Cells: Organization and Reproduction
CHAPTER 5: The Cell Membrane: Interacting with the Environment	**TOPIC(S): 4.** The Life of Cells: Membranes
CHAPTER 6: The Energy of Life	**TOPIC(S): 6.** Enzyme Action
CHAPTER 7: Photosynthesis: Capturing Energy	**TOPIC(S): 7.** Photosynthesis
CHAPTER 8: Energy-Releasing Pathways: Cellular Respiration and Fermentation	**TOPIC(S): 8.** Cellular Respiration
CHAPTER 9: Chromosomes, Mitosis, and Meiosis	**TOPIC(S): 3.** The Life of Cells: Organization and Reproduction **9.** Meiosis and Heredity
CHAPTER 10: Patterns of Inheritance	**TOPIC(S): 9.** Meiosis and Heredity **10.** Mendelian Genetics and the Analysis of Data **11.** Human Genetics
CHAPTER 11: DNA: The Molecular Basis of Inheritance	**TOPIC(S): 13.** DNA: The Secret of Life
CHAPTER 12: Gene Function and Regulation	**TOPIC(S): 13.** DNA: The Secret of Life
CHAPTER 14: The Diversity of Life; Microbial Life and Fungi	**TOPIC(S): 14.** Classification of Living Things **15.** Kingdom Monera and Kingdom Protista **16.** Kingdom Fungi and the Simpler Plants

World of Biology 3rd ed. by Davis & Solomon	*General Biology Laboratory Manual* by Eberhard
CHAPTER 15: Plant Life	**TOPIC(S):** 5. The Life of Cells: Tissues and Organs
	16. Kingdom Fungi and the Simpler Plants
	17. Vascular Plants: Division Tracheophyta
CHAPTER 16: Animal Life	**TOPIC(S):** 5. The Life of Cells: Tissues and Organs
	18. Kingdom Animalia: Animals Without a Coelom
	19. Kingdom Animalia: Mollusks and Annelids
	20. Kingdom Animalia: Arthropods
	21. Kingdom Animalia: Vertebrates
	31. Development in Animals (Echinoderms)
CHAPTER 17: The Plant Body	**TOPIC(S):** 22. The Plant Body: Structure and Function
CHAPTER 18: Reproduction in Complex Plants	**TOPIC(S):** 23. Reproduction in Seed Plants
CHAPTER 19: Plant Growth, Development and Nutrition	**PROJECT(S):** A. Plant Hormones
	B. Plant Nutrition
CHAPTER 20: Animal Tissues, Organs and Organ Systems	**TOPIC(S):** 5. The Life of Cells: Tissues and Organs
CHAPTER 21: Skin, Muscle and Bone	**TOPIC(S):** 24. Skin, Bone, and Muscle
CHAPTER 22: Responsiveness: Neural Control	**TOPIC(S):** 30. Neural Control: Neurons, Nervous System, and Sense Organs
CHAPTER 23: Responsiveness: Nervous Systems	**TOPIC(S):** 30. Neural Control: Neurons, Nervous System, and Sense Organs
CHAPTER 24: Internal Transport	**TOPIC(S):** 26. Internal Transport in Vertebrates
CHAPTER 26: Gas Exchange	**TOPIC(S):** 28. Gas Exchange
CHAPTER 27: Processing Food	**TOPIC(S):** 25. Processing Food
CHAPTER 28: Nutrition	**TOPIC(S):** 1. Biologically Important Molecules
	25. Processing Food
CHAPTER 29: Disposal of Metabolic Wastes	**TOPIC(S):** 29. Excretion and Reproduction
CHAPTER 30: Responsiveness: Endocrine Regulation	**TOPIC(S):** 25-29 (throughout)
CHAPTER 31: Reproduction: Perpetuation of the Species	**TOPIC(S):** 29. Excretion and Reproduction
CHAPTER 32: Development: The Origin of the Organism	**TOPIC(S):** 31. Development in Animals
CHAPTER 33: Variability and Evolution	**TOPIC(S):** 12. Population Genetics
CHAPTER 35: Behavior	**TOPIC(S):** 32. Behavior
CHAPTER 36: Ecology: The Basic Principles	**PROJECT(S):** C. The Pond Ecosystem
CHAPTER 37: Ecology: Community Interactions	**PROJECT(S):** C. The Pond Ecosystem

INDEX

369